Britain's Best BED & BREAKFAST

Maps prepared by the Cartography Department of The Automobile Association.

Advertising Sales:
advertisementsales@theAA.com

Editorial:
lifestyleguides@theAA.com

Assessments of AA inspected establishments are based on the experience of the hotel and restaurant inspectors on the occasion of their visit(s) and therefore descriptions given in this guide necessarily dictate an element of subjective opinion which may not reflect or dictate a reader's own opinion on another occasion. We have tried to ensure accuracy in this guide but things do change and we would be grateful if readers would advise us of any inaccuracies they may encounter.

Typeset by Keenes, Andover, Hampshire, UK

Printed and bound by Graficas Estella, Spain

Editorial contributors: Apostrophe S

A CIP catalogue record for this book is available from the British Library

ISBN-10: 0-7495-4829-0
ISBN-13: 978-0-7495-4829-0

Published by AA Publishing, which is a trading name of Automobile Association Developments Limited, whose registered office is:
Fanum House, Basing View
Basingstoke
Hampshire RG21 4EA

www.theAA.com

Registered number 1878835

A02836

Contents

Using the guide

Finding the location

The guide is divided into sections covering England, Scotland and Wales, with the Channel Islands and the Isle of Man following the England section. Town or village locations are listed approximately alphabetically under county order (see map and index on pages 13 and 14). County names are shown at the top left or top right side of each page in the England section. The town and village locations marked on the atlas at the front of the guide are listed in the index at the back of the guide.

1 Symbols

 Diamond classification

All establishments in the guide have been inspected by the AA and at the time of going to press belong to the AA Guest Accommodation Scheme. Each accommodation in the scheme is classified for quality from one to five Diamonds (see page 8); all establishments in this guide have four or five Diamonds.

 Egg cups & pies

These symbols denote either breakfast or dinner exceeded the quality level for the Diamond classification achieved by the establishment.

 Rosette awards

The AA's food award - see page 8.

2 Map reference

The map reference number indicates the atlas page at the front of the guide, and is followed by the National Grid Reference. To find the town or village location, read the first figure across and the second figure vertically within the lettered square. Maps locating each establishment and also a route planner are available on www.theAA.com.

3 Address & directions

4 Contact details

Telephone and fax numbers, and e-mail and website addresses are given where available. See page 11 for international dialling. The telephone and fax numbers are believed correct at the time of going to press but changes may occur during the currency of the book. The latest establishment details are on the B&B pages at www.theAA.com.

Website addresses have been supplied by the establishments and lead you to websites that are not under the control of Automobile Association Developments Ltd. AADL has no control over and accepts no responsibility or liability in respect of the material on any such websites. By including the addresses of third-party websites AADL does not intend to solicit business.

5 Rooms

The number of rooms is shown after the contact details. Further details of room facilities appear in the main description. Check when booking to ensure that all the facilities you require will be available.

Prices

Prices are provided by the proprietors and are believed to be correct at the time of going to press.

Smoking restrictions

Although we request accurate information about smoking restrictions, the situation may change during the currency of the guide.

6 Description

The description of the establishment includes information about the various facilities and special features.

7 Recommended in the area

Places to visit in the area that the establishments recommend to their guests.

www.theAA.com

At the beginning of each county section there is a selection of AA recommended pubs and restaurants. Click on to www.theAA.com to find more AA listed guest houses, hotels, pubs and restaurants - some 12,000 establishments.

Routes & Traffic on the home page leads to a route planner. Simply enter your postcode and the establishment postcode given in this guide and click Confirm. Check your details and then click Get my route and you are on your way.

Or else search on the home page for Hotels & B&Bs or Restaurants & Pubs by location or establishment name. Scroll down the list of finds for the interactive map and local routes.

Postcode searches can also be done on www.ordnancesurvey.co.uk and www.multimap.com, and the latter provides useful aerial views of your destination.

Sample Entry

Molly's Farmhouse ♦♦♦♦ — 1

Map ref 2 - SY99 — 2

Address, LOCATION, County — 3
LXX 1XX

From A338 onto A3060 to Christchurch, at 2nd rdbt turn right, 1m to traffic lights, left signed Beaches, in 1m right down Grand Ave to end and turn right.

T 02524 734248 — 4
F 02524 734248
E email@address.co.uk
W www.mfarmhouse.co.uk

6 rooms, S £38-£45, D £56-£70, No Smoking — 5

A lovely stone farmhouse set in well-tended gardens on the outskirts of town. Molly Smith is the perfect host, offering afternoon tea, suppertime drinks and generous breakfasts. The warm hospitality and home comforts extend to the bedrooms, with spacious en suite accommodation and stunning views across the gardens to the surrounding countryside. — 6

RECOMMENDED IN THE AREA — 7
St Mawes Castle; Trelissick Garden; Glendurgan Garden

Where to stay

Guest houses

The guest houses selected for this guide are among some of the very best establishments in the AA scheme, with many of the services and facilities you can expect of a hotel. Some guest houses include the word 'hotel' in their name, which can be confusing. Small and private hotels are included in the AA Guest Accommodation Scheme when they cannot offer all the services required for the AA hotel scheme (for example, evening meals). There may also be restricted guest access to the house, particularly in the late morning and during the afternoon, so check when booking.

AA guest accommodation in London includes small hotels, which may not be privately owned. London prices tend to be higher than outside the capital and usually only include bed and breakfast.

Farmhouses

Farmhouse accommodation can provide good value for money and excellent home cooking. Many of the farmhouses in the guide are on working farms, and some farmers may allow guests to look around, or even to help feed the animals. However, guests should be careful and never leave children unsupervised around the farm. Some farmhouses are in remote locations - ask for further directions when booking.

Inns

Traditional inns provide a cosy bar, convivial atmosphere, good beer and pub food. Entries in the guide will provide breakfast in a suitable room, and should also serve light meals during licensing hours. Some small licensed hotels are classified as inns, and the character of the properties vary according to whether they are country inns or town establishments. Arrival times may be restricted to opening hours.

Breakfast & evening meals

Guest houses usually offer a full, cooked breakfast in the British tradition, or else a substantial continental breakfast. Many guest houses also provide dinner or evening meals, ranging from a set meal to a full menu - some even have their own restaurants. Dinner is often arranged in advance, at breakfast or on the previous day. If you book on bed, breakfast and evening meal terms, the tariff may include only a set menu, or you may have to pay a supplement if a carte is available. On Sundays, many establishments serve the main meal at midday, and provide only a cold supper in the evening. In some parts of Britain, particularly in Scotland, high tea (a savoury dish followed by bread and butter, scones or cakes) is sometimes served instead of dinner; dinner may be available as an alternative. Where guest houses offer bed and breakfast only, guests must go out for an evening meal.

Booking

Advance booking is always recommended to avoid disappointment. The peak holiday periods in the UK are Easter, and from June to September; public holidays are also busy times. In some parts of Scotland the winter skiing season is a peak holiday period. Some establishments may only accept weekly bookings from Saturday, and others require a deposit on booking. Please quote this guide in any enquiry. Guest houses may not accept credit or debit cards - ask when booking. VAT (Value Added Tax at 17.5%) is payable in the UK and in the Isle of Man, on basic prices and additional services. VAT does not apply in the Channel Islands. Always confirm the current price before booking; the prices in this guide are indications rather than firm quotations. It is a good idea also to confirm exactly what is included in the price when booking. Remember that all details, especially prices, may change without notice during the currency of the guide.

Cancellation

Advise the proprietor immediately if you must cancel a booking. If the room cannot be re-let you may be held legally responsible for partial payment. This could include losing your deposit or being liable for compensation. You should consider taking out cancellation insurance.

AA classification & awards

 Diamond classification

The AA inspects and classifies small private hotels, guest houses, farmhouses and inns at five levels of quality, from one Diamond at the simplest, to five Diamonds offering the highest quality. The emphasis for a Diamond rating is on guest care, housekeeping, and the quality and maintenance of all the bedrooms, bathrooms and public areas, rather than the provision of extra facilities. The establishments in this guide have been recommended by the AA inspectors for their excellent hospitality, accommodation and food.

Establishments applying for AA recognition are visited on a 'mystery guest' basis by one of the AA's qualified accommodation inspectors. The inspector stays overnight to make a thorough test of the accommodation, food, and hospitality offered. After paying the bill the following morning they identify themselves and ask to be shown round the premises. Each inspector completes a full report, resulting in a recommendation for the appropriate diamond award. After this first visit, the establishment will receive an annual visit to check that standards are maintained. If it changes hands, the new owners must re-apply for classification.

Red diamonds indicate the best establishments within the three, four and five Diamond classifications.

 AA Rosette awards

Some of the establishments in this guide have been awarded AA Rosettes for their food. Rosettes are awarded annually, from one to five, on the basis of a meal visit or visits by one or more of our restaurant inspectors.

An establishment awarded one rosette serves food prepared with care, understanding and skill, using good quality ingredients. To gain two rosettes, the chef achieves higher standards and better consistency, and a greater precision is apparent in the cooking. There is obvious attention to the selection of quality ingredients.

Three rosettes are awarded to outstanding restaurants that demand recognition well beyond their local area. The cooking is underpinned by the sympathetic treatment of the highest quality ingredients. Timing, seasoning and flavour combinations are consistently excellent. At the four rosette level there is a passion for excellence, superb technical skills and remarkable consistency. An appreciation of culinary traditions is combined with a passionate desire for further exploration and improvement.

Five rosettes are awarded to the finest restaurants in the British Isles, where the cooking stands comparison with the best in the world. These restaurants have highly individual voices, exhibit breathtaking culinary skills, and set the standards to which others aspire.

It is important to remember that many places serve very enjoyable food but do not qualify for the AA Rosette awards.

Useful information

Codes of practice

The AA encourages the use of The Hotel Industry Voluntary Code of Booking Practice in appropriate establishments. The prime objective of the code is to ensure that the customer is clear about the price and the exact services and facilities being purchased, before entering into a contractually binding agreement. If the price has not been previously confirmed in writing, the guest should be handed a card at the time of registration, stipulating the total obligatory charge.

The Tourism (Sleeping Accommodation Price Display) Order 1977 compels hotels, motels, guest houses, farmhouses, inns and self-catering accommodation with four or more letting bedrooms to display in entrance halls the minimum and maximum prices charged for each category of room. This order complements the Voluntary Code of Booking Practice.

Fire precautions and safety

Many of the establishments listed in the guide are subject to the requirements of the Fire Precautions Act 1971. This Act does not apply to the Channel Islands or the Isle of Man, where their own rules are exercised. All establishments should display details of how to summon assistance in the event of an emergency at night.

Licensed premises

Whereas inns hold a licence to sell alcohol, not all guest houses are licensed. Some may have a full liquor licence, or others may have a table licence and wine list. Licensed premises are not obliged to remain open throughout the permitted hours, and they may do so only when they expect reasonable trade.

Children

Restrictions for children may be mentioned in the description. Some establishments may offer free accommodation to children when they share their parents' room. Such conditions are subject to change without notice, therefore always check when booking.

Dogs

Some establishments that do not normally accept dogs may accept guide or hearing dogs. Establishments that do accept dogs may restrict the size and breed and the rooms into which they can be taken. Check any conditions when booking.

Complaints

Readers who have cause to complain are urged to do so on the spot. This should provide an opportunity for the proprietor to correct matters. If this approach fails, please inform AA Hotel Services, Fanum House, Basingstoke, Hampshire, RG21 4EA. The AA does not, however, undertake to obtain compensation for complaints.

International information

Air travel

London Heathrow and London Gatwick are the principal international airports in the UK. Some regional airports also accept international flights, including Birmingham, Edinburgh, Glasgow, Manchester, Southampton and Leeds Bradford. There are domestic airports in many cities and internal flights can be a relatively cheap option for longer distances. Ask your travel agent or browse the Internet for the best prices.

Ferries

Vehicle and passenger ferries operate regularly from mainland Britain to the Isle of Wight, the Isle of Man, the Channel Islands and the Scottish islands. Ferry services are subject to seasonal variations so check with a travel agent - you may have to book in advance.

Driving

In the UK you drive on the left and overtake on the right. Seat belts are worn by every occupant of the car, whether they sit in the front or the rear. Speed limits are displayed in miles per hour.

Car rental

You will need to present your driving licence and credit or debit card. You can also provide an International Driving Permit along with your driving licence (a document with a photograph that confirms you as the holder of a valid driving licence in your own country). Further identification, such as a passport, may be required for certain rental vehicles.

It is advisable to book in advance and check that you have the appropriate insurance, mileage allowance and transmission (an automatic is more expensive). A minimum age limit will apply. When collecting the car, check whether it takes diesel or unleaded fuel.

Trains

The UK has an extensive rail network. When booking accommodation check that it is accessible by train if this is your main method of transport. To find out about routes, special offers or passes, contact a travel agent or National Rail (www.nationalrail.co.uk, telephone 08457 484950; from overseas +44 20 7278 5240, and international rates apply). It may be advisable to book more popular routes - e.g. London to Edinburgh - well in advance.

Money

Some establishments may not accept traveller's cheques, or credit or debit cards, so ask about payment methods when you book. There are exchange offices at airports and usually at town banks and post offices, where current exchange rates are displayed. Make sure you have enough currency for your everyday needs, particularly in rural areas, where there may be little opportunity to exchange currency. Some European and American credit and debit cards allow you to withdraw cash from British ATMs; check with your bank before travelling.

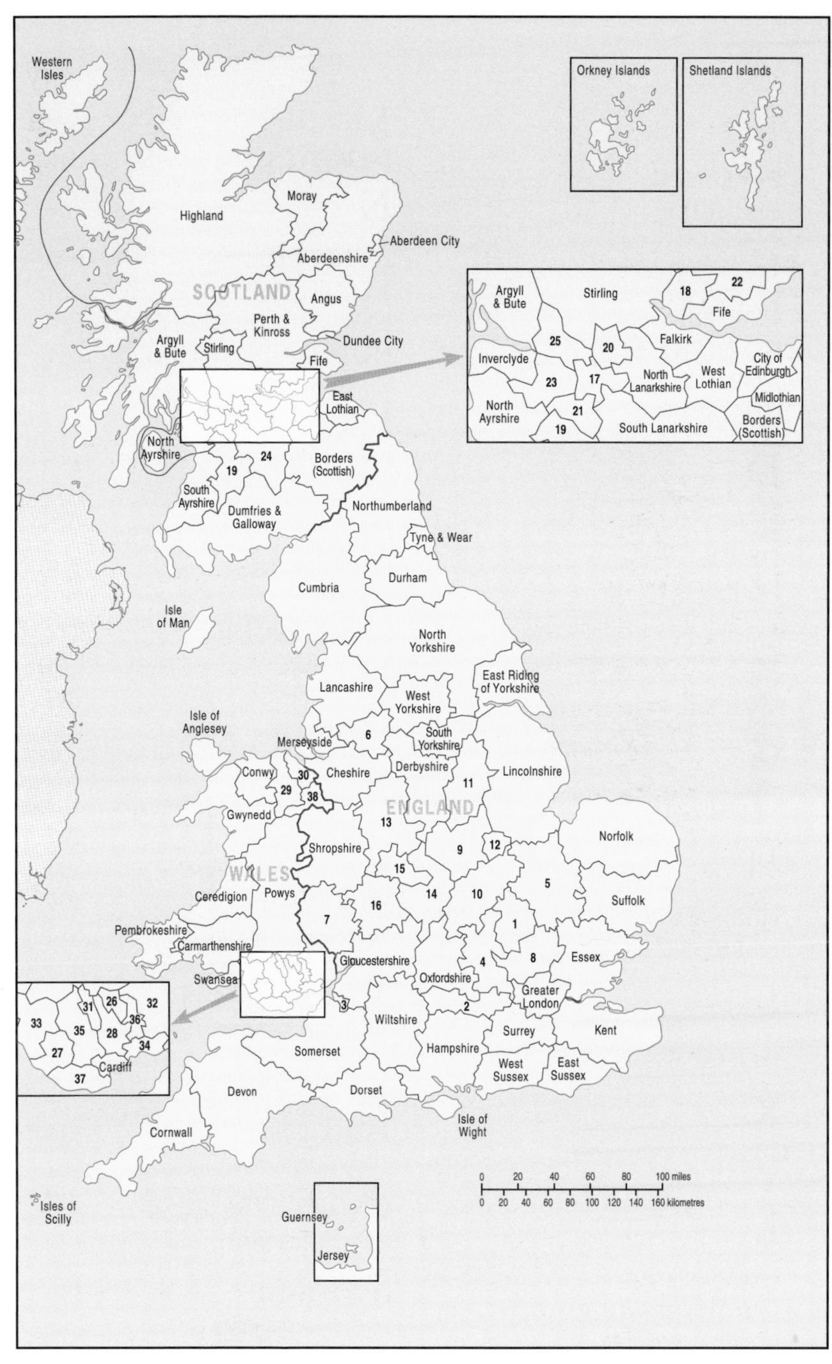
Western Isles
Highland
Moray
Aberdeen City
Aberdeenshire
SCOTLAND
Angus
Perth & Kinross
Argyll & Bute
Stirling
Dundee City
Fife
East Lothian
North Ayrshire
24
19
Borders (Scottish)
South Ayrshire
Dumfries & Galloway
Northumberland
Tyne & Wear
Durham
Cumbria
Isle of Man
North Yorkshire
East Riding of Yorkshire
Lancashire
West Yorkshire
Isle of Anglesey
Merseyside
6
South Yorkshire
Conwy
30
Cheshire
Derbyshire
11
Lincolnshire
29
38
Gwynedd
ENGLAND
13
Norfolk
Shropshire
12
9
WALES
15
5
Ceredigion
Powys
14
10
Suffolk
16
7
1
Pembrokeshire
Carmarthenshire
8
Essex
Gloucestershire
4
Swansea
Oxfordshire
Greater London
3
2
Wiltshire
Surrey
Kent
Hampshire
Somerset
West Sussex
East Sussex
Devon
Dorset
Isle of Wight
Cornwall
Isles of Scilly
Guernsey
Jersey
Orkney Islands
Shetland Islands
Argyll & Bute
Stirling
18
22
Fife
25
20
Falkirk
Inverclyde
23
17
North Lanarkshire
West Lothian
City of Edinburgh
Midlothian
North Ayrshire
21
19
South Lanarkshire
Borders (Scottish)
31
26
32
33
35
36
28
34
27
Cardiff
37
0 20 40 60 80 100 miles
0 20 40 60 80 100 120 140 160 kilometres

County & country index

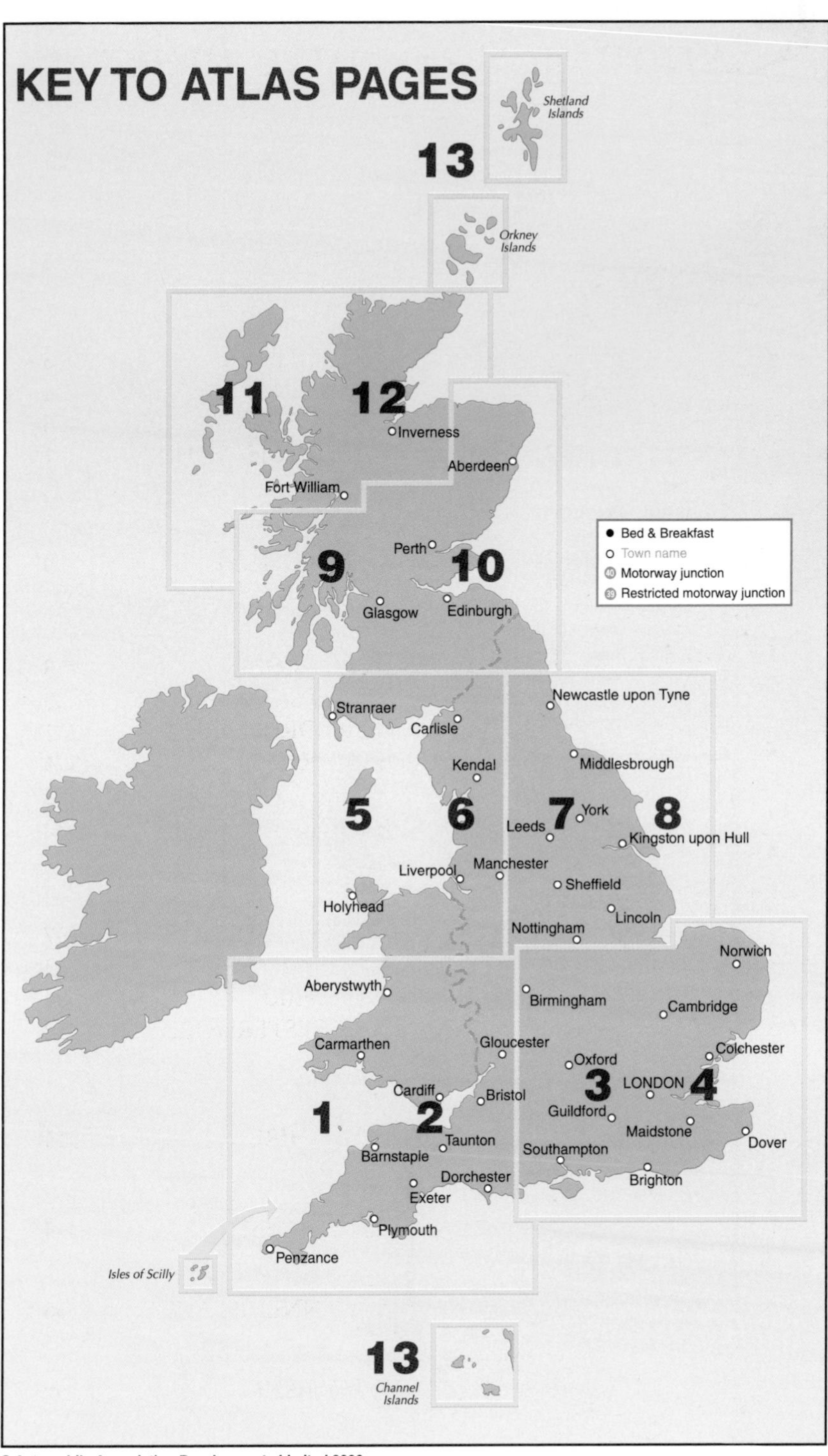
KEY TO ATLAS PAGES
13
Shetland Islands
Orkney Islands
11
12
Inverness
Aberdeen
Fort William
Perth
9
10
Glasgow
Edinburgh
Bed & Breakfast
Town name
Motorway junction
Restricted motorway junction
Stranraer
Carlisle
Newcastle upon Tyne
Middlesbrough
Kendal
5
6
7
8
Leeds
York
Kingston upon Hull
Liverpool
Manchester
Sheffield
Holyhead
Lincoln
Nottingham
Norwich
Aberystwyth
Birmingham
Cambridge
Carmarthen
Gloucester
Colchester
Oxford
3
LONDON
4
Cardiff
Bristol
1
2
Guildford
Maidstone
Dover
Taunton
Barnstaple
Southampton
Brighton
Dorchester
Exeter
Plymouth
Penzance
Isles of Scilly
13
Channel Islands

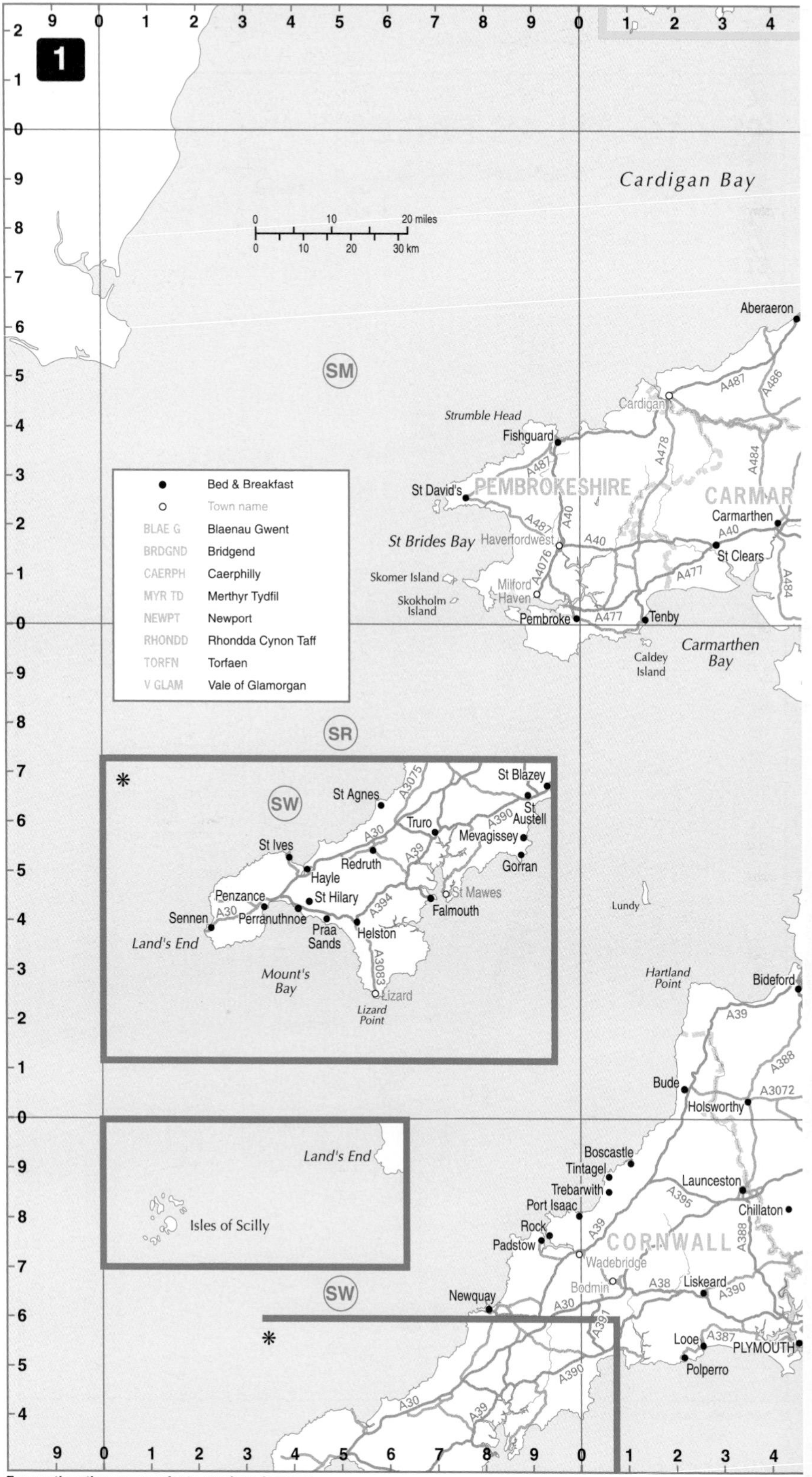

1
Cardigan Bay
0 10 20 miles
0 10 20 30 km
Aberaeron
Cardigan
Strumble Head
Fishguard
St David's
PEMBROKESHIRE
CARMAR
Carmarthen
St Brides Bay
Haverfordwest
St Clears
Skomer Island
Skokholm Island
Milford Haven
Pembroke
Tenby
Caldey Island
Carmarthen Bay
Bed & Breakfast
Town name
BLAE G Blaenau Gwent
BRDGND Bridgend
CAERPH Caerphilly
MYR TD Merthyr Tydfil
NEWPT Newport
RHONDD Rhondda Cynon Taff
TORFN Torfaen
V GLAM Vale of Glamorgan
SM
SR
SW
St Agnes
St Blazey
St Austell
Truro
Mevagissey
Gorran
St Ives
Redruth
Hayle
Penzance
St Hilary
St Mawes
Falmouth
Sennen
Perranuthnoe
Praa Sands
Helston
Land's End
Mount's Bay
Lizard
Lizard Point
Lundy
Hartland Point
Bideford
Bude
Holsworthy
Isles of Scilly
Boscastle
Tintagel
Trebarwith
Port Isaac
Launceston
Chillaton
Rock
Padstow
CORNWALL
Wadebridge
Bodmin
Liskeard
Newquay
Looe
Polperro
PLYMOUTH

For continuation pages refer to numbered arrows

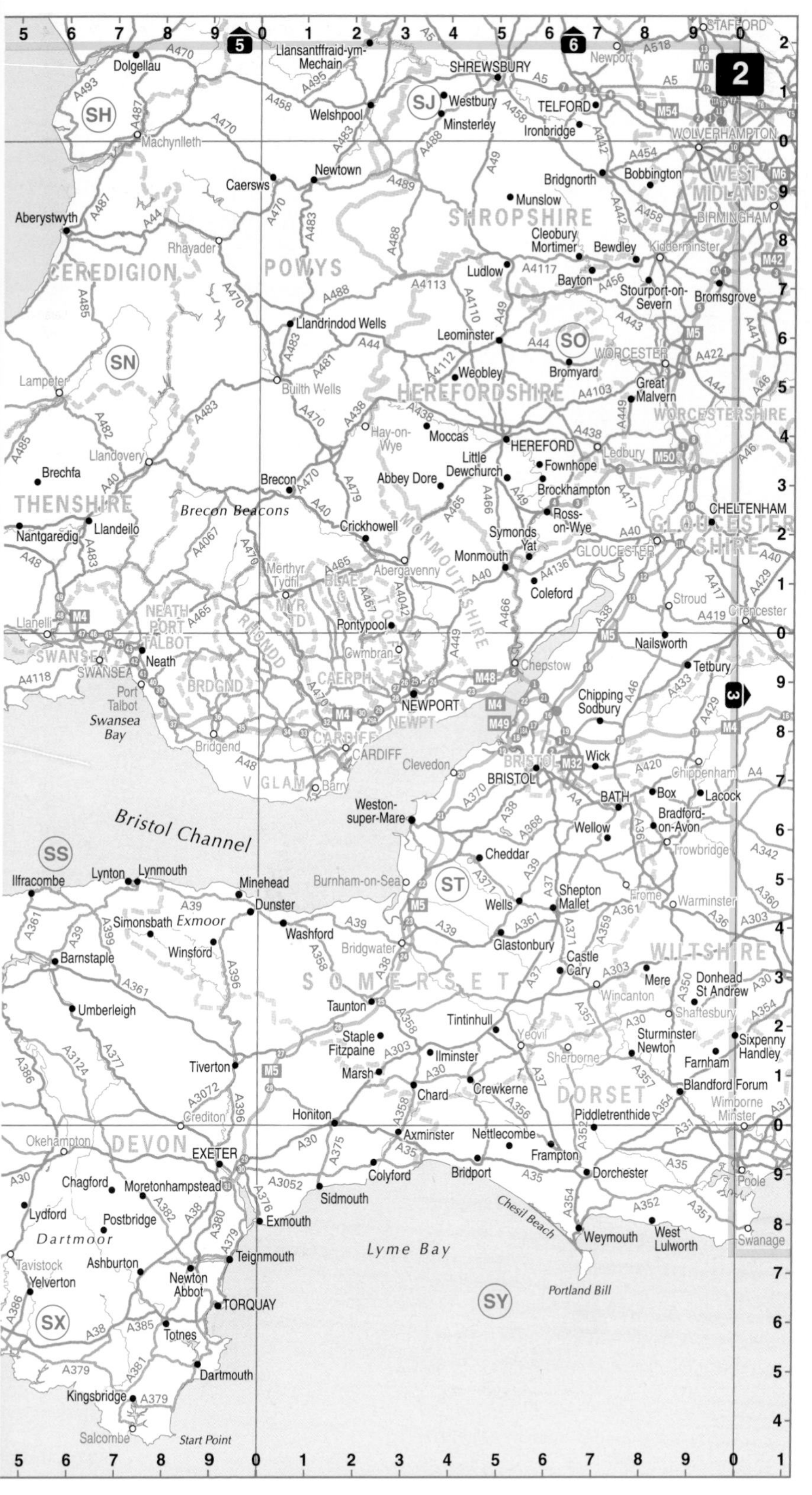

2
5
6
Dolgellau
SH
Machynlleth
Aberystwyth
CEREDIGION
Llansantffraid-ym-Mechain
Welshpool
SJ
Westbury
Minsterley
SHREWSBURY
TELFORD
Ironbridge
Newport
STAFFORD
WOLVERHAMPTON
WEST MIDLANDS
BIRMINGHAM
Caersws
Newtown
Rhayader
POWYS
SHROPSHIRE
Bridgnorth
Bobbington
Munslow
Cleobury Mortimer
Bewdley
Kidderminster
Ludlow
Bayton
Stourport-on-Severn
Bromsgrove
Llandrindod Wells
Leominster
SO
WORCESTER
Bromyard
Weobley
SN
Lampeter
Builth Wells
HEREFORDSHIRE
Great Malvern
WORCESTERSHIRE
Hay-on-Wye
Moccas
HEREFORD
Ledbury
Llandovery
Brechfa
THENSHIRE
Brecon
Brecon Beacons
Abbey Dore
Little Dewchurch
Fownhope
Brockhampton
Ross-on-Wye
CHELTENHAM
GLOUCESTERSHIRE
GLOUCESTER
Nantgaredig
Llandeilo
Crickhowell
Symonds Yat
Monmouth
Abergavenny
MONMOUTHSHIRE
Merthyr Tydfil
Coleford
Stroud
Cirencester
Llanelli
NEATH PORT TALBOT
Pontypool
Nailsworth
SWANSEA
Neath
Cwmbran
Chepstow
Tetbury
Port Talbot
Swansea Bay
BRDGND
CAERPH
NEWPORT
NEWPT
Chipping Sodbury
3
Bridgend
CARDIFF
Clevedon
BRISTOL
Wick
Chippenham
V GLAM
Barry
BATH
Box
Lacock
Bristol Channel
Weston-super-Mare
Wellow
Bradford-on-Avon
Trowbridge
SS
Cheddar
Ilfracombe
Lynton
Lynmouth
Minehead
Dunster
Burnham-on-Sea
ST
Wells
Shepton Mallet
Frome
Warminster
Simonsbath
Exmoor
Winsford
Washford
Bridgwater
Glastonbury
Barnstaple
SOMERSET
Castle Cary
WILTSHIRE
Mere
Donhead St Andrew
Wincanton
Umberleigh
Taunton
Shaftesbury
Tintinhull
Staple Fitzpaine
Yeovil
Sherborne
Sturminster Newton
Sixpenny Handley
Ilminster
Farnham
Tiverton
Marsh
Chard
Crewkerne
DORSET
Blandford Forum
Crediton
Honiton
Wimborne Minster
Piddletrenthide
Okehampton
DEVON
Axminster
Nettlecombe
Frampton
EXETER
Colyford
Bridport
Dorchester
Poole
Chagford
Moretonhampstead
Sidmouth
Chesil Beach
Lydford
Postbridge
Exmouth
West Lulworth
Swanage
Dartmoor
Weymouth
Tavistock
Ashburton
Teignmouth
Lyme Bay
Yelverton
Newton Abbot
Portland Bill
TORQUAY
SY
SX
Totnes
Dartmouth
Kingsbridge
Salcombe
Start Point

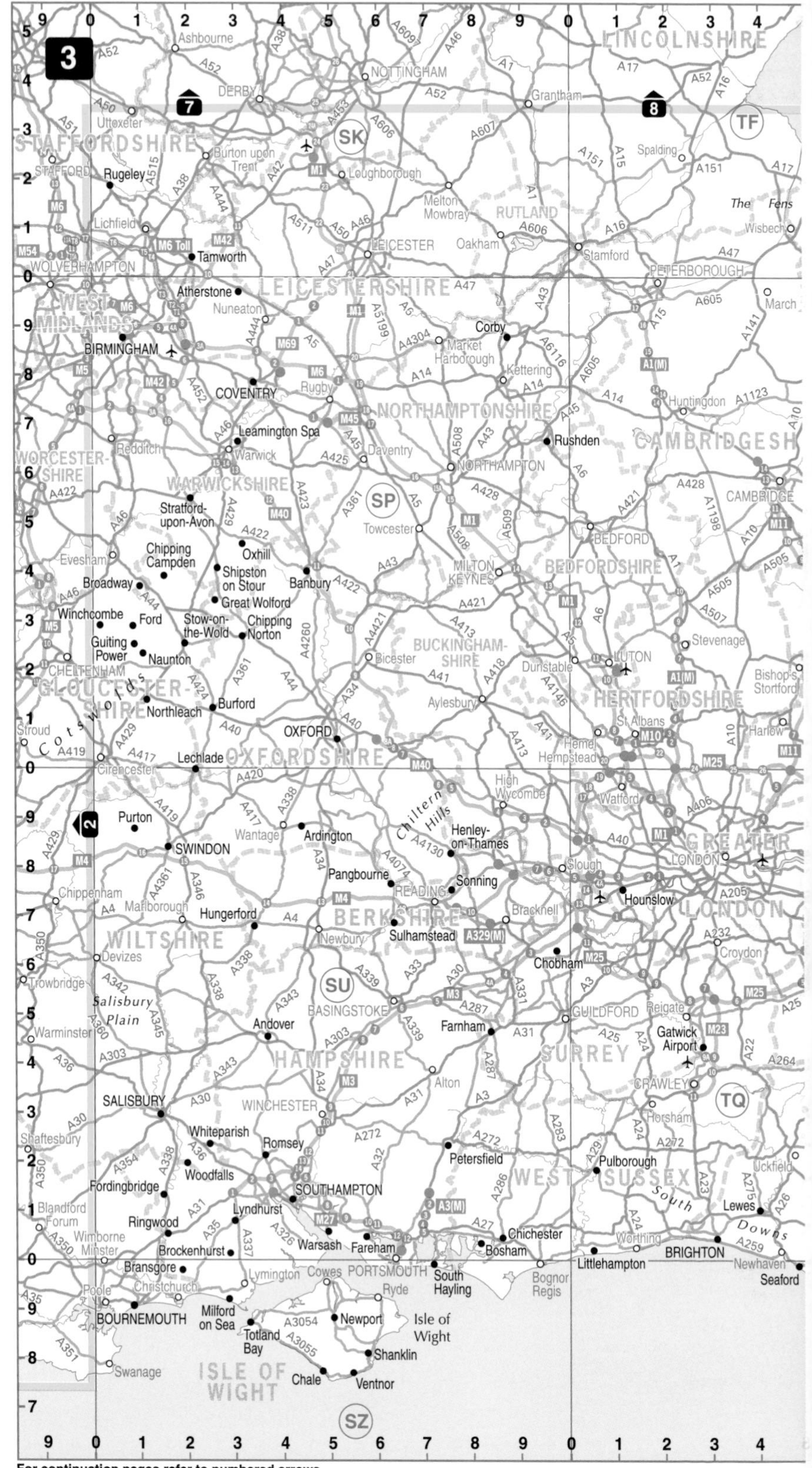

For continuation pages refer to numbered arrows

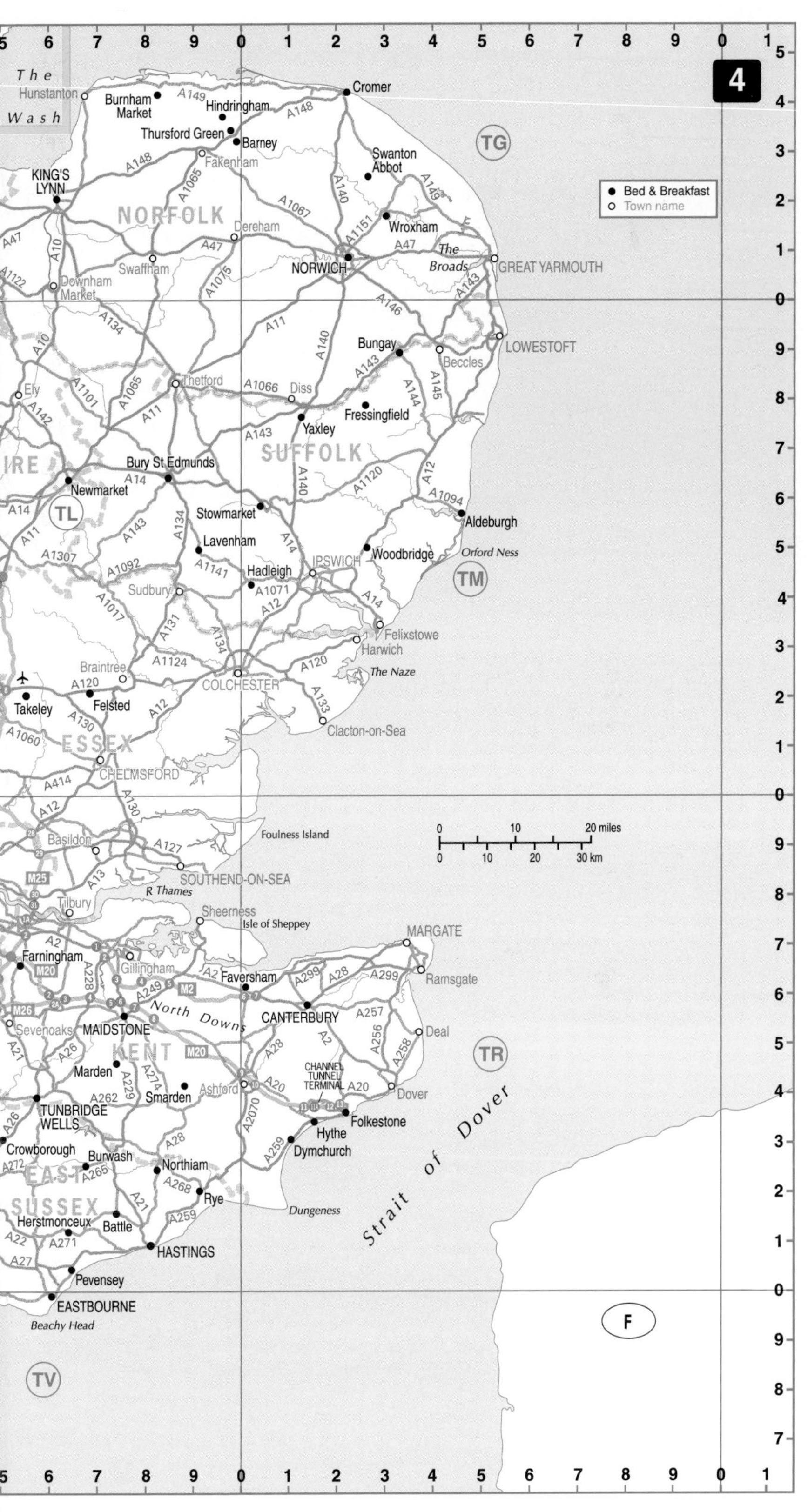
4
Bed & Breakfast
Town name
The Wash
Hunstanton
Burnham Market
Hindringham
Thursford Green
Barney
Fakenham
Cromer
Swanton Abbot
KING'S LYNN
NORFOLK
Dereham
Wroxham
Swaffham
Downham Market
NORWICH
The Broads
GREAT YARMOUTH
Bungay
Beccles
LOWESTOFT
Ely
Thetford
Diss
Fressingfield
Yaxley
SUFFOLK
Bury St Edmunds
Newmarket
Stowmarket
Aldeburgh
Lavenham
Woodbridge
Orford Ness
Hadleigh
IPSWICH
Sudbury
Felixstowe
Harwich
The Naze
Braintree
COLCHESTER
Takeley
Felsted
Clacton-on-Sea
ESSEX
CHELMSFORD
Foulness Island
Basildon
SOUTHEND-ON-SEA
R Thames
Tilbury
Sheerness
Isle of Sheppey
MARGATE
Farningham
Gillingham
Faversham
Ramsgate
CANTERBURY
North Downs
Sevenoaks
MAIDSTONE
Deal
KENT
Marden
Smarden
Ashford
CHANNEL TUNNEL TERMINAL
Dover
TUNBRIDGE WELLS
Folkestone
Hythe
Dymchurch
Crowborough
Burwash
Northiam
EAST SUSSEX
Rye
Dungeness
Strait of Dover
Herstmonceux
Battle
HASTINGS
Pevensey
EASTBOURNE
Beachy Head
TG
TL
TM
TR
TV
F
0 10 20 miles
0 10 20 30 km

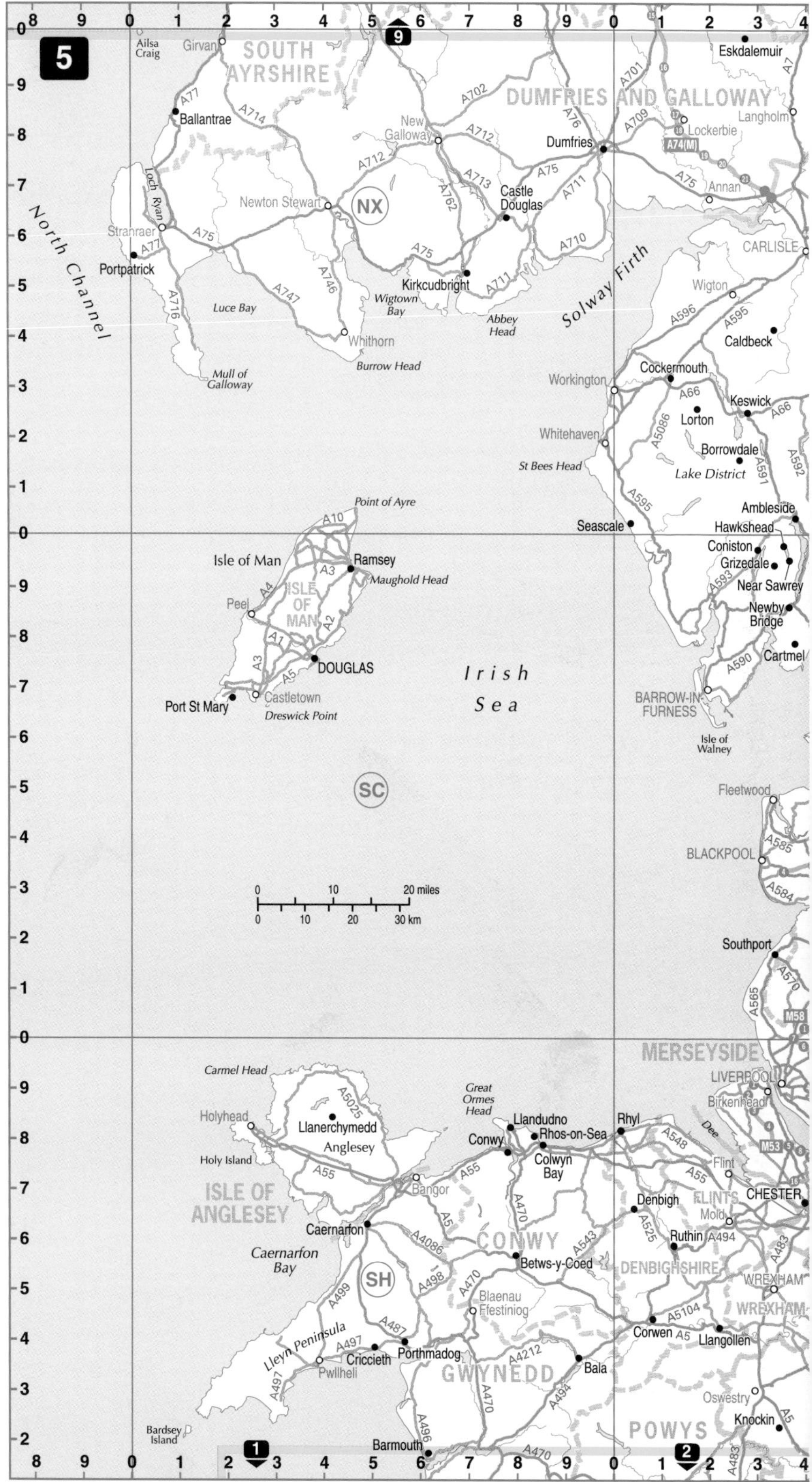

For continuation pages refer to numbered arrows

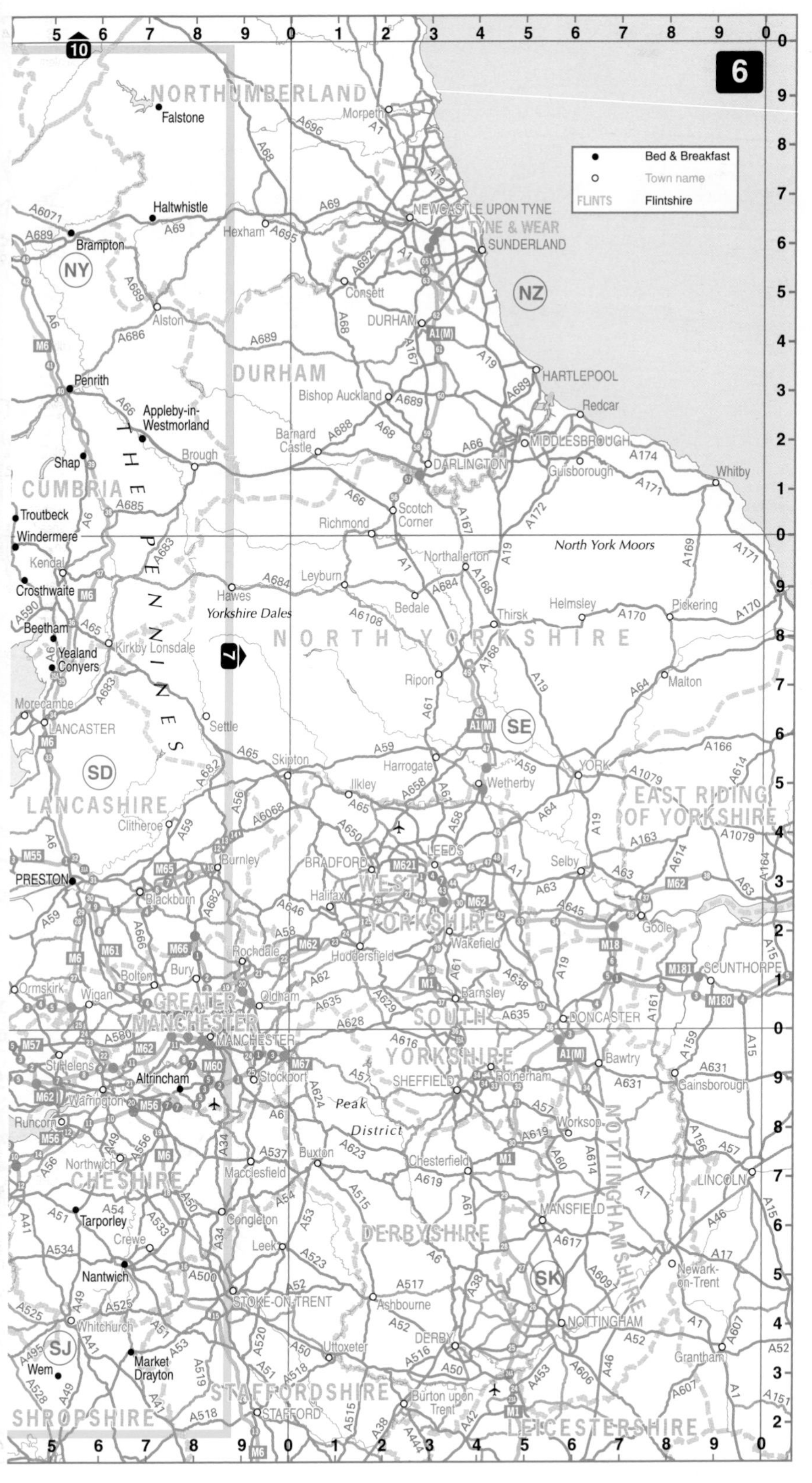
6
10
7
Bed & Breakfast
Town name
FLINTS Flintshire
NORTHUMBERLAND
Falstone
Morpeth
Haltwhistle
Brampton
Hexham
NEWCASTLE UPON TYNE
TYNE & WEAR
SUNDERLAND
Consett
Alston
DURHAM
Penrith
Bishop Auckland
HARTLEPOOL
Redcar
Appleby-in-Westmorland
Barnard Castle
MIDDLESBROUGH
Shap
Brough
DARLINGTON
Guisborough
Whitby
CUMBRIA
THE PENNINES
Troutbeck
Windermere
Scotch Corner
Richmond
North York Moors
Kendal
Northallerton
Crosthwaite
Leyburn
Hawes
Yorkshire Dales
Bedale
Thirsk
Helmsley
Pickering
Beetham
NORTH YORKSHIRE
Yealand Conyers
Kirkby Lonsdale
Ripon
Malton
Morecambe
LANCASTER
Settle
Skipton
Harrogate
YORK
Ilkley
Wetherby
EAST RIDING OF YORKSHIRE
LANCASHIRE
Clitheroe
Burnley
BRADFORD
LEEDS
Selby
PRESTON
Blackburn
Halifax
WEST YORKSHIRE
Wakefield
Goole
Rochdale
Huddersfield
Bury
Bolton
Oldham
Barnsley
SCUNTHORPE
Ormskirk
Wigan
GREATER MANCHESTER
SOUTH YORKSHIRE
DONCASTER
MANCHESTER
St Helens
Stockport
Altrincham
SHEFFIELD
Rotherham
Bawtry
Gainsborough
Warrington
Peak District
Runcorn
Worksop
NOTTINGHAMSHIRE
Northwich
CHESHIRE
Macclesfield
Buxton
Chesterfield
LINCOLN
Tarporley
Congleton
MANSFIELD
Crewe
Leek
DERBYSHIRE
Newark-on-Trent
Nantwich
STOKE-ON-TRENT
Ashbourne
Whitchurch
NOTTINGHAM
Uttoxeter
DERBY
Grantham
Market Drayton
Wem
STAFFORDSHIRE
Burton upon Trent
SHROPSHIRE
STAFFORD
LEICESTERSHIRE
NY
NZ
SD
SE
SJ
SK

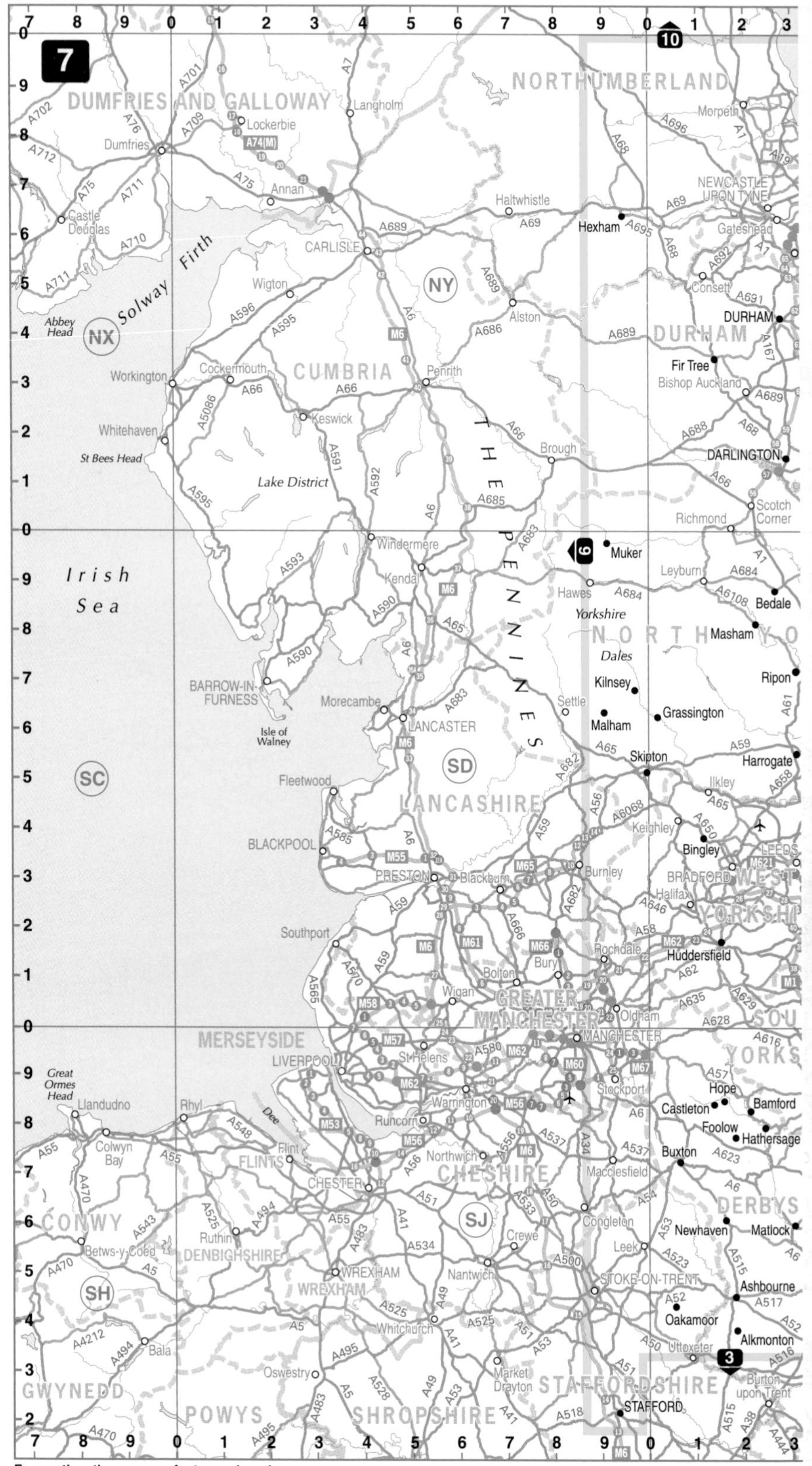

For continuation pages refer to numbered arrows

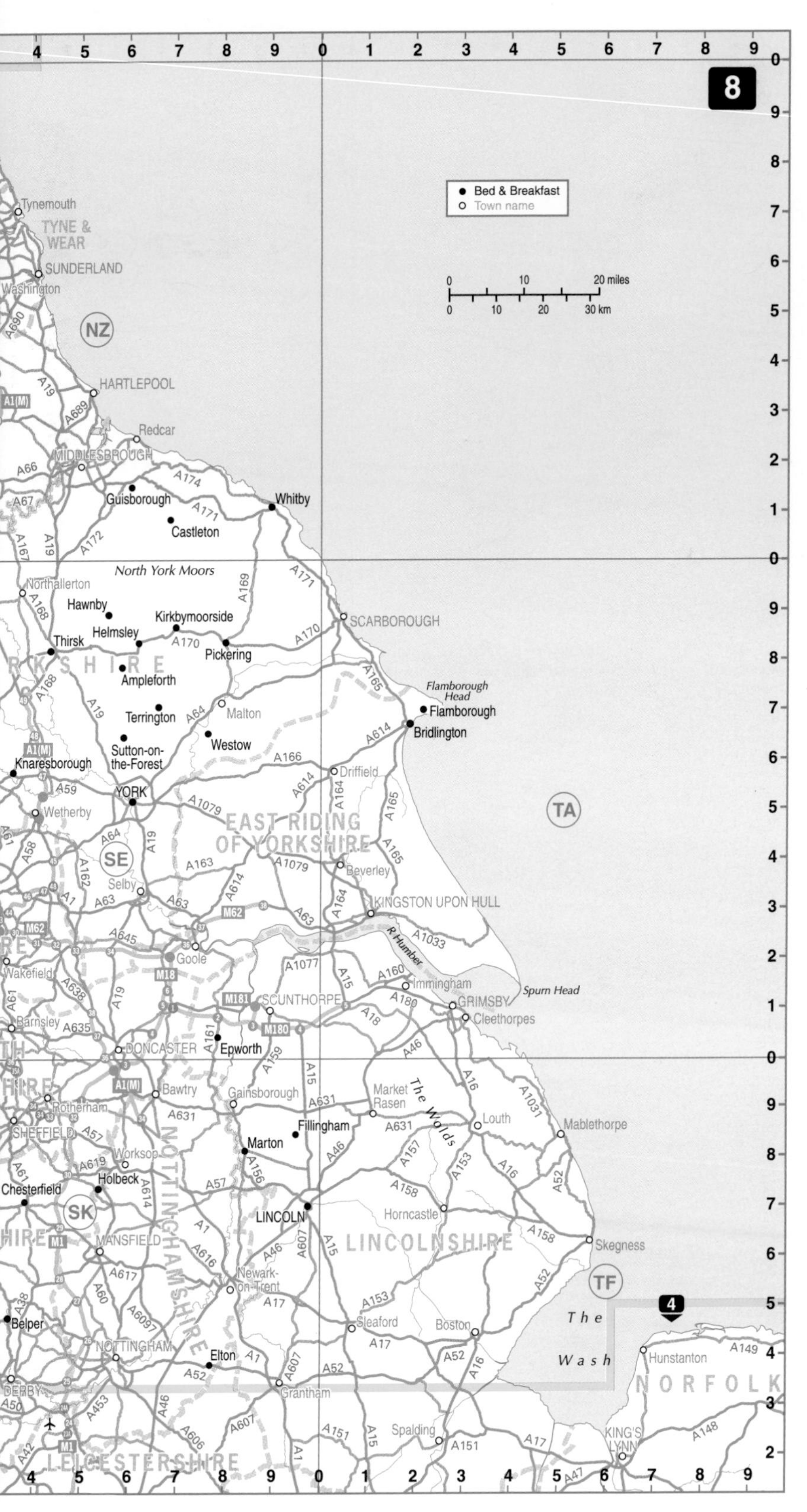
8
Bed & Breakfast
Town name
0 10 20 miles
0 10 20 30 km
Tynemouth
TYNE & WEAR
SUNDERLAND
Washington
NZ
HARTLEPOOL
Redcar
MIDDLESBROUGH
Guisborough
Castleton
Whitby
North York Moors
Northallerton
Hawnby
Kirkbymoorside
Helmsley
Thirsk
Pickering
SCARBOROUGH
Ampleforth
Flamborough Head
Flamborough
Bridlington
Malton
Terrington
Westow
Sutton-on-the-Forest
Knaresborough
Driffield
YORK
Wetherby
EAST RIDING OF YORKSHIRE
TA
SE
Beverley
Selby
KINGSTON UPON HULL
R Humber
Goole
Wakefield
Immingham
SCUNTHORPE
GRIMSBY
Spurn Head
Cleethorpes
Barnsley
DONCASTER
Epworth
Bawtry
Gainsborough
Rotherham
Market Rasen
The Wolds
Louth
Mablethorpe
SHEFFIELD
Fillingham
Marton
Worksop
Holbeck
Chesterfield
SK
LINCOLN
Horncastle
NOTTINGHAMSHIRE
LINCOLNSHIRE
Skegness
MANSFIELD
Newark-on-Trent
TF
The Wash
Belper
Sleaford
Boston
NOTTINGHAM
Elton
Hunstanton
NORFOLK
DERBY
Grantham
Spalding
KING'S LYNN
LEICESTERSHIRE

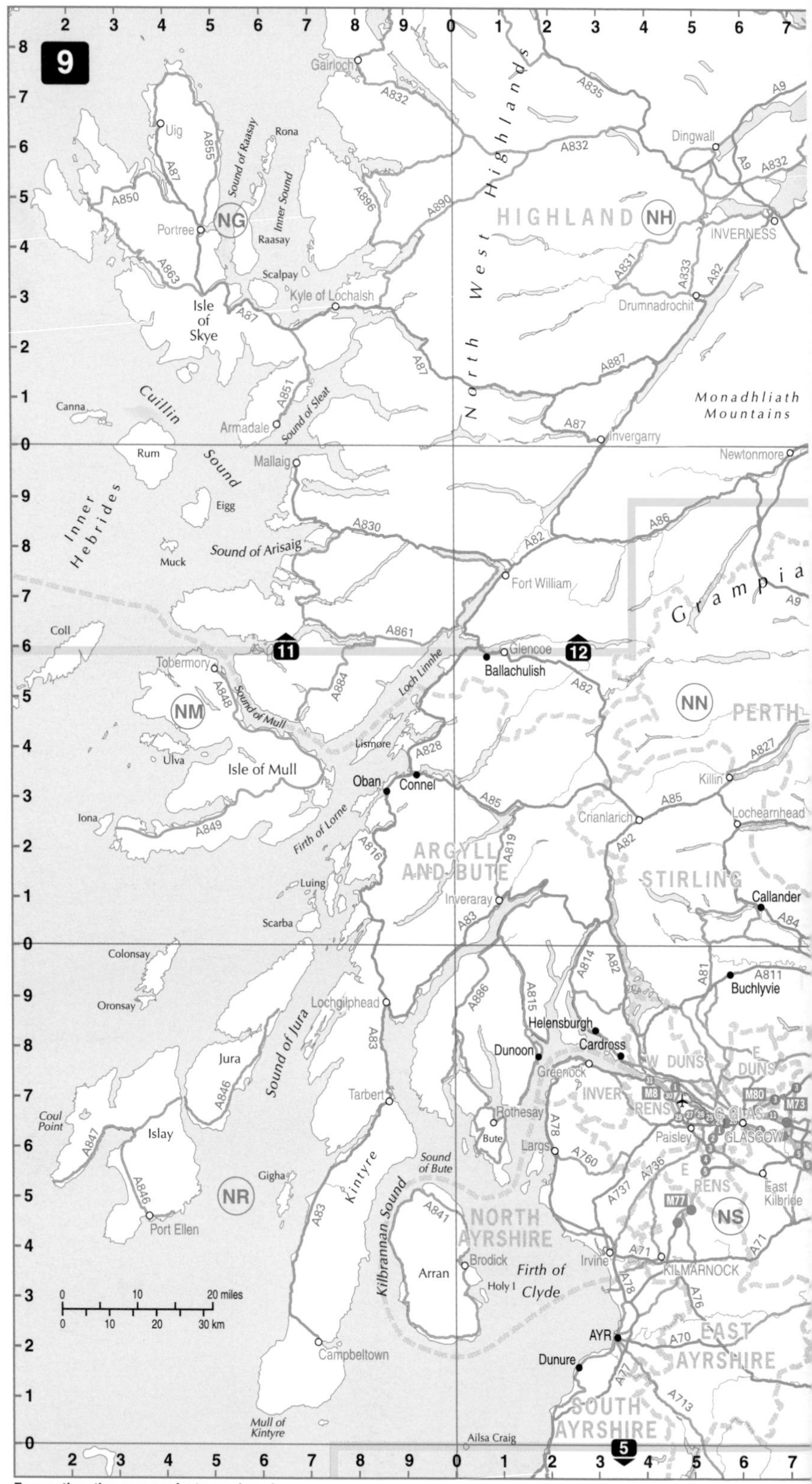

For continuation pages refer to numbered arrows

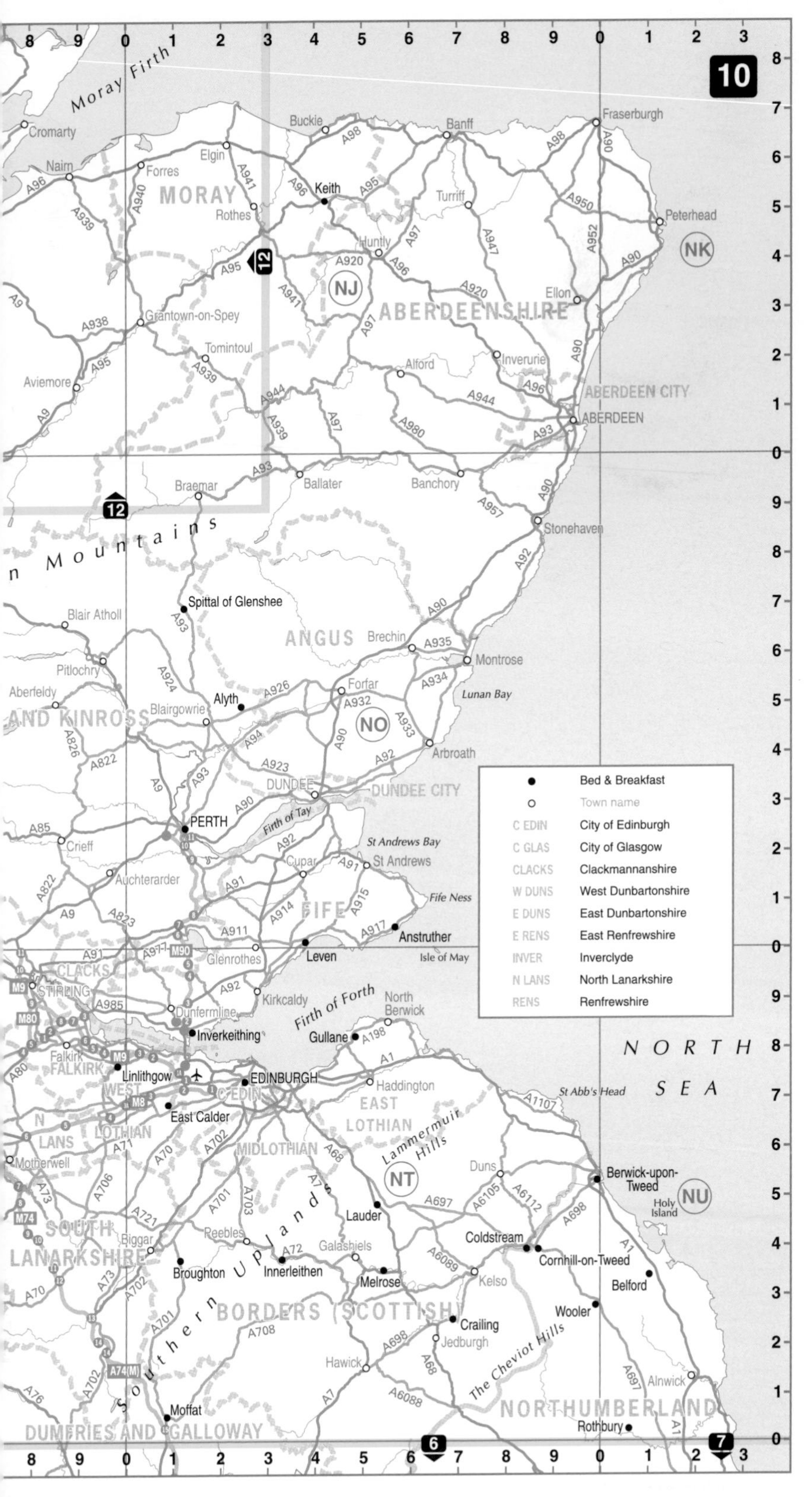
10
Moray Firth
Cromarty
Nairn
Forres
Elgin
MORAY
Rothes
Buckie
Keith
Banff
Turriff
Fraserburgh
Peterhead
Huntly
ABERDEENSHIRE
Ellon
Inverurie
Alford
ABERDEEN CITY
ABERDEEN
Grantown-on-Spey
Tomintoul
Aviemore
Braemar
Ballater
Banchory
Stonehaven
Mountains
Spittal of Glenshee
Blair Atholl
Pitlochry
Aberfeldy
AND KINROSS
Blairgowrie
Alyth
ANGUS
Brechin
Montrose
Forfar
Lunan Bay
Arbroath
DUNDEE
DUNDEE CITY
PERTH
Firth of Tay
Crieff
Auchterarder
Cupar
St Andrews Bay
St Andrews
FIFE
Fife Ness
Anstruther
Glenrothes
Leven
Isle of May
CLACKS
STIRLING
Kirkcaldy
Dunfermline
Firth of Forth
North Berwick
Inverkeithing
Gullane
Falkirk
FALKIRK
Linlithgow
EDINBURGH
C EDIN
Haddington
WEST LOTHIAN
East Calder
EAST LOTHIAN
Lammermuir Hills
N LANS
MIDLOTHIAN
Motherwell
SOUTH LANARKSHIRE
Biggar
Peebles
Broughton
Innerleithen
Galashiels
Melrose
Lauder
Duns
Berwick-upon-Tweed
Holy Island
Coldstream
Cornhill-on-Tweed
Kelso
Belford
Wooler
Southern Uplands
BORDERS (SCOTTISH)
Crailing
Jedburgh
The Cheviot Hills
Hawick
Alnwick
Moffat
NORTHUMBERLAND
Rothbury
DUMFRIES AND GALLOWAY
St Abb's Head
NORTH SEA
NJ
NK
NO
NT
NU
Bed & Breakfast
Town name
C EDIN City of Edinburgh
C GLAS City of Glasgow
CLACKS Clackmannanshire
W DUNS West Dunbartonshire
E DUNS East Dunbartonshire
E RENS East Renfrewshire
INVER Inverclyde
N LANS North Lanarkshire
RENS Renfrewshire

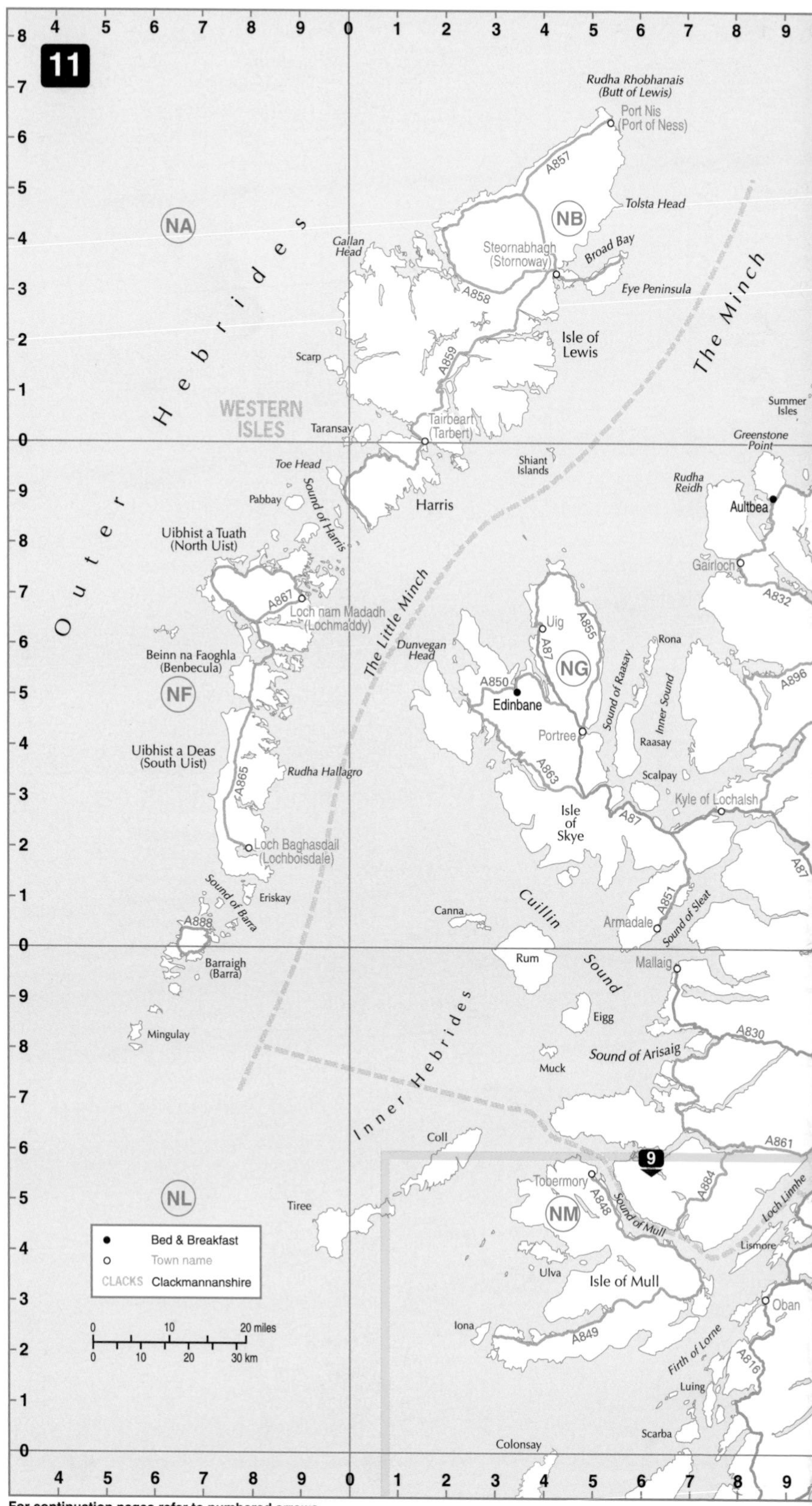
11
Rudha Rhobhanais (Butt of Lewis)
Port Nis (Port of Ness)
A857
Tolsta Head
NA
NB
Outer Hebrides
Gallan Head
Steornabhagh (Stornoway)
Broad Bay
Eye Peninsula
A858
The Minch
Isle of Lewis
Scarp
A859
WESTERN ISLES
Taransay
Tairbeart (Tarbert)
Summer Isles
Greenstone Point
Toe Head
Shiant Islands
Rudha Reidh
Pabbay
Sound of Harris
Harris
Aultbea
Uibhist a Tuath (North Uist)
Gairloch
A832
A867
Loch nam Madadh (Lochmaddy)
The Little Minch
Uig
A855
Rona
Beinn na Faoghla (Benbecula)
Dunvegan Head
A87
NG
Sound of Raasay
Inner Sound
A896
NF
A850
Edinbane
Portree
Uibhist a Deas (South Uist)
Raasay
A865
Rudha Hallagro
A863
Scalpay
Kyle of Lochalsh
Isle of Skye
Loch Baghasdail (Lochboisdale)
Sound of Barra
Eriskay
Cuillin
A851
Canna
Armadale
Sound of Sleat
A888
Rum
Sound
Mallaig
Barraigh (Barra)
Eigg
Mingulay
A830
Sound of Arisaig
Muck
Inner Hebrides
Coll
A861
9
Tobermory
A848
A884
Loch Linnhe
NL
Tiree
NM
Sound of Mull
Bed & Breakfast
Town name
CLACKS Clackmannanshire
Lismore
Ulva
Isle of Mull
Oban
0 10 20 miles
0 10 20 30 km
Iona
A849
Firth of Lorne
A816
Luing
Scarba
Colonsay
For continuation pages refer to numbered arrows

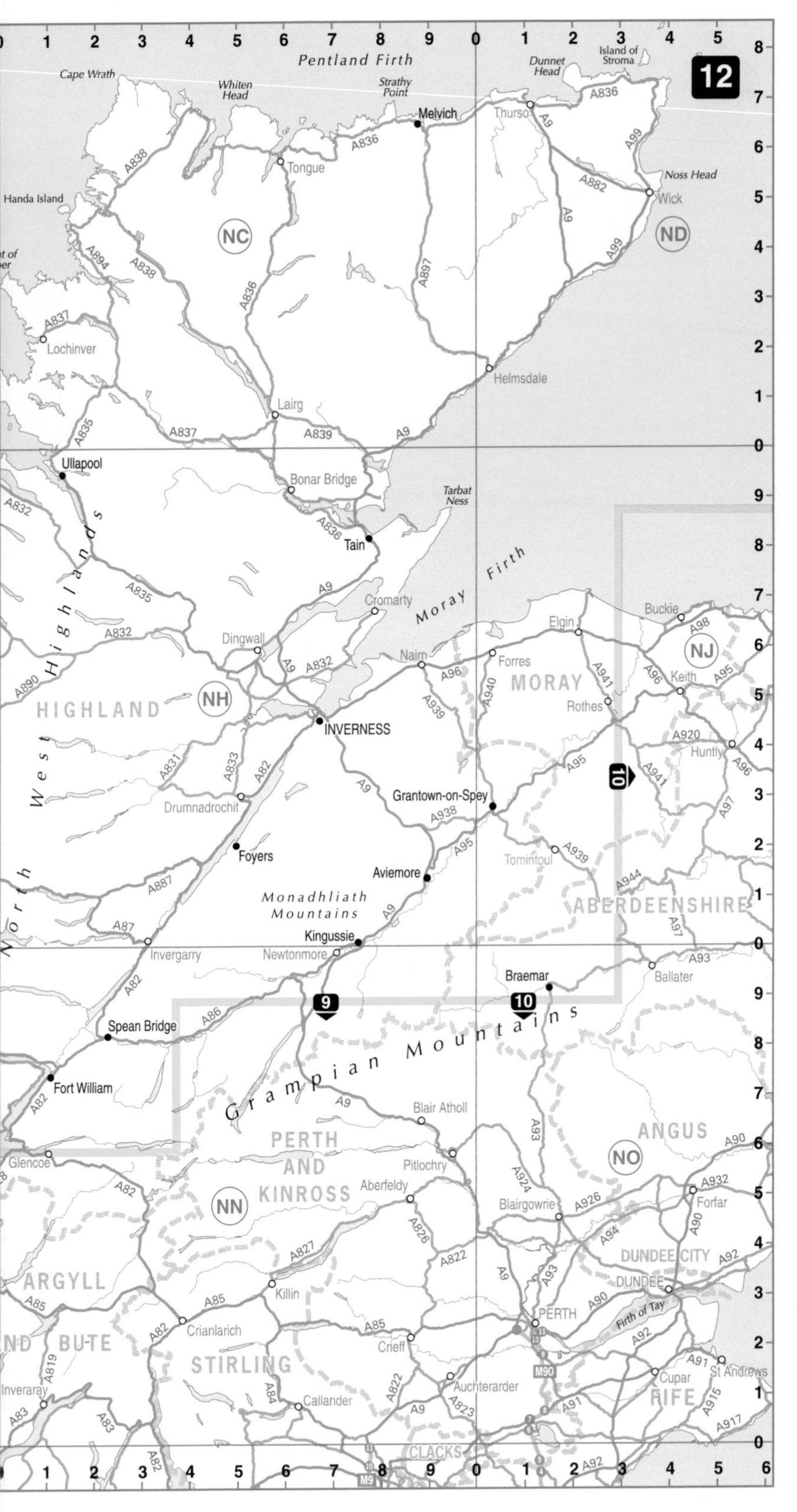
12
Pentland Firth
Cape Wrath
Whiten Head
Strathy Point
Dunnet Head
Island of Stroma
Melvich
Thurso
Tongue
Noss Head
Wick
Handa Island
NC
ND
Lochinver
Helmsdale
Lairg
Ullapool
Bonar Bridge
Tarbat Ness
Tain
Moray Firth
Cromarty
Buckie
Elgin
Dingwall
Nairn
Forres
NJ
Keith
MORAY
Rothes
HIGHLAND
NH
INVERNESS
Huntly
North West Highlands
Drumnadrochit
Grantown-on-Spey
Foyers
Tomintoul
Aviemore
Monadhliath Mountains
ABERDEENSHIRE
Kingussie
Invergarry
Newtonmore
Braemar
Ballater
Spean Bridge
Grampian Mountains
Fort William
Blair Atholl
PERTH AND KINROSS
ANGUS
NO
Glencoe
Pitlochry
Aberfeldy
Blairgowrie
Forfar
NN
DUNDEE CITY
DUNDEE
ARGYLL AND BUTE
Killin
PERTH
Firth of Tay
Crianlarich
Crieff
STIRLING
St Andrews
Cupar
Auchterarder
FIFE
Inveraray
Callander
CLACKS

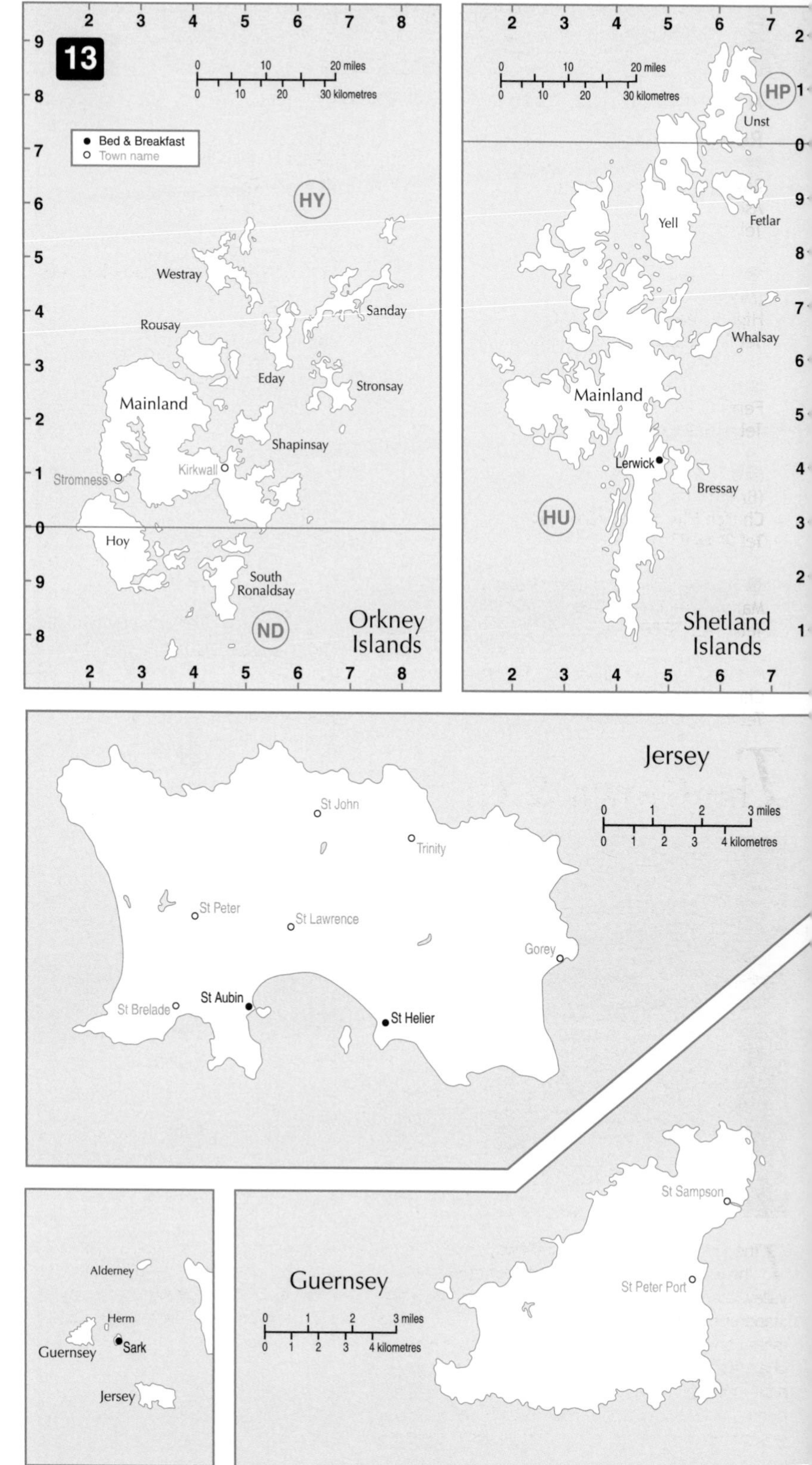

13
0
10
20 miles
0
10
20
30 kilometres
Bed & Breakfast
Town name
HY
Westray
Rousay
Sanday
Eday
Stronsay
Mainland
Shapinsay
Kirkwall
Stromness
Hoy
South Ronaldsay
ND
Orkney Islands
HP
Unst
Yell
Fetlar
Whalsay
Mainland
Lerwick
Bressay
HU
Shetland Islands
Jersey
3 miles
4 kilometres
St John
Trinity
St Peter
St Lawrence
Gorey
St Aubin
St Brelade
St Helier
St Sampson
St Peter Port
Guernsey
Alderney
Herm
Sark
Guernsey
Jersey

Berkshire

A selection of places to eat from the AA Restaurant & AA Pub guides

Restaurants

The Berystede (International)
Bagshot Road, Sunninghill
Ascot SL5 9JH
Tel 01344 623311

The Fat Duck (Modern British)
High Street, Bray SL6 2AQ
Tel 01628 580333

Waterside Inn (French)
Ferry Road, Bray SL6 2AT
Tel 01628 620691

Castle Brasserie (British, Pacific Rim)
Church Hill, Hurst RG10 0SJ
Tel 0118 934 0034

The Red House (International)
Marsh Benham RG20 8LY
Tel 01635 582017

L'Ortolan (French, British)
Church Lane, Shinfield RG2 9BY
Tel 0118 988 8500

Pubs

The Bell Inn
Aldworth RG8 9SE
Tel 01635 578272

Chequers Inn Brasserie
Dean Lane, Cookham Dean SL6 9BQ
Tel 01628 481234

The Horns
Crazies Hill RG10 8LY
Tel 0118 940 1416

The Yew Tree Inn
Hollington Cross, Andover Road
Highclere RG20 9SE
Tel 01635 253360

The Swan
Craven Road, Lower Green, Inkpen
Hungerford RG17 9DX
Tel 01488 668326

The Dundas Arms
53 Station Road
Kintbury RG17 9UT
Tel 01488 658263

The Crown & Garter ♦♦♦♦

Map ref 3 - SU36
Great Common, Inkpen,
HUNGERFORD, RG17 9QR
4m SE of Hungerford. Off A4 into Kintbury, opp corner stores onto Inkpen Rd, straight for 2m

T 01488 668325
E enquiries@crownandgarter.com
W www.crownandgarter.com

8 rooms, No smoking

Recommended in the Area

Historic Marlborough; Lambourn Downs; Salisbury Plain & Stonehenge

The 16th-century inn is tucked away in the village of the Inkpen in the heart of the beautiful Kennet valley. Owner Gillian Hern continues to raise all-round standards and friendly service is assured. The bar and restaurant were refurbished in 2004, in keeping with the character of the building, and real ales, spiced wine and a selection of malt whiskies are available. The en suite bedrooms are in a modern courtyard around a tranquil garden. Each room has a bath and power shower, a hairdryer, television and video, and tea and coffee facilities. The restaurant offers an interesting range of country dishes prepared by the resident chef from local produce.

The Swan Inn ♦♦♦♦

Map ref 3 - SU36
Craven Rd, Inkpen, HUNGERFORD, RG17 9DX
3.5m SE of Hungerford. S on Hungerford High St past railway bridge, left to Hungerford Common, right signed Inkpen

T 01488 668326
F 01488 668306
E enquiries@theswaninn-organics.co.uk
W www.theswaninn-organics.co.uk

10 rooms, S £60-£70, D £85-£95, No smoking in bedrooms or dining room, Closed 25-26 Dec

The peaceful north Wessex downs provide an idyllic setting for this 17th-century inn, located close to the highest point in the south. Outside it is a delightful picture, with white-painted walls, old tiled roof and pretty terraces. Inside there are oak beams, open fires and a warm welcome from the Harris family. The owners are organic farmers, and both the restaurant and an adjoining farm shop feature superb produce. The spacious en suite bedrooms are firmly rooted in the 21st century, with direct-dial and Internet connections. There's even a beautifully decorated bridal suite for newly weds.

Recommended in the Area
Combe Gibbet; Kennet & Avon Canal; Avebury stone circle

Weir View House Hotel ♦♦♦♦

Map ref 3 - SU67
9 Shooters Hill, PANGBOURNE, RG8 7DZ
A329 N from Pangbourne, after minirdbt opp Swan pub

T 0118 984 2120
F 0118 984 3777
E info@weirview.co.uk
W www.weirview.co.uk

9 rooms, S £75-£90, D £75-£90, No smoking, Closed 23 Dec-1 Jan

Recommended in the Area
Basildon Park (NT); Child Beale Wildlife Park; The Living Rainforest in Hampstead Norreys

As well as an enchanting setting beside the River Thames, this inviting guesthouse offers spacious en suite bedrooms (many with four-poster beds and views over the water) equipped with minibar, telephone with modem lines, tea and coffee facilities, hairdryer and trouser press. A continental breakfast is served in the bright and airy dining room, and cooked meals can be delivered to your room from the pub across the road. At weekends breakfast is arranged in your fridge the night before, so you can have a lie in. During the day coffee and tea are served in the lounge, where Internet access is available free of charge.

Bull Inn ♦♦♦♦

Map ref 3 - SU77
High St, SONNING, RG4 6UP
T 0118 969 3901
F 0118 969 7188
E bullinn@accommodating-inns.co.uk
W www.accommodating-inns.co.uk/bullinn.html
5 rooms, S £85-£125, D £85-£125, No smoking in bedrooms

The 16th-century Bull Inn stands opposite the village church. Refurbished in keeping with the original character, its lovely bedrooms are individually furnished with with high-quality fabrics and carpets, and their facilities include flat-screen televisions and DVDs. Jerome K Jerome mentions the Bull Inn in his comedy novel *Three Men in a Boat* and rooms are named from this book. Manager Dennis Mason is a real card and the epitome of a great barman. The bar blackboards display an extensive range of good pub grub and award-winning ales are sold.

RECOMMENDED IN THE AREA
River Thames; Windsor; Reading

The Old Manor ♦♦♦♦♦

Map ref 3 - SU66
Whitehouse Green, SULHAMSTEAD, RG7 4EA
M4 junct 12, A4 W, left for Theale Station, over railway, over river, right after 0.4km. Continue for 1km and turn left at x-rds & Old Manor entrance on left
T 0118 983 2423
F 0118 983 6262
E rags-r@theoldmanor.fsbusiness.co.uk
3 rooms, S £40-£60, D £80, No smoking, Closed 23 Dec-2 Jan

A haven for the discerning guest, this one-time manor house stands in 10 acres of well-kept grounds. Outside you may meet the owners' four grandchildren playing with their pony and dog, while indoors you can relish being treated like a family friend by Rosemary and Peter Sanders-Rose. The charming couple are very involved in local affairs and maintain an impeccable property. The elegant bedrooms, all with bathrooms en suite, include one with a four-poster bed and a spa bath. Good food and a complimentary glass of wine are served in the dining room, and afternoon tea is provided in the drawing room.

RECOMMENDED IN THE AREA
Basildon Park (NT); The Vyne (NT); Kennet & Avon Canal

Bristol

A selection of places to eat from the AA Restaurant & AA Pub guides

Restaurants

Arno's Manor Hotel (British, Mediterranean)
470 Bath Road, Arn's Vale BS4 3HQ
Tel 0117 971 1461

Bells Diner (European)
1-3 York Road, Montpellier BS6 5QB
Tel 0117 924 0357

Michael Caines at The Bristol Marriott Royal (European)
College Green BS1 5TA
Tel 0117 925 5100

City Café (European)
Temple Way BS1 6BF
Tel 0117 925 1001

Conrad at Jamesons (European)
Upper Maudlin Street BS2 8BJ
Tel 0117 927 6565

Glass Boat Restaurant (International)
Welsh Back BS1 4SB
Tel 0117 929 0704

Hotel du Vin & Bistrol (British, Mediterranean)
The Sugar House, Narrow Lewins Mead BS1 2NU
Tel 0117 925 5577

Howards Restaurant (British, French)
1a-2a Avon Crescent, Hotwells BS1 6XQ
Tel 0117 926 2921

riverstation (European)
The Grove BS1 4RB
Tel 0117 914 4434

Pubs

Brewery Tap
Upper Maudlin Street BS1 5BD
Tel 0117 921 3668

Highbury Vaults
164 St Michael's Hill, Cotham BS2 8DE
Tel 0117 973 3203

Downs Edge ♦♦♦♦

Map ref 2 - ST57
Saville Rd, Stoke Bishop, BRISTOL, BS9 1JA
M5 junct 17, onto A4018. At 4th rdbt right onto Parrys Ln B4054. 1st left Saville Rd, 3rd right Hollybush Ln, after 2nd speed ramp, left onto drive

T 0117 968 3264
F 0117 968 7063
E welcome@downsedge.com
W www.downsedge.com

7 rooms, S £49-£55, D £72-£75, No smoking in bedrooms or dining room, Closed Xmas-New Year

This fetching, Arts and Crafts style country house has a quiet countryside setting in the heart of the city, on the edge of Bristol's famous Durdham Downs. It stands in glorious gardens and is furnished with period pieces and paintings. The pleasant, well-equipped bedrooms have facilities en suite and the added bonus of sweeping views across the Downs - a nice finishing touch to each room is a basket full with life's little necessities. Breakfast is an impressive variety of hot and cold dishes served around one large table. There is a refined lounge and a library containing many books on Bristol.

Recommended in the Area

Clifton Suspension Bridge; Bristol Zoo; Bristol city centre

*D*ownlands House ♦♦♦♦

Map ref 2 - ST57
33 Henleaze Gardens, Henleaze, BRISTOL, BS9 4HH
M5 junct 17, signs Westbury on Trym/City Centre, past private girls' schools, Henleaze Gdns on left
T / F 0117 962 1639
E mjdownlands@blueyonder.co.uk
W www.downlandshouse.co.uk
10 rooms, S £38-£50, D £55-£72, No smoking

Combining Victorian elegance and the comforts of a family home, Downlands is perfect for a weekend break or longer holiday. The quiet setting is not far from the centre of Bristol and the smart residential area of Clifton with Brunel's spectacular suspension bridge. There are plenty of pretty, well-equipped rooms to choose from, including a large double on the ground floor. There are smart facilities en suite, and each room is thoughtfully supplied with a hairdryer, a hospitality tray and other homely touches. Relax in the lounge after a day spent exploring Bristol or its environs. The day begins with a tasty cooked breakfast served either in the delightful conservatory or the stylish dining room. The patio is a charming place on warm days.

RECOMMENDED IN THE AREA

Durdham Downs; SS Great Britain; Clifton Suspension Bridge

*W*estfield House ♦♦♦♦

Map ref 2 - ST57
37 Stoke Hill, Stoke Bishop,
BRISTOL, BS9 1LQ
T / F 0117 962 6119
E admin@westfieldhouse.net
W www.westfieldhouse.net
3 rooms, S £49.50-£79.50,
D £69.50-£95, No smoking

This large Georgian-style, family-run guesthouse makes an ideal retreat from the city lights, close to Durdham Downs and set in 2.5 acres of grounds. The very cosy bedrooms are well equipped and decorated in pastel shades. The living room centres round a fireplace while large bay windows lead onto a terrace. Owner Ann cooks more or less to order using quality local ingredients. A typical meal may include salmon en croute with pureed spinach and hollandaise sauce accompanied by potatoes dauphinoise, followed by home-made apple pie - all the better in summer when served on the patio overlooking the lovely rear garden. If you still hanker for the the city lights, Westfield house is just a short walk from Bristol city centre.

RECOMMENDED IN THE AREA

Clifton Suspension Bridge; SS Great Britain; Bristol Zoo

Cheshire

A selection of places to eat from the AA Restaurant & AA Pub guides

Restaurants

The Arkle, Chester Grosvenor (French)
Eastgate, Chester CH1 1LT
Tel 01244 324024

Crewe Hall (British)
Weston Road, Crewe CW1 6UZ
Tel 01270 253333

The Pheasant Inn (British)
Higher Burwardsley CH3 9PF
Tel 01829 770434

Mere Court Hotel (British)
Warrington Road, Mere, Knutsford WA16 0RW
Tel 01565 831000

White House Restaurant (British)
Prestbury SK10 4DG
Tel 01625 829376

Stannylands (European)
Stannylands Road, Wilmslow SK9 4EY
Tel 01625 525225

Pubs

The Grosvenor Arms
Chester Road, Aldford CH3 6HJ
Tel 01244 620228

The Bhurtpore Inn
Wrenbury Road, Aston CW5 8DQ
Tel 01270 780917

The Dysart Arms
Bowes Gate Road, Bunbury CW6 9PH
Tel 01829 260183

The Cholmondeley Arms
Cholmondeley SY14 8HN
Tel 01829 720300

The Dog Inn
Well Bank Lane, Over Peover,
Knutsford WA16 8UP
Tel 01625 861421

The Swettenham Arms
Swettenham Lane, Swettenham
CW12 2LF
Tel 01477 571284

Ash Farm Country House ♦♦♦♦♦

Map ref 6 - SJ78
Park Ln, Little Bollington,
ALTRINCHAM, WA14 4TJ
Off A56 beside Stamford Arms
T 0161 929 9290
F 0161 928 5002
E jan@ashfarm97.fsnet.co.uk
W www.ashfarm.co.uk
3 rooms, No smoking, Closed
22 Dec-5 Jan

RECOMMENDED IN THE AREA
Manchester city centre; Dunham Massey (NT); Tatton Park (NT)

An appealing 18th-century farmhouse with peaceful country views, Ash Farm is full of character and extends a warm welcome. Situated in a quiet village at the heart of National Trust countryside, the property is a short walk from Dunham Deer Park and the Bridgewater Canal and convenient for the M56 and M6 - Manchester Airport is just 6 miles away. Several rooms have antique beds and all provide facilities en suite. Finishing touches include bathrobes, fresh fruit, mineral water, biscuits and toiletries. There is an attractive lounge and a smart breakfast room with views over the valley. No children under 12 years.

Alton Lodge Hotel ♦♦♦♦

Map ref 5 - SJ46
78 Hoole Rd, CHESTER, CH2 3NT
M53 junct 12, A56 into Chester, house 0.5m on right opp playing field

T 01244 310213
F 01244 319206
E enquiries@altonlodge.co.uk
W www.altonlodge.co.uk

17 rooms, S £60-£68, D £80-£98, No smoking in bedrooms or dining room, Closed Xmas-New Year

Alton Lodge is a delightful, well-cared for property only 1 mile from the city centre and well placed for the Chester ring road. The smart, lodge-style bedrooms have been thoughtfully designed and fitted with quality pine furniture - you can be sure of finding all of the comforts of home and more. Business and leisure guests are equally well catered for, and your own key allows you to come and go at will. The open-plan public areas are bright and include a comfortable, spacious bar-lounge where snacks are served, and an attractive dining room offering à la carte. The bar and restaurant are only open Monday to Thursday, and during weekends the hotel operates solely as a motel-style bed and breakfast. There is plenty of parking on the premises.

Recommended in the Area

Chester Zoo; Blue Planet Aquarium; Cheshire Oaks

Oakland House ♦♦♦♦

Map ref 6 - SJ65
252 Newcastle Rd, Shavington, NANTWICH, CW5 7ET
2m E of Nantwich. Off A500 into Shavington, house 500yds W of village
T 01270 567134
E enquiries@oaklandhouseonline.co.uk
W www.oaklandhouseonline.co.uk
9 rooms, S £34-£39, D £49-£54, No smoking

There are splendid views from the front and rear of Oakland House, and a warm welcome awaits you from the friendly hosts, Sue and Tony Murphy. The family-run guesthouse is in a semi-rural location convenient for the M6 and various attractions. The en suite bedrooms, some of which are in an adjacent chalet, are attractively furnished and well equipped with hairdryers and tea and coffee facilities. There is a spacious sitting room and the modern conservatory looks across a pretty garden to Cheshire countryside. Enjoy substantial breakfasts, or simpler alternatives, in a relaxed atmosphere around a large family table.

RECOMMENDED IN THE AREA

Stapeley Water Gardens; Nantwich; Bridgemere Garden World

Hill House Farm ♦♦♦♦

Map ref 6 - SJ56
Rushton, TARPORLEY, CW6 9AU
1.5m E of Tarporley. Off A51-A49 to Eaton, continue E for Rushton, right onto The Hall Ln, farm 0.5m
T 01829 732238
F 01829 733929
E enquiries@hillhousefarm-cheshire.co.uk
W www.hillhousefarm-cheshire.co
3 rooms, S £35-£40, D £60-£65, No smoking, Closed Xmas-New Year

Elegant decor and furnishings highlight the original features of this Victorian house. It stands amid Cheshire countryside in a peaceful garden surrounded by 14 acres of paddocks and pasture. The stylish bedrooms balance practicality and homeliness, with lots of thoughtful extras to enhance your comfort - all the rooms are en suite. The spacious drawing room epitomises the period character of the house, and the log fire makes this a cosy spot to retire to in cold weather. The very friendly owners serve delicious breakfasts in the traditional breakfast room.

RECOMMENDED IN THE AREA

Historic Chester; Beeston Castle; Oulton Park

A selection of places to eat from the AA Restaurant & AA Pub guides

Restaurants

Langmans Restaurant (British)
3 Church Street, Callington PL17 7RE
Tel 01579 384933

Harbourside Restaurant (British)
Greenbank Hotel, Harbourside, Falmouth
TR11 2SR
Tel 01326 312440

Well House Hotel (British)
St Keyne, Liskeard PL14 4RN
Tel 01579 342001

The Seafood Restaurant (International)
Riverside, Padstow PL28 8BY
Tel 01841 532700

The Summerhouse (Mediterranean)
Cornwall Terrace, Penzance TR18 4HL
Tel 01736 363744

Idle Rocks Hotel (European)
Harbour Side, St Mawes TR2 5AN
Tel 01326 270771

Pubs

Godolphin Arms
Marazion TR17 0EN
Tel 01736 710202

The Halfway House Inn
Fore Street, Kingsand PL10 1NA
Tel 01752 822279

The Halzephron Inn
Gunwalloe TR12 7QB
Tel 01326 240406

Pandora Inn
Restronguet Creek, Mylor Bridge TR11 5ST
01326 372678

Royal Oak Inn
Duke Street, Lostwithiel PL22 0AQ
Tel 01208 872552

The Shipwright Arms
Helford TR12 6JX
Tel 01326 231235

Tolcarne House Hotel ♦♦♦♦

Map ref 1 - SX09
Tintagel Rd, BOSCASTLE,
PL35 0AS
At junct B3266 & B3263 in Boscastle
T / F 01840 250654
E crowntolhouse@eclipse.co.uk
W www.milford.co.uk/go/tolcarne.html
8 rooms, S £36-£38, D £60-£78,
Closed Nov-Feb

Graham and Margaret Crown have lived and worked at Tolcarne House for over 11 years, providing friendly service in a beautiful environment. The house stands in an elevated position 800 yards from the sea amid delightful grounds. A short walk through the village takes you to the Elizabethan harbour, now a National Trust property. Bedrooms, each named after a local beauty spot, are individually decorated and offer sea or valley views. All have facilities en suite, hospitality trays, clock radios and hairdryers. Guests eat at individual tables in the dining room, where the home-cooked dinner is a choice of meat or fish dishes.

Recommended in the Area

Tintagel Castle; Bodmin Moor; Pencarrow House

Bude Haven Hotel ♦♦♦♦

Map ref 1 - SS20
Flexbury Av, BUDE, EX23 8NS
Off A39 at Stratton, signs to town centre. Through town centre & round right bend. Continue 300yds with golf course either side. 1st left & 1st right, right onto Creathorne Rd, hotel on corner

Ⓣ 01288 352305
Ⓕ 01288 352662
Ⓔ enquiries@budehavenhotel.com
Ⓦ www.budehavenhotel.com

10 rooms, S £25.50-£35, D £53-£70, No smoking

Bude Haven is a charming building in a quiet residential area, with the town centre and two lovely beaches just a short walk away. Natural hosts Alison and Richard Long foster a friendly, homely atmosphere. They offer comfortable en suite bedrooms, each with a clock radio, hairdryer and a beverage tray. An inviting lounge features a television, video and DVD, music centre, books and games. There is a well-stocked bar and interesting meals are served in the evening. For complete pampering retreat to the hot tub in the secluded garden, or the services of the qualified masseuse.

RECOMMENDED IN THE AREA

South West Coast Path; Tintagel; The Eden Project

Cotswold House Hotel ♦♦♦♦

Map ref 1 - SW83
49 Melvill Rd, FALMOUTH, TR11 4DF
Signs for station and beaches, onto Dracaena Av, over 2 rdbts onto Melvill Rd, house on right

Ⓣ 01326 312077
Ⓔ info@cotswoldhousehotel.com
Ⓦ www.cotswoldhousehotel.com

10 rooms, D £50-£75, No smoking

With the beach and harbour just a short walk away, this small family-run hotel is ideal for a holiday or short stay. The smart Victorian property is also close to the picturesque cobbled town centre. All bedrooms have a bath or shower room en suite, hospitality trays, and many have lovely views of the sea and the river. Well-cooked traditional cuisine is a feature of a stay here, and the friendly owners offer attentive service. The convivial bar is another plus at this relaxed house, and a popular place for socializing in the evening.

RECOMMENDED IN THE AREA

Falmouth National Maritime Museum; The Eden Project; Trebah & Glendurgan gardens

Dolvean Hotel ♦♦♦♦♦

Map ref 1 - SW83
50 Melvill Rd, FALMOUTH, TR11 4DQ
On road to Pendennis Castle & National Maritime Museum

T 01326 313658
F 01326 313995
E reservations@dolvean.co.uk
W www.dolvean.co.uk

11 rooms, S £35-£40, D £70-£90, No smoking, Closed Xmas

Recommended in the Area

Pendennis Castle; Falmouth National Maritime Museum; Trebah Garden

The Dolvean is a Victorian residence situated between the beach and Falmouth's internationally renowned harbour, which shelters everything from tall ships to cruise liners. Paul and Carol Crocker, resident proprietors since 1994, are passionate collectors of antiques, curios, old books (on travel, cookery, remedies, household hints and woodwork), advertising memorabilia, sewing machines and sewing ephemera. These fascinating collections have spilled out of their home and into every corner of Dolvean, and the Crockers enjoy sharing their interests with guests, some of whom have contributed to the collections. Pretty pictures and an abundance of lace and ribbon bring a special touch to the bedrooms, each of which has its own character. All the rooms have full facilities en suite with fluffy towels and luxury toiletries. Thoughtful extras include hospitality trays, Cornish mineral water and chocolates by your bed. The traditional breakfast menu uses only the finest Cornish produce available. Enclosed car park provided.

Rosemullion Private Hotel ♦♦♦♦

Map ref 1 - SW83
Gyllyngvase Hill, FALMOUTH, TR11 4DF
Ⓣ 01326 314690
Ⓕ 01326 210098
Ⓔ gail@rosemullionhotel.demon.co.uk
13 rooms, S £30-£35, D £53-£60, No smoking, Closed 23-27 Dec

Built towards the end of the 19th century, this striking mock-Tudor hotel caters for the discerning guest. Hospitality and customer care are top of the owners' priorities, and the peaceful atmosphere draws people back again and again. Bedrooms are beautifully decorated and furnished, and some have glorious views over the bay - two have their own balconies. Breakfast is served in a smart wood-panelled dining room, and the drawing room with its tranquil colour scheme and flower arrangements is delightful for relaxing. Rosemullion is just a stroll from Falmouth's main beach, and handy for the town and harbour.

RECOMMENDED IN THE AREA
Gyllyngvase Beach & Pendennis Castle; Helford River & Trebah Garden; The Eden Project

---

Tregerrick Farm B & B ♦♦♦♦

Map ref 1 - SW94
GORRAN, PL26 6NF
B3273 S from St Austell. After Pentewan Sands campsite, right at top of hill for Heligan Gardens. Continue past entrance for 3m, farm on left
Ⓣ / Ⓕ 01726 843418
Ⓔ fandc.thomas@btconnect.com
Ⓦ www.tregerrickfarm.co.uk
4 rooms, D £60-£70, No smoking

A traditional farm with a pedigree South Devon herd provides the peaceful setting for this Victorian guesthouse. Host Christine Thomas is passionate about painting and design, and her work can be admired in the gallery dining room. Elsewhere the double en suite bedrooms and an annexe are ideal for families or two couples, are well furnished and equipped with hairdryers, hospitality trays and toiletries. Tasty breakfasts of local and home-made produce are served around a large dining table. Cream teas offered on arrival are another special feature of Tregerrick.

RECOMMENDED IN THE AREA
The Lost Gardens of Heligan; The Eden Project; South West Coast Path

Calize Country House ◆◆◆◆

Map ref 1 - SW53
Prosper Hill, Gwithian, HAYLE, TR27 5BW
B3301 Hayle to Portreath. In Gwithian at Red River Inn, house 350yds up hill on left

T / F 01736 753268
E jillywhitaker@firenet.uk.net
W www.calize.co.uk

4 rooms, S £35-£45, D £70-£80, No smoking

This refurbished establishment has superb views of the sea and countryside, and is close to the beaches and coves of West Penwith. Jilly and Nigel Whitaker are naturally friendly and their hospitality is outstanding (home-made cake and tea are offered on arrival). Guests are invited to share their comfortable lounge, which has a log-burning fire during colder months. Memorable breakfasts are served around a communal table with sea views - treats include home made walnut bread and blackberry jelly, seeded toast, fresh fruit, creamy scrambled eggs and fresh smoked salmon. And don't forget to ask about the local seals.

RECOMMENDED IN THE AREA

South West Coast Path; St Ives Bay; St Michael's Mount (NT)

Colvennor Farmhouse ◆◆◆◆

Map ref 1 - SW62
Cury, HELSTON, TR12 7BJ
A3083 Helston-Lizard, across rdbt at end of airfield, next right to Cury/Poldhu Cove, continue 1.4m, farm on right at top of hill

T 01326 241208
E colvennor@aol.com
W www.cornwall-online.co.uk/colvennor

3 rooms, S £30-£36, D £46-£54, No smoking, Closed Dec-Jan

Expect far-reaching rural views from this peaceful setting, where Bob and Jackie Royds ensure a comfortable stay and excellent customer care at their granite farmhouse. Set in 1 acre of secluded and tranquil gardens, the Grade II listed building dates from the 17th century and is an ideal base for touring the Lizard peninsula. The delightful cottage-style bedrooms, two double and one twin, have good outlooks and facilities en suite. Very good freshly cooked breakfasts using local produce are served in the dining room, which overlooks the cottage garden, and a beamed lounge complete with a stone fireplace provides a comfortable retreat.

RECOMMENDED IN THE AREA

Lizard Point; The Eden Project; St Ives

Hurdon Farm ♦♦♦♦

Map ref 1 - SX38
LAUNCESTON, PL15 9LS
A30 onto A388 to Launceston, at rdbt exit for hospital, 2nd right signed Trebullett, premises 1st on right
01566 772955
6 rooms, No smoking, Closed Nov-Apr

RECOMMENDED IN THE AREA
The Eden Project; South West Coast Path; Dartmoor & Bodmin Moor

Hurdon Farm is particularly appealing for its delightful setting and the high standard of accommodation provided in the 18th-century farmhouse. Fresh flowers and a well-stocked tea tray welcome guests to the individually decorated bedrooms. Single, double, triple and family rooms are available, all with bathrooms en suite and useful extras include hairdryers. Guests also have use of telephone and ironing facilities. Evening meals are available by arrangement, using only the best of local produce - don't miss the home-made puddings and farm-fresh clotted cream - and special diets can be catered for. This is a non-smoking house and children are welcome.

Withnoe Farm ♦♦♦♦

Map ref 1 - SX38
Tavistock Rd, LAUNCESTON, PL15 9LG
On A388 towards Plymouth, opp route sign Tavistock (B3362) 13, Liskeard (A390) 19 and Plymouth (A38) 24
01566 772523
3 rooms, S £25-£30, D £48-£52, No smoking, Closed Dec-Jan

RECOMMENDED IN THE AREA
The Eden Project; South West Coast Path; Dartmoor

Mrs Avril Colwill's bed and breakfast business has been established at Withnoe Farm for over 30 years, and she prides herself on her friendly and helpful service. Her spacious home is immaculately kept, set back from the Tavistock road in large gardens with far reaching views of the valley and grazing cattle. Accommodation is provided in double rooms, either en suite or with private facilities. A good breakfast is served in the dining room, from where the views are quite breathtaking. The farmhouse is convenient for the A30 and many attractions, and just 1 mile from the centre of Launceston. There is plenty of parking space.

Trecarne House ♦♦♦♦

Map ref 1 - SX26

Penhale Grange, St Cleer, LISKEARD, PL14 5EB

B3254 N from Liskeard to St Cleer. Right at Post Office, 3rd left after church, 2nd right, house on right

T / F 01579 343543
E trish@trecarnehouse.co.uk
W www.trecarnehouse.co.uk

3 rooms, S £45-£55, D £66-£99, No smoking

RECOMMENDED IN THE AREA

The Eden Project; The Hurlers Stone Circle; The Lost Gardens of Heligan

With Bodmin Moor right on the doorstep, this friendly guesthouse has beautiful rural views and plenty of peace and quiet. The large garden is a haven for children, who are made to feel very welcome. A trampoline, outdoor table tennis and a pool table are provided, and indoors the atmosphere is relaxed and informal. Breakfast can be taken at any time before 11.30 am, in either the smart dining room or a spacious conservatory, and there is a comfortable lounge with a large Cornish slate and stone fireplace. The individually named bedrooms have a Scandinavian feel with their stripped pine floors, and all come equipped with hairdryers and tea and coffee facilities, plus many thoughtful extras and videos. Some rooms have sofas, armchairs and French windows, and are either en suite or have a private bathroom. Trecarne House is at the end of a country lane, and the village, with its pubs serving evening meals, is just a stroll away. Children are half price when sharing with their parents.

*B*ay View Farm ♦♦♦♦

Map ref 1 - SX25
St Martins, LOOE, PL13 1NZ
2m NE of Looe. Off B3253 for Monkey Sanctuary, farm signed
Ⓣ / Ⓕ 01503 265922
Ⓦ www.looedirectory.co.uk/bay-view-farm.htm
2 rooms, S £25-£27, D £50-£55, No smoking

RECOMMENDED IN THE AREA

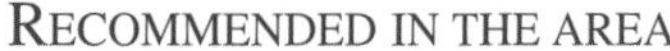

The Lost Gardens of Heligan; The Eden Project; Looe

A genuine Cornish welcome, tranquillity and great food are the hallmarks of Bay View Farm. Host Mrs Elford is a delightful lady and it's easy to see why you are drawn back to this special place again and again. The renovated and extended bungalow has a truly spectacular spot with ever-changing views across Looe Bay, and is beautifully decorated and furnished throughout to give a light, spacious feel. The en suite bedrooms are very individual - one is huge with comfy sofas and a spectacular view, the other smaller but still very inviting. Relax at the end of the day either in the lounge or on the lovely patio and watch the sun set over Looe. Breakfasts are substantial and the evening meals feature home-made desserts accompanied by clotted cream - not be missed. If you do choose to eat out there are numerous restaurants and pubs nearby. The coastal path outside the entrance takes you to Millendreath beach and on to Looe and Polperro.

Bucklawren Farm ♦♦♦♦

Map ref 1 - SX25
St Martin-by-Looe, LOOE,
PL13 1NZ
B3253 from Looe to Plymouth, 2m right to Monkey Sanctuary, 1m right to Bucklawren, farmhouse 0.5m on left
T 01503 240738
F 01503 240481
E bucklawren@btopenworld.com
W www.bucklawren.com
6 rooms, S £28.50-£35, D £50-£57, No smoking, Closed Nov-Feb

With the sea and a lovely beach just 1 mile away, this spacious 19th-century farmhouse is the perfect setting for a holiday. Set in 500 acres of farmland close to Looe, you are assured of peace and quiet. Front-facing rooms have spectacular sea views, and all bedrooms are attractively furnished; one room is on the ground floor. Tasty farm breakfasts are served in the dining room, while the Granary restaurant in an adjacent converted barn is the setting for evening meals made from fresh local produce. Jean Henly is a charming and friendly hostess.

RECOMMENDED IN THE AREA
The Eden Project; Fishing villages of Looe & Polperro; Lanhydrock (NT)

Coombe Farm ♦♦♦♦

Map ref 1 - SX25
Widegates, LOOE, PL13 1QN
3.5m E of Looe on B3253 just S of Widegates
T 01503 240223
E coombe_farm@hotmail.com
W www.coombefarmhotel.co.uk
3 rooms, S £55-£73, D £68-£78, No smoking

RECOMMENDED IN THE AREA
The Eden Project; Bodmin Moor; West & East Looe

Distinctive accommodation and perfect solitude - you cannot fail to relax here in the 11 acres of lawns and woods with views down a valley to the sea. An additional bonus is the outdoor heated swimming pool. This appealing house is admired for its warm, friendly atmosphere and is convenient for sandy beaches, attractions and glorious walks. Spacious garden rooms are housed in a converted stone barn and have beamed ceilings and stone features. Each has their own door into the gardens and a dining area with breakfast delivered to your room. Decorated in a fresh and cheerful fashion, they have shower rooms en suite, modern facilities, and one room is ideal for families.

Dovers House ♦♦♦♦

Map ref 1 - SX25
St Martins Rd, LOOE, PL13 1PB
On B3253 towards Looe, 1.7m from harbour

Ⓣ 01503 265468
Ⓔ twhyte@btconnect.com
Ⓦ www.dovershouse.co.uk

3 rooms, D £55-£85, No smoking, Closed 21-27 Dec

RECOMMENDED IN THE AREA

Lanhyrock (NT); Dobwalls Adenuture Park; The Eden Project

Bright and cheerful holiday accommodation away from the hustle, but only a short drive from the historic fishing port of Looe - this is an ideal base for exploring north Cornwall's many attractions, splendid scenery and sandy beaches. The charming hosts take hospitality and good housekeeping most seriously. Refurbished, the bright pretty bedrooms, including a family room, are surprisingly spacious and very well equipped, are en suite, and have large picture windows with wide views across the attractive grounds. A good traditional English breakfast, served in the lovely, sunny conservatory, provides a hearty start to the day.

Trehaven Manor Hotel ♦♦♦♦

Map ref 1 - SX25
Station Rd, LOOE, PL13 1HN
In East Looe between railway station & bridge

Ⓣ 01503 262028
Ⓕ 01503 265613
Ⓔ enquiries@trehavenhotel.co.uk
Ⓦ www.trehavenhotel.co.uk

7 rooms, D £60-£110, No smoking

RECOMMENDED IN THE AREA

Polperro; Looe town & beach; St Mellion Golf Course

The enthusiastic owners of Trehaven Manor are a young family attracted to the hotel because of its stunning location. Neil and Ella Hipkiss are friendly and committed to providing the best service. Originating in the mid-18th century and built from Cornish stone, the house offers a taste of gracious living in spacious surroundings. The en suite bedrooms mostly have a spectacular outlook over the estuary and the bridge that connects East and West Looe. With attractive coordinated fabrics, quality furnishings and thoughtful extras such as clocks and hairdryers, the rooms provide a high level of comfort and style. Guests are welcomed on arrival with home-made scones and Cornish clotted cream in the lounge. Fresh local produce again features at breakfast, served in the bay-fronted dining room overlooking the estuary. For evening meals, Neil and Ella can recommend restaurants, and have a collection of local menus; evening meals are available on request.

Woodlands ♦♦♦♦

Map ref 1 - SX25
St Martins Rd, LOOE, PL13 1LP
On B3253, 1m from St Martin's Church
T 01503 264405
W www.looedirectory.co.uk
5 rooms, D £56-£70, No smoking, Closed Dec-Jan

Woodlands is a lovely Victorian country house with stunning views over the peaceful Looe estuary and valley. An attractive wood borders one side of the property, and the harbour and beaches are within walking distance. Bedrooms are well equipped, including double, twin and single rooms, with facilities en suite; two rooms are easily adapted into family accommodation. Wherever possible, local produce goes into the enjoyable breakfasts which are served at a relaxed pace in the elegant dining room. Delicious three-course dinners are available by arrangement. Woodlands has on-site parking.

RECOMMENDED IN THE AREA

The Eden Project; South West Coast Path; Lanhydrock (NT)

Kerryanna Country House ♦♦♦♦

Map ref 1 - SX04
Treleaven Farm, Valley Rd, MEVAGISSEY, PL26 6SA
B3273 into village, turn right by bowling green
T / F 01726 843558
E linda.hennah@btinternet.com
W www.kerryanna.co.uk
6 rooms, D £64-£80, No smoking, Closed Nov-Feb

RECOMMENDED IN THE AREA

The Lost Gardens of Heligan; The Eden Project; sandy beaches

Set on the outskirts of this peaceful fishing village, and just a stroll from bustling harbour, Kerryanna was once a dairy and beef farm, the Hennah family home since the 1950s. Now retired from farming, the owners concentrate on ensuring your stay is as comfortable as possible. Furnished with flair, the en suite bedrooms have personal touches such as beverage trays, fresh flowers, pot-pourri and toiletries; two have romantic lace canopies over the beds. Breakfast presents plenty of choice, including a vegetarian option and dishes using locally caught fish. There are three lounge areas - one is a conservatory full of exotic plants. The well-tended mature gardens have an added attraction of a secluded swimming pool.

Degembris Farmhouse ♦♦♦♦

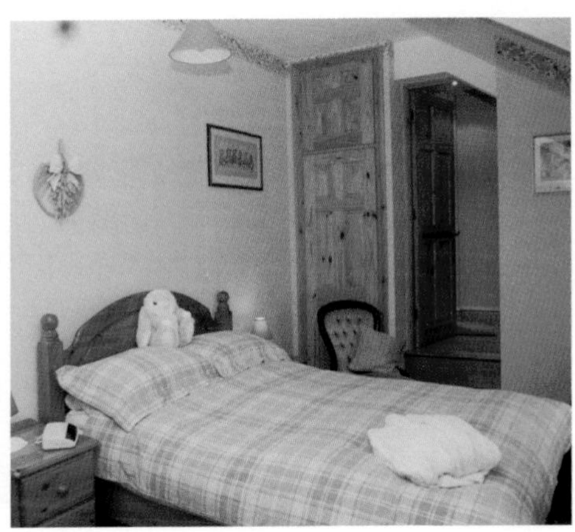

Map ref 1 - SW86

St Newlyn East, NEWQUAY,
TR8 5HY

A30 onto slip road for Summercourt, at x-rds right towards Newquay on A3058, 3rd left to St Newlyn East & 2nd left

T 01872 510555
F 01872 510230
E kathy@degembris.co.uk
W www.degembris.co.uk

5 rooms, S £28, D £54-£60, No smoking, Closed Xmas

RECOMMENDED IN THE AREA

The Eden Project; Trerice (NT); The Lost Gardens of Heligan

Degembris is a Grade II listed farmhouse, dating from the 16th to the early 17th century with 18th-century additions. The stone building has an unusual slate-hung exterior. The Woodley family first owned the farm in 1893 and these days it is in the capable hands of Roger and Kathy Woodley. Their farm overlooks a wooded valley, where they have established a country trail to help preserve the wildlife and the bluebell walks in spring. A good choice of accommodation includes single, double, twin and family rooms, three with facilities en suite. Bedrooms are individually decorated and each one has a hairdryer, complimentary tea and coffee, electric blanket and heating. The comfortable sitting room comes with books and games, and traditional farmhouse cooking is served at separate tables in the beamed dining room. Numerous attractions are within easy reach - the coastline, National Trust properties and famous Cornish gardens.

Cross House Hotel ♦♦♦♦♦

Map ref 1 - SW97
Church St, PADSTOW, PL28 8BG
A389 into town, one way past church, sharp left 50yds
T 01841 532391
F 01841 533633
E info@crosshouse.co.uk
W www.crosshouse.co.uk
11 rooms, D £70-£125, No smoking

RECOMMENDED IN THE AREA

Camel Trail Cycle Path; Prideaux Place; Tintagel Castle

Nestling in the heart of popular Padstow, Cross House is one of the town's most historic buildings. It was formerly owned by John Tredwen, Padstow's last sailing ship builder. A friendly and relaxed atmosphere prevails at this delightful Grade II listed Georgian house, which is a short walk from the picturesque harbour, and close to all amenities including some excellent restaurants. The house has been lovingly refurbished to a high standard of luxury and relaxation. The elegant bedrooms and bathrooms are spacious, attractively furnished and complemented by an impressive range of accessories. Two sumptuous lounges are available and the property is licensed. A choice of full English or continental breakfast is served in the cosy dining room.

The Old Mill House ♦♦♦♦

Map ref 1 - SW97
PADSTOW, PL27 7QT
A389 between Wadebridge & Padstow, in centre of Little Petherick
T 01841 540388
F 01841 540406
E enquiries@theoldmillhouse.com
W www.theoldmillhouse.com
7 rooms, S £70-£105, D £70-£105, No smoking, Closed Nov-Jan

The Grade II listed Old Mill House stands next to a gentle stream in an Area of Outstanding Natural Beauty just 2 miles from Padstow. The idyllic converted corn mill and millhouse date from the 18th and 19th centuries and have attractive secluded gardens with a variety of resident wildlife. The rooms are individually decorated, well equipped and have tea and coffee facilities - all have good views, either over the garden or the village and bridge. An extensive breakfast is served in the original mill room where the mill wheel still turns. Four-course dinners are also served here with a daily-changing menu using local ingredients, plus a comprehensive wine list. No pets or children under 14.

RECOMMENDED IN THE AREA

The Eden Project; The Lost Gardens of Heligan; Camel Trail Cycle Path

Chy-an-Mor Hotel ♦♦♦♦♦

Map ref 1 - SW43

15 Regent Ter, PENZANCE, TR18 4DW

A30 to Penzance, at railway station follow road along harbour front onto Promenade Rd, pass Jubilee Pool, right at Stanley Hotel

T / F 01736 363441
E reception@chyanmor.co.uk
W www.chyanmor.co.uk

10 rooms, S £32-£41, D £56-£88, No smoking, Closed Nov-Jan

RECOMMENDED IN THE AREA

St Michael's Mount (NT); Minack Theatre; Land's End

This elegant Georgian property has an attractive sea-facing location near to Mount's Bay and the Promenade. The terrace was built in the 1830s and the house is now Grade II listed. Smart black railings and a short flight of steps lead to the impressive front door, and inside are spacious, high-ceilinged public rooms that are a feature of this period dwelling. Linger over the changing sea views in the stylish lounge, or there is the large, welcoming dining room with parquet flooring and individual tables.

Owners Valerie and David Smith have refurbished their home to a high standard, and bedrooms have been thoughtfully designed for your comfort. Some of the en suite rooms are less spacious than others, but the many thoughtful extras bring a homely touch. All rooms have showers, and there are clock radios, hairdryers and courtesy trays. Breakfast is a tasty and satisfying start to the day. The hotel is totally non-smoking.

The Summerhouse ♦♦♦♦♦

Map ref 1 - SW43
Cornwall Ter, PENZANCE, TR18 4HL
A30 to Penzance, at railway station follow road along harbour front onto Promenade Rd, pass Jubilee Pool, right after Queens Hotel, Summerhouse 30yds on left

T 01736 363744
F 01736 360959
E reception@summerhouse-cornwall.com
W www.summerhouse-cornwall.com

5 rooms, D £80-£95, No smoking in bedrooms or dining room, Closed Dec-Feb

RECOMMENDED IN THE AREA

St Michael's Mount (NT); Land's End; The Minack Theatre

The philosophy of the Summerhouse is great food, beautiful surroundings and a happy atmosphere - the perfect seaside retreat for jaded townies. It is a stunning Grade II listed Regency house with bold decor and a curving glass-walled tower filling the house with light. Fresh flowers are among the thoughtful extras provided in the en suite bedrooms, and interesting family pieces and collectables enhance the individually decorated rooms. Fresh local and regional produce is simply prepared to provide memorable dining from a daily changing menu. Dishes are distinctively Mediterranean, echoing the bistro food of France and Italy. Fish and shellfish always feature, and the rich Cornish puddings are hard to resist. The restaurant opens out on to a walled garden with terracotta pots, sub-tropical planting and attractive blue tables and chairs, where in warmer weather evening drinks and dinner can be enjoyed.

Blue Seas Hotel ♦♦♦♦

Map ref 1 - SW43
13 Regent Ter, PENZANCE, TR18 4DW
A30 to Penzance, at railway station follow road along harbour front onto Promenade Rd. Opp Jubilee Bathing Pool, Regent Ter 2nd right

T / F 01736 364744
E blueseas@ukonline.co.uk
W www.blueseashotel-penzance.co.uk

9 rooms, S £30-£35, D £56-£70, No smoking, Closed Dec-Jan

RECOMMENDED IN THE AREA

St Michael's Mount (NT); The Minack Theatre; Mousehole

Genuine hospitality is assured at this family-run hotel situated in a south-facing Georgian terrace overlooking Mount's Bay. The attractive Grade II listed house has a sheltered front garden where guests can sit and enjoy the mild Cornish weather. Bedrooms are pleasantly appointed and most have stunning views across the bay towards Newlyn - nice touches include fresh flowers and chocolates. The lounge and reading room have information to help you plan the next excursion. Breakfast choices range from full English (savour the scrambled eggs and smoked salmon) to a continental buffet, with fresh fruit and a vegetarian option.

Ednovean Farm ♦♦♦♦♦

Map ref 1 - SW52
PERRANUTHNOE, TR20 9LZ
Off A394 Penzance-Helston towards Perranuthnoe at Dynasty Restaurant, farm drive on left on bend by post box

T 01736 711883
E info@ednoveanfarm.co.uk
W www.ednoveanfarm.co.uk

3 rooms, S £72.50-£85, D £72.50-£90, No smoking, Closed 24-28 Dec, New Year

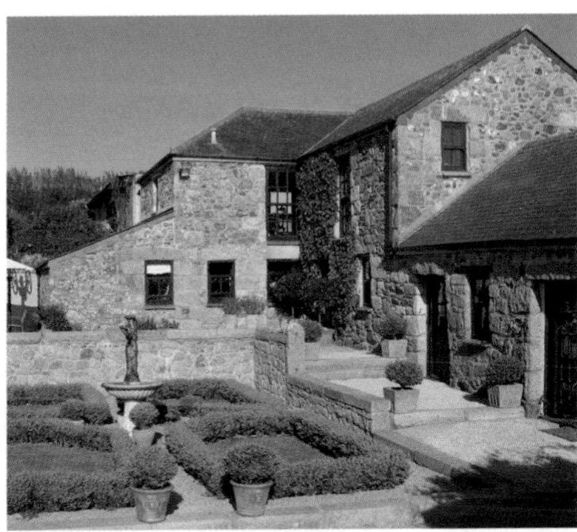

Spectacular sea views over St Michael's Mount and Mount's Bay are a delightful feature of this converted 17th-century farmhouse. The impressive property, which the owners continuously upgrade, stands high above the village in beautiful grounds that include an Italianate garden. The stylish bedrooms are furnished with comfortable beds and quality pieces, chintz fabrics, and thoughtful extras like flowers, magazines and fruit. You can relax in the elegant sitting room, the garden room and on several sunny patios, and breakfast is served at a magnificent oak table in the dining room. The coastal footpath and the beach are just three minutes away.

RECOMMENDED IN THE AREA

St Michael's Mount (NT); Godolphin House; Penlee House Gallery (Newlyn School paintings)

Allhays Country Bed & Breakfast ♦♦♦♦

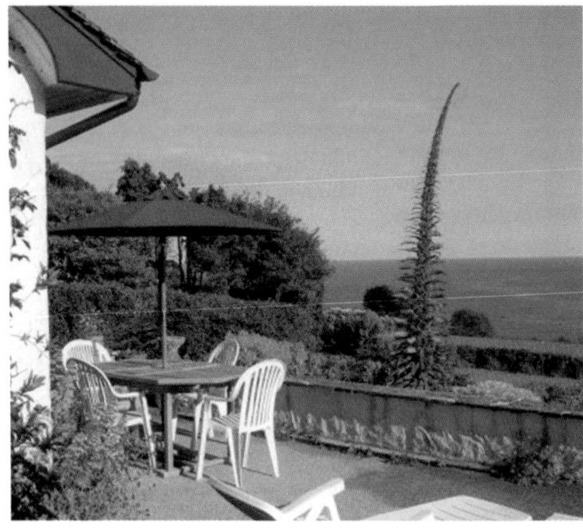

Map ref 1 - SX25
Porthallow, POLPERRO, PL13 2JB
2m from Looe on Polperro road, left signed Talland, 1m down lane

T 01503 273188
E info@allhays.co.uk
W www.allhays.co.uk

4 rooms, S £45-£75, D £70-£90, No smoking, Closed Dec

Recommended in the Area

The Eden Project; The Lost Gardens of Heligan; Lanydrock (NT)

Allhays is a spacious family house set in peaceful gardens with breathtaking views over the rugged and unspoiled beauty of Talland Bay. The country house was built in the late 1930s for Lady Mary Cook, a direct descendant of both the Nelson and Hood naval families. Just a short drive from the bustling tourist and fishing villages of Polperro and Looe, the peaceful hideaway is an ideal base for touring the area. The standard throughout is high with all bedrooms furnished with comfort and quality in mind, and come with bath robes, complimentary tea and coffee and other useful extras. Two of the rooms have spectacular sea views. In addition to extensive gardens, the public areas include a snug lounge and conservatory with great views.

Imaginative and enjoyable breakfasts, using excellent local produce, are served against the scenic backdrop. There is a good choice of hot dishes plus home-made breads, preserves and freshly squeezed orange juice.

*T*renderway Farm ♦♦♦♦♦

Map ref 1 - SX25
Pelynt, POLPERRO, PL13 2LY
A387 from Looe to Polperro, farm signed, onto 2nd signed turning
Ⓣ 01503 272214
Ⓕ 01503 272991
Ⓔ enquiries@trenderwayfarmholidays.co.uk
Ⓦ www.trenderwayfarmholidays.co.uk
6 rooms, S £35-£40, D £70-£90, No smoking, Closed Xmas, New Year

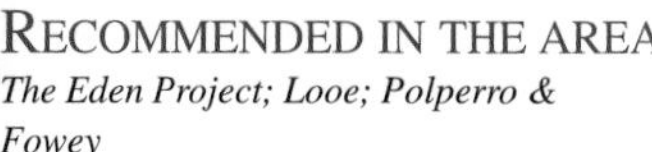

RECOMMENDED IN THE AREA
The Eden Project; Looe; Polperro & Fowey

Warm hospitality is offered at this delightful working farm, set in 300 acres of beautiful Cornish countryside. The 16th-century farmhouse offers luxury and tranquillity, and its ideal location makes a great base for walking, exploring the magnificent coastal scenery or visiting some of Cornwall's best attractions. The smart bedrooms (in the farmhouse or the adjacent barns) are splendid, luxuriously furnished and well equipped. The newest, the charmingly named Granary and Hayloft, are in a converted granite barn with plenty of light and space - contemporary decor complements the exposed stonework. Substantial four-course breakfasts, with free-range eggs from the farm, are served in the conservatory or on the decking that looks across fields to the lakes beyond. In winter an open fire warms the restful sitting room. The owners are always happy to recommend excellent restaurants nearby and can supply sample menus. With no children, families or pets, this is a perfect retreat for world-weary couples.

Penryn House Hotel ♦♦♦♦

Map ref 1 - SX25

The Coombes, POLPERRO,
PL13 2RQ

A387 to Polperro, at minirdbt left down hill into village (ignore restricted access). Hotel 200yds on left

Ⓣ 01503 272157
Ⓕ 01503 273055
Ⓔ chrispidcock@aol.com
Ⓦ www.hotelscornwall.org

12 rooms, S £31, D £62-£80, No smoking in bedrooms or dining room

The picturesque fishing village of Polperro is a firm favourite with visitors to Cornwall, and this country hotel is close to its centre. Wander through the narrow lanes among whitewashed cottages, and explore the fishing harbour. Further afield there are breathtaking walks along the coastal path. Owners Anna and Chris Pidcock give a memorable welcome, and their neat en suite bedrooms are equally hospitable, with well-stocked courtesy trays. In the evening relax in the licensed bar, or enjoy a candlelit meal in the smart restaurant, where locally caught fish and fresh produce are stars.

RECOMMENDED IN THE AREA

The Eden Project; Lanhydrock (NT); Bodmin Moor

The Corn Mill ♦♦♦♦

Map ref 1 - SW98

Port Isaac Rd, Trelill, PORT ISAAC,
PL30 3HZ

Off B3314, between Pendoggett and Trelill

Ⓣ 01208 851079

3 rooms, D £70, No smoking in bedrooms or dining room, Closed 24 Dec-5 Jan

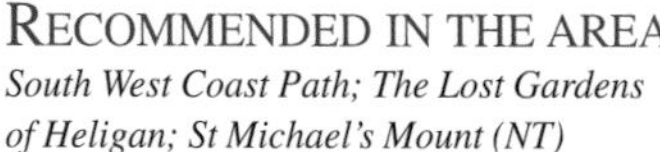

RECOMMENDED IN THE AREA

South West Coast Path; The Lost Gardens of Heligan; St Michael's Mount (NT)

Dating from the 18th century, this former mill has been lovingly restored to provide a beautiful home packed with character. The delightful garden and charming hostess add to the pleasure of a stay here. Bedrooms are individually styled, and personal touches create a wonderfully relaxed and homely atmosphere. Most rooms have their own shower room, while the twin room uses a bathroom with an enormous Victorian bathtub, and plenty of hot water. Luxury extras such as huge towels and cotton bed linen are pampering touches. Delicious breakfasts with home-made nutty bread are served in the farmhouse kitchen. The Eden Project is only a half-hour drive away.

Gwynoon Guest House ♦♦♦♦

Map ref 1 - SW52
Chy-an-Dour Rd, PRAA SANDS, TR20 9SY
Off A394 at Germoe x-rds into village, 2nd left after Post Office, house on left

T 01736 763508
E enquiries@gwynoon.co.uk
W www.gwynoon.co.uk

3 rooms, S £28, D £56, No smoking

RECOMMENDED IN THE AREA

St Michael's Mount (NT); Penzance; St Ives

Beautifully positioned on dazzling Praa Sands, this seafront property has excellent views from its front rooms. All the bedrooms are en suite and supplied with toiletries, tea and coffee facilities, Cornish spring water, biscuits and fruit. The enthusiastic hosts work hard to provide a restful atmosphere and make your stay memorable. You can use the first-floor balcony overlooking the bay, and are encouraged to bring your own wine to enjoy as you watch the sunset. Cream teas, light snacks and drinks are served in the tea garden throughout the day. The extensive breakfast features fresh local produce and you can opt for continental breakfast in your room.

Aviary Court Hotel ♦♦♦♦

Map ref 1 - SW64
Mary's Well, Illogan, REDRUTH, TR16 4QZ
Off A30 at A3047 Camborne, Pool and Portreath sign. Follow Portreath and Illogan signs for 2m to Alexander Rd

T 01209 842256
F 01209 843744
E info@aviarycourthotel.co.uk
W www.aviarycourthotel.co.uk

6 rooms, S £49, D £72-£75, No smoking in bedrooms or dining room

Attractive gardens and a very appealing exterior give a positive first impression to this 300-year-old property. Considerably modernised, it offers a relaxing stay with the friendly Studley family. The en suite bedrooms are spacious and well equipped, with easy chairs, quality towels, fresh fruit, and mineral water and biscuits. Direct-dial telephones and radio alarms are also provided. Dinner is notable for its fresh produce and imaginative cooking skills, and the licensed bar is well stocked. You are welcome to stroll in the lovely gardens, use the tennis court or simply play table tennis.

RECOMMENDED IN THE AREA

St Michael's Mount (NT); Tate St Ives; The Eden Project

The Eden Project, near St Austell

Gleneglos Hotel ♦♦♦♦

Map ref 1 - SW97
Trewint Ln, ROCK, PL27 6LU
Wadebridge B3314 to St Minver signed Pityme & Rock. At Texaco garage turn right, hotel 200yds

T 01208 862369
F 01208 862797
E franklin.gleneglos@btopenworld.com
W www.gleneglos.co.uk

6 rooms, D £57-£65, Closed Dec

The popular village of Rock is tucked up the Camel estuary on the north Cornish coast. There are country views from every bedroom of this Edwardian house, and glimpses of the Atlantic here and there. The Gleneglos has spacious gardens in which to unwind when it is warm, and blazing fires to relax in front on cooler days. The well-equipped accommodation includes a four-poster bedroom and all rooms are en suite or have private bathrooms. Dinner in the pleasant dining room is a highlight, with local produce on the daily-changing menu. The licensed bar is a popular meeting place, before and after dinner.

Recommended in the Area

Camel estuary; South West Coast Path; St Enedoc Golf Course

*M*ayon Farmhouse ♦♦♦♦

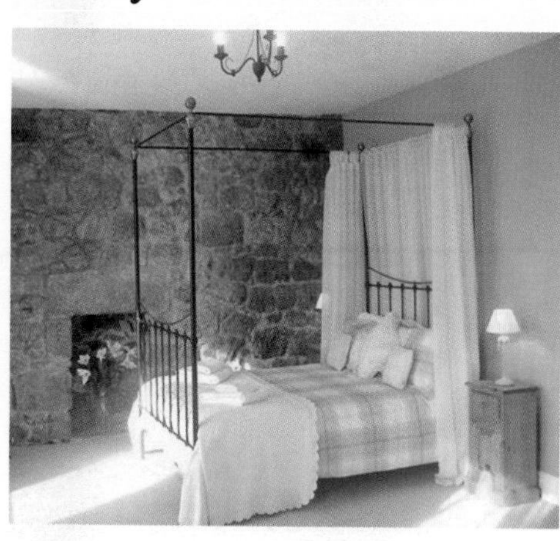

Map ref 1 - SW32
SENNEN, TR19 7AD
A30 into Sennen, driveway opp Post Office

Ⓣ 01736 871757
Ⓔ enquiries@mayonfarmhouse.co.uk
Ⓦ www.mayonfarmhouse.co.uk

3 rooms, S £35-£40, D £54-£70, No smoking in bedrooms or dining room

RECOMMENDED IN THE AREA
Sennen Cove; Land's End; The Minnack Theatre

You will receive a genuine welcome at this former Victorian farmhouse just over 1 mile from Land's End. The granite building stands on an elevated position with sea and country views. This part of west Cornwall has some of the most spectacular coastal walks in the British Isles, the path undulating from towering granite cliffs to tiny coves and fishing villages. This area is also a birdwatcher's paradise with both native and migrating birds to spot. Other local activities include horse riding, golf, surfing and rock climbing. The pretty bedrooms at Mayon are all en suite, have lovely sea or country views, and extras include tea and coffee with biscuits. There are also two four-poster bedrooms. The pleasant sitting room makes a restful retreat with wood-burning open fires in winter. A huge open-plan lounge-dining room is the venue for a wide choice of delicious Aga-cooked breakfasts. An on-site beauty room, providing a range of holistic treatments, is exclusively available for guests.

Driftwood Spars Hotel ♦♦♦♦

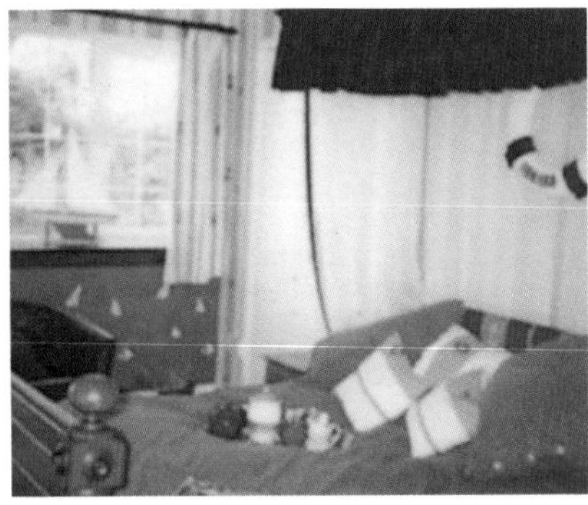

Map ref 1 - SW75

Trevaunance Cove, ST AGNES, TR5 0RT

Off A30 at rdbt signed St Agnes, through village bear right past church, left at bottom of hill, hotel on right

T 01872 552428
F 01872 553701
E driftwoodspars@hotmail.com
W www.driftwoodspars.com

15 rooms, S £39-£50, D £78, Closed 24-25 Dec

A magnificent setting right by the sea at St Agnes is just one compelling reason for making the Driftwood Spars Hotel your holiday destination. The sound of waves lull you to sleep at night, and in the morning the sands of Trevaunance Beach are an inspiration and pleasure. This property was built as a marine warehouse in 1660, and its white walls are bedecked with flowering baskets in the summer. Out of season it is quiet and calm, but at weekends it buzzes with visitors to the bars and restaurant. Refurbishment and modernisation now provide comfortable en suite bedrooms decorated in jolly seaside colours, all with telephones and hospitality trays. The spacious garden rooms are ideal for families and pet owners. Massive beams (the hotel was built from wrecked timbers), blazing log fires, a cosy lounge, atmospheric bars with hand-pulled ales, a microbrewery and lots of eating areas complete the attractive picture.

Recommended in the area

St Agnes Marine Conservation Area; Blue Hills Tin Streams; St Agnes Arts & Crafts Trail

Bedruthan Steps

Anchorage House ♦♦♦♦♦

Map ref 1 - SX05
Nettles Corner, Tregrehan Mills,
ST AUSTELL, PL25 3RH
T 01726 814071
E stay@anchoragehouse.co.uk
W www.anchoragehouse.co.uk
4 rooms, S £80, D £105-£130,
No smoking, Closed Dec-Feb

RECOMMENDED IN THE AREA

The Eden Project; The Lost Gardens of Heligan; Carlyon Bay beach & golf course

Anchorage House is a modern building in the Georgian style, set in landscaped gardens and furnished with beautiful antiques. Steve and Jane Epperson offer a truly personal service where extras such as fresh fruit, flowers, chocolates and robes are available, as is the superb 15-metre pool and a hot tub. Buffet-style breakfasts and (by arrangement) four-course candlelit dinners are served in the magnificent Glass Room using fresh Cornish produce. Each of the spacious and individually furnished bedrooms features controllable central heating, hair dryers, satellite television and power showers, while beds are either king size or super king size.

Highcroft Guest House ♦♦♦♦

Map ref 1 - SX05
Highcroft, Truro Rd, Sticker,
ST AUSTELL, PL26 7JA
2m SW of St Austell. Off A390 S into Sticker, pass Hewas Inn, B&B at top of hill
T 01726 63549
E highcroft.bnb@virgin.net
W www.highcroftguesthouse.co.uk
3 rooms, D £55-£70, No smoking

For a slower pace of life in a rural setting, head for the village of Sticker. Whether you want to explore the Cornish coastline, walk in the countryside or visit picturesque fishing villages, or else spend your time, this small guesthouse is a great place to start. Light and modern double bedrooms are impressively appointed, each with facilities en suite, a minifridge, tea and coffee facilities, DVD player and country views. The freshly cooked full English breakfast is a highlight of the day, served in the spacious dining room or on the sun deck. Attentive proprietor Jane Lang makes you feel at home and has a wealth of local knowledge she is more than willing to share. Discount on green fees at selected local golf courses is available to guests.

RECOMMENDED IN THE AREA
The Eden Project; The Lost Gardens of Heligan; Mevagissey

Hunter's Moon ♦♦♦♦

Map ref 1 - SX05
Chapel Hill, Polgooth, ST AUSTELL,
PL26 7BU
A390/B2373 follow signs to Polgooth. Pass village shop on left, Chapel Hill 1st right
T / F 01726 66445
E enquiries@huntersmooncornwall.co.uk
W www.huntersmooncornwall.co.uk
4 rooms, S £36-£40, D £52-£60, No smoking

A friendly welcome and a pot of tea or coffee in the conservatory await when you arrive at this spacious modern house in the picturesque village of Polgooth, less than 2 miles from the centre of St Austell. This part of Cornwall has a large number of attractions - beaches, gardens and historic houses, and activities including golf, coastal walks and cycling. The bedrooms have been redecorated and furnished to a high standard, all with facilities en suite and tea and coffee trays - two of the rooms have super king-size beds. There is plenty of space to sit and relax in the attractive gardens. Tasty traditional breakfasts are a feature and packed lunches are available on request.

RECOMMENDED IN THE AREA
The Eden Project; The Lost Gardens of Heligan; Charlestown harbour

Highland Court Lodge ♦♦♦♦♦

Map ref 1 - SX05
Biscovey Rd, Biscovey, ST AUSTELL, PL24 2HW
A390 from St Austell to St Blazey Gate, right onto Biscovey Rd, Lodge 300yds on right
T / F 01726 813320
E enquiries@highlandcourt.co.uk
W www.highlandcourt.co.uk
3 rooms, S £55-£95, D £90-£150, No smoking

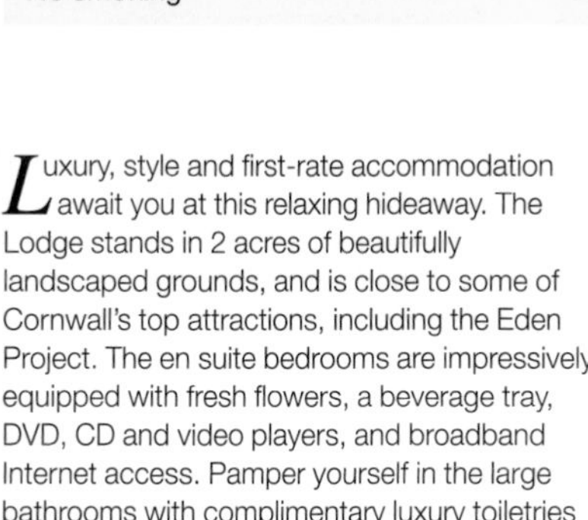

Luxury, style and first-rate accommodation await you at this relaxing hideaway. The Lodge stands in 2 acres of beautifully landscaped grounds, and is close to some of Cornwall's top attractions, including the Eden Project. The en suite bedrooms are impressively equipped with fresh flowers, a beverage tray, DVD, CD and video players, and broadband Internet access. Pamper yourself in the large bathrooms with complimentary luxury toiletries - some have Jacuzzi spa baths and each bedroom has a private patio. There is a lounge with deep sofas, and a terrace with fine views, where dinner can be enjoyed on summer evenings. The freshly prepared breakfast, with daily specials, and dinner feature local produce and are not to be missed. The local butcher in Tywardreath provides the sausages, Cornish hog's pudding and steak, and delectable fish comes from Charlestown just down the road.

Recommended in the Area

The Eden Project; Carlyon beach & golf course; The Lost Gardens of Heligan

Lower Barn ♦♦♦♦♦

Map ref 1 - SX05

Bosue, St Ewe, ST AUSTELL, PL26 6EU

3.5m SW of St Austell. Off B3273 at x-rds signed Lost Gardens of Heligan. Follow road until sharp left bend, Lower Barn signed 1m on right

T 01726 844881
E janie@bosue.co.uk
W www.bosue.co.uk

3 rooms, No smoking, Closed Dec-Jan

RECOMMENDED IN THE AREA

The Eden Project; The Lost Gardens of Heligan; Mevagissey

Tucked away in down a meandering country lane yet having easy access to local attractions, this converted barn has huge appeal and proprietors Mike and Janie Cooksley fully deserve the award AA Guest Accommodation of the Year for England 2005. The warm colours and decoration create a Mediterranean feel, complemented by informal and genuine hospitality. It is the attention to detail that puts Lower Barn a cut above the rest. The bedrooms have a host of extras from daily fresh towels and fridges to tea and coffee facilities. Breakfast is an extensive menu, served round a large table or on the patio deck overlooking the garden, which also has a luxurious hot tub. You can even collect your own free-range eggs for breakfast. A candlelit dinner is available on most nights, served in the conservatory or on the terrace - bring your own wine. After exploring the area unwind with some gorgeous massage and therapy treatments to complete your Lower Barn experience.

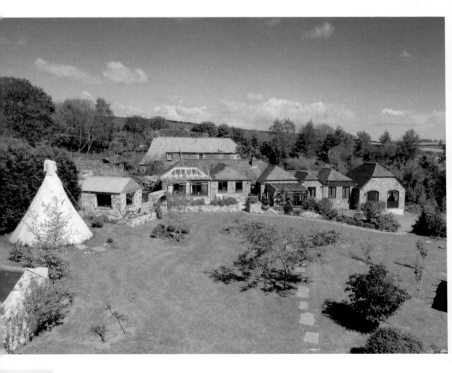

Sunnyvale Bed & Breakfast ♦♦♦♦

Map ref 1 - SX05
Hewaswater, ST AUSTELL,
PL26 7JF
A390 from St Austell through Sticker. Sunnyvale on right in the centre of Hewaswater

T 01726 882572
E jmuden@aol.com
W www.sunny-vale.co.uk

2 rooms, S £30-£35, D £56-£60, No smoking

RECOMMENDED IN THE AREA
The Eden Project; The Lost Gardens of Heligan; South West Coast Path

The visitors' book tells it all: guests from near and far enthuse about the friendly atmosphere, impressively equipped bedrooms, and the delicious breakfasts. Judy and Richard Uden are natural hosts who have made their beautiful home a gem of a retreat. The en suite bedrooms are in an annexe, and include smart bathrooms, easy chairs and videos, plus access to a hospitality tray and fridge. An extensive range of extras guarantees a comfortable stay. Freshly cooked breakfasts are served in the dining room, and there are also lovely gardens to enjoy.

Wisteria Lodge ♦♦♦♦♦

Map ref 1 - SX05
Boscundle, Tregrehan,
ST AUSTELL, PL25 3RJ
Off A390 1m W of St Blazey, 2m east of St Austell

T 01726 810800
E info@wisterialodgehotel.co.uk
W www.wisterialodgehotel.co.uk

5 rooms, No smoking

The stylish Wisteria Lodge stands in lovingly tended gardens close to St Austell. Sally and James Wilkins offer high levels of personal service and a relaxed atmosphere at their delightful guesthouse. One room comes complete with spa whirlpool bath and private lounge, or you can choose the opulent suite with four-poster bed. Complimentary chocolates and fluffy bathrobes are pampering touches. Skilfully prepared meals are served in the conservatory-dining room, which overlooks the large garden - breakfast is a triumph and the candlelit dinner a delight. Wisteria Lodge is well placed to visit many attractions and there are excellent beaches within a 20-minute walk.

RECOMMENDED IN THE AREA
The Eden Project; The Lost Gardens of Heligan; Lanhydrock (NT)

Penarwyn House ♦♦♦♦♦

Map ref 1 - SX05
ST BLAZEY, PL24 2DS
A390 W through St Blazey, left at 2nd speed camera, house past school

T / F 01726 814224
E mrussell@fsbdial.co.uk
W www.penarwyn.co.uk

3 rooms, S £80-£90, D £95-£120, No smoking, Closed 21 Dec-9 Jan

RECOMMENDED IN THE AREA
The Eden Project; Lanhydrock (NT); The Lost Gardens of Heligan

True Cornish hospitality and memorable breakfasts complement this spacious Victorian residence set in tranquil surroundings, yet close to main routes and many attractions. Since 2003, owners Mike and Jan Russell - who have many years experience successfully running bed and breakfast establishments - have been painstakingly restoring Penarwyn House to its original glory. Many old features have been faithfully restored alongside luxury new en suites, which include a bath by candlelight for romantics and a separate shower. The bedrooms are most impressive, spacious, delightfully appointed, and equipped with a host of extras including tea and coffee facilities and hairdryers. Breakfast is another highlight , and along with the friendly and attentive service, this all makes for a pleasurable stay. Children welcome over 10 years of age.

Ennys ♦♦♦♦♦

Map ref 1 - SW43
Trewhella Ln, ST HILARY, TR20 9BZ
1m N of B3280 Leedstown-Goldsithney road at end of Trewhella Ln

T 01736 740262
F 01736 740055
E ennys@ennys.co.uk
W www.ennys.co.uk

5 rooms, D £75-£95, No smoking, Closed Nov-15 Mar

Set off the beaten track in the valley of the River Hayle, this 17th-century manor house is a perfect place to unwind. A friendly welcome awaits you from travel writer Gill Charlton, and a complimentary afternoon tea is laid out in the kitchen. Ennys retains much original character and the rooms are stylish and impressively furnished with antiques. Two family suites are available in the large stone barn conversion adjoining the main house. A delightful Cornish breakfast is served in the dining room, using fresh local ingredients and home-produced fresh eggs. A heated outdoor pool is available from early May to late September and there is also a grass tennis court.

RECOMMENDED IN THE AREA

St Michael's Mount (NT); Land's End; St Ives

Chy Roma Guest House ♦♦♦♦

Map ref 1 - SW54
2 Seaview Ter, ST IVES, TR26 2DH
A3074 into St Ives, fork left at Porthminster Hotel, 1st left, 1st right, down slope 2nd guesthouse on left

T / F 01736 797539
E jenny@omshanti.demon.co.uk
W www.connexions.co.uk/chyroma

6 rooms, S £26-£35, D £52-£90, No smoking

RECOMMENDED IN THE AREA

Tate St Ives; Bernard Leach Pottery; Barbara Hepworth Museum

From the terrace of this property you can gaze across the picturesque town and harbour to the sea beyond. Inside, the house is equally conducive to relaxing. Jenny Marks provides genuine hospitality, welcoming her guests with a delicious Cornish cream tea. Relish too her cooking skills at breakfast, and there are also home-made preserves, marmalade, bread and muesli. The smart bedrooms, some having spectacular views, come with impressive bathrooms, tea and coffee facilities, and clock radios. The lounge comes with a CD player, books and games.

*B*ay View ♦♦♦♦

Map ref 1 - SW54

Headland Rd, Carbis Bay, ST IVES, TR26 2NX

A3074 into Carbis Bay, 1st right onto Porthrepta Rd, 3rd right onto Headland Rd

T / F 01736 796469
E sandie@bayview1.freeserve.co.uk
W www.bayview-hotel.co.uk

9 rooms, S £26-£34, D £52-£68, No smoking, Closed 24-28 Dec

Sandie and Andy Neal score highly in hospitality and maintain impressive standards in their house, where guests leave as friends. The modern and immaculately presented guesthouse is in a peaceful residential area within easy reach of St Ives. It is also close to the sweeping silver sands of Carbis Bay beach, where a train from the tiny station takes you on a coastal ride into town. The en suite bedrooms are well equipped, and each is fitted with a hairdryer and a courtesy tray. A large homely lounge is well stocked with games and books, and the licensed bar serves drinks in the evening. Sandie's memorable breakfasts herald the start of another pleasurable day.

Recommended in the Area

Tate St Ives; St Michael's Mount (NT) & Marazion; Land's End

*B*orthalan ♦♦♦♦

Map ref 1 - SW54
Off Boskerris Rd, Carbis Bay, ST IVES, TR26 2NQ
A3074 into Carbis Bay, right onto Boskerris Rd, 1st left onto cul-de-sac
T / F 01736 795946
E borthalanhotel@btconnect.com
W www.borthalan-hotel.co.uk
7 rooms, D £70-£80, No smoking in bedrooms or dining room, Closed 20-28 Dec

RECOMMENDED IN THE AREA

Barbara Hepworth Museum; The Eden Project; Tate St Ives

Lovely gardens and views over the golden sands of Carbis Bay and St Ives Bay are among the attractions of this smart guesthouse. The friendly Talbot family - Debbie, Robert and daughter Aimee - take great pleasure in looking after their guests. Most of the well-appointed bedrooms look over the coast, and with facilities en suite, courtesy trays and thoughtful extras, you are promised a relaxing stay. All rooms are on the first and second floors. Cooked breakfasts are served in the sunny dining room looking out over the sea, and there is a small licensed bar and a cosy lounge. The pretty gardens are a treat on warm days and evenings. The picturesque fishing harbour of St Ives is just a few minutes away, and can be reached by a short train journey or a breathtaking walk along the coastal path. Parking is available at the hotel.

Chy-Garth ♦♦♦♦

Map ref 1 - SW54
Sea View Meadows, St Ives Rd, Carbis Bay, ST IVES, TR26 2JX
A3074 to Carbis Bay, hotel on right opp Methodist church
Ⓣ 01736 795677
Ⓔ ann@chy-garth.demon.co.uk
Ⓦ www.chy-garth.co.uk
8 rooms, S £35-£38, D £60-£74, No smoking

RECOMMENDED IN THE AREA
Tate St Ives; St Michael's Mount (NT); Porthcorno

Sea views and close proximity to lovely beaches are bonuses at this detached guesthouse. Chy-Garth stands in sub-tropical gardens overlooking a bay ranked as one of the 40 most beautiful in the world. The good range of accommodation includes twin, double and double coronet, and one room with a king-size four-poster. Some rooms are on the ground floor, which are en suite, and all have central heating, double-glazing, remote-control televisions, hairdryers and hospitality trays. There is a comfortable lounge and a separate dining room where a full English, vegetarian or continental breakfast is served. Private parking on the premises, and minimum stay two nights.

Kynance Guest House ♦♦♦♦

Map ref 1 - SW54
The Warren, ST IVES, TR26 2EA
A3074 into town centre, sharp right before bus/coach station onto railway station approach road, Kynance 20yds on left
Ⓣ 01736 796636
Ⓔ enquiries@kynance.com
Ⓦ www.kynance.com
6 rooms, D £56-£64, No smoking, Closed Nov-Mar

RECOMMENDED IN THE AREA
Tate St Ives; St Michael's Mount (NT); Land's End

Kynance is a charming, former tin-miner's cottage in the cobbled conservation area of scenic St Ives known as the Warren, and just yards from the picturesque harbour and the Blue Flag Porthminster beach. The attractive bedrooms are well equipped, including tea and coffee facilities, and some have superb sea and harbour views. The varied choice at breakfast includes a vegetarian option and a range of smoked fish - coffee lovers can indulge in a cafetière, espresso or cappuccino. This charming house has a south-facing patio garden and a large shady pergola, reached from the second floor. Reserved parking is also available, a real bonus as it is hard to find space in the town.

The Old Vicarage Hotel ♦♦♦♦

Map ref 1 - SW54
Parc-an-Creet, ST IVES, TR26 2ES
Off A3074 in town centre onto B3306, 0.5m right into Parc-an-Creet
T 01736 796124
E holidays@oldvicaragehotel.com
W www.oldvicaragehotel.com
7 rooms, S £50-£60, D £64-£80, No smoking in bedrooms or dining room, Closed Oct-Etr

An atmospheric Victorian vicarage set in very attractive grounds in a peaceful part of St Ives. Dianne Sykes is an accomplished artist and textile designer whose work is showcased throughout the property. Jack Sykes, her father, has run the business for more than 30 years, and is a popular figure behind the welcoming Victorian bar where his many stories are legendary. The stylish bedrooms have hospitality trays and facilities en suite, and there is capacity for families in many cases. Breakfast is a feast of local and home-made produce, including yoghurt and preserves.

Recommended in the Area
Porthmeor Beach; Tate St Ives; Bernard Leach Pottery

Pebble Private Hotel ♦♦♦♦

Map ref 1 - SW54
4 Parc Av, ST IVES, TR26 2DN
A3074 to St Ives, left at NatWest bank, left at minirdbt, pass car park, house 150yds on right
T 01736 794168
E info@pebble-hotel.co.uk
W www.pebble-hotel.co.uk
7 rooms, S £28-£40, D £56-£80, No smoking

Recommended in the Area
Tate St Ives; Barbara Hepworth Museum; The Eden Project

Owners Jenny and Ricky have spent over a year refurbishing this elegant Victorian house with stunning views over St Ives Bay, set in the centre of the popular resort. They have produced an impeccably maintained house offering well-equipped accommodation, paying great attention to detail and hospitality. The lovely bedrooms, all with facilities en suite, come with flat-screen televisions and DVD players. You can treat yourself to breakfast in bed or relax in the stylish sea-view lounge with a glass of wine. The breakfast menu is an impressive range of choices, including vegetarian and fish dishes, and local produce is used whenever possible.

Regent Hotel ♦♦♦♦

Map ref 1 - SW54
Fernlea Ter, ST IVES, TR26 2BH
In town centre, close to bus & railway station
T 01736 796195
F 01736 794641
E keith@regenthotel.com
W www.regenthotel.com
9 rooms, S £32.50-£45, D £65-£84, No smoking

RECOMMENDED IN THE AREA

Tate St Ives; Barbara Hepworth Museum; Paradise Park Wildlife Sanctuary

The Regent Hotel was established 78 years ago when a local architect purchased Penwyn House from a retired sea captain and converted it to provide an interest for his wife and daughter. In 1972 the late Mr and Mrs SH Varnals bought the property and in due course passed it on to Keith and Sandi Varnals, the present proprietors. Sandi, a former lingerie designer, has worked her magic on the interior of the old building, while Keith, an engineer turned chef, has modernised the hotel's facilities to appeal to the modern traveller. Bedrooms are well equipped, seven have facilities en suite, and most have spectacular sea views. The breakfast menu offers a good choice of hot dishes, cooked to order, and an extensive buffet of cereals, yoghurts, pastries, fruit and juice. Also on offer are espresso, cappuccino, and cafetière coffee, hot chocolate and a choice of teas. There is a lounge and bar for evening relaxation, and parking is provided for all rooms.

Porthglaze ♦♦♦♦♦

Map ref 1 - SW54
Steeple Ln, ST IVES, TR26 2AY
A3074 to St Ives, left at Cornish Arms, left onto Steeple Ln, Porthglaze 500yds on left

T 01736 799409
E info@porthglaze.co.uk
W www.porthglaze.co.uk

2 rooms, D £75-£85, No smoking

Porthglaze lies in a quiet lane just a stroll from golden sands. The spacious bedrooms are classically furnished with either Sanderson or Liberty fabrics, and have bath-shower rooms en suite with luxury towels, bathrobes, hairdryers and toiletries. The Roseberry Suite to the rear has French doors leading to the pleasant garden, while the Cornflower Suite has a fabulous antique bed made up with fine linen - both have tea and coffee facilities. The continental breakfast is an impressive choice served in a sunny breakfast room, mostly using fresh local produce and home-made jams and preserves. Parking is available.

Recommended in the Area

Tate St Ives; Bernard Leach Pottery; Barbara Hepworth Museum

The Rookery ♦♦♦♦

Map ref 1 - SW54
8 The Terrace, ST IVES, TR26 2BL
A3074 through Carbis Bay, right fork at Porthminster Hotel, The Rookery 500yds on left

T 01736 799401
E therookerystives@hotmail.com
W www.rookerystives.com

6 rooms, S £32.50-£35, D £55-£75, No smoking

This friendly establishment stands on an elevated position overlooking the harbour, sandy beaches and St Ives Bay. The Rookery is near the town's train and bus stations, and only a short walk to the shops, galleries and restaurants for which St Ives is famed. Ron and Barbara Rook make guests feel very welcome and maintain a programme of constant refurbishment. The rooms are attractively decorated, and are well equipped with considerate extras such as a chiller to keep soft drinks and wines cool. A choice of full English, continental or vegetarian breakfast is served at separate tables in the first-floor dining room.

RECOMMENDED IN THE AREA
Tate St Ives; Barbara Hepworth Museum; The Minack Theatre

Tregony Guest House ♦♦♦♦

Map ref 1 - SW54
1 Clodgy View, ST IVES, TR26 1JG
A3074 into St Ives, left at NatWest, pass cinema, right at minirdbt up Bullars Ln, right at T-junct, over next junct, house 100yds on right

T 01736 795884
E info@tregony.com
W www.tregony.com

5 rooms, D £56-£68, No smoking

Ideal for a holiday at any time, Tregony has a wonderful position overlooking Porthmeor beach towards Clodgy Point. The town centre, harbour and sands are all within easy access, with glorious coastal walks, rocky coves and sandy inlets waiting to be explored. The en suite bedrooms are homely and comfortable, with attractive decor, showers, televisions, clock radios and hospitality trays. The freshly cooked breakfasts provide plenty of choice. Parking is available in the nearby public car park.

RECOMMENDED IN THE AREA
Tate St Ives; Barbara Hepworth Museum; The Eden Project

Woodside Hotel ♦♦♦♦

Map ref 1 - SW54

The Belyars, ST IVES, TR26 2DA

A3074 to St Ives, left at Porthminster Hotel onto Talland Rd, 1st left onto Belyars Ln, Woodside 4th on right

T 01736 795681
E woodsidehotel@btconnect.com
W www.woodside-hotel.co.uk

10 rooms, S £33-£51, D £66-£108, No smoking

RECOMMENDED IN THE AREA

Tate St Ives; Land's End; The Eden Project

Suzanne and Chris Taylor are welcoming hosts who diligently attend to their beautiful hotel. They promise personal attention, ensuring an enjoyable holiday here. Woodside stands in peaceful grounds above St Ives Bay, with fantastic views from most bedrooms and all of the public rooms. The lovely beaches, picturesque harbour and narrow cobbled streets of St Ives are just a 5-minute walk away. The comfortable en suite bedrooms range from single to family rooms, and are each well equipped with a radio-alarm clock and a hospitality tray. Guests can relax in the lounge or bar, or relish the sea views from the attractive gardens or terrace. A heated swimming pool is open from May to September. Breakfast is another delight, a hearty choice of full English, continental or vegetarian dishes.

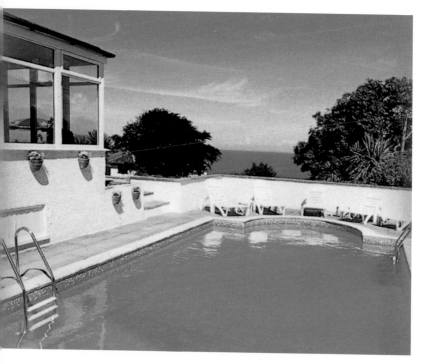

Treliska ♦♦♦♦

Map ref 1 - SW54
3 Bedford Rd, ST IVES, TR26 1SP
A3074 to St Ives, fork at Porthminster Hotel into town, at T-junct facing Barclays Bank left onto Bedford Rd, house on right
T / F 01736 797678
E info@treliska.com
W www.treliska.com
5 rooms, S £30-£35, D £56-£64, No smoking

A warm welcome awaits you at this modern and friendly guesthouse located close to the shops, galleries and museums of this artistic town, and only a 2-minute walk from the harbour. The mid-terrace house is furnished to a high degree of comfort with all modern amenities. Bedrooms are exceptionally well equipped with tea and coffee facilities, hairdryers, and bathrooms with very smart fittings. Breakfast is an enjoyable experience with a good choice and quality ingredients accurately cooked.

Recommended in the Area

Tate St Ives; Bernard Leach Pottery; Paradise Park Wildlife Sanctuary, Hayle

---

Port William Inn ♦♦♦♦

Map ref 1 - SX08
Trebarwith Strand, TINTAGEL, PL34 0HB
Off B3263 Camelford to Tintagel
T 01840 770230
F 01840 770936
E theportwilliam@btinternet.com
W www.theportwilliam.com
8 rooms, S £67-£74, D £85-£99, No smoking in bedrooms

Perched on the side of a cliff, the inn overlooks the cove and beach at Trebarwith Strand, one of Cornwall's loveliest and most unspoiled places. The incoming tide is a spectacular sight as the surf pounds the rocks, while low tide reveals a mile of gleaming sand. All bedrooms have breathtaking views over the sea and offer well-equipped accommodation. The nautical theme bar is furnished with old pews and large wooden tables. The popular restaurant in the conservatory dining room serves a wide range of dishes but with an emphasis on locally caught fish.

Recommended in the Area

Tintagel Castle; Bodmin Moor; Launceston Castle

Upton Farm ♦♦♦♦

Map ref 1 - SX08
TREBARWITH, PL33 9DG
A39 onto B3314, through Delabole. Atlantic garage on left, sharp right onto Treligga Downs Rd. 0.5m right at T-junct, farm 1m on right

T 01840 770225
F 01840 770377
E ricardo@dorich.co.uk
W www.upton-farm.co.uk

3 rooms, S £50, D £70-£80, No smoking

Having splendid sea views, this attractive stone house is close to the breathtaking coastal path that leads to nearby Boscastle, Port Isaac and Tintagel. Elizabeth and Ricardo Dorich provide warm hospitality and smart accommodation, and welcome guests on arrival with tea in the drawing room. Breakfast is served in the garden room around one large table, where local produce and home-made muesli taste that much better with the morning sun and sea views. The neat en suite bedrooms have tea and coffee facilities, and a share of the views. Sunsets from the terrace are not to be missed, and the rural location is convenient for good, local dining.

RECOMMENDED IN THE AREA

South West Coast Path; Tintagel Castle; Bodmin Moor

Bodrean Manor Farm ♦♦♦♦

Map ref 1 - SW84
Trispen, TRURO, TR4 9AG
A30 onto A39 at Carland Cross rdbt towards Truro, left after Trispen village signed Frogmore & Trehane, farm driveway 100yds

T 01872 273227
F 01872 273225
W www.bodrean.co.uk

2 rooms, S £30-£35, D £50, No smoking

This friendly and characterful farmhouse lies with in attractive gardens and countryside with splendid views, yet is only minutes from the cathedral city of Truro. It is an ideal touring base for visiting many of Cornwall's top attractions and is surrounded by excellent walking country. The farmhouse has been restored to a high standard and the spacious, luxurious bedrooms, all with facilities en suite, are thoughtfully and extensively equipped. The bathrooms are well provisioned with soft towels and a host of toiletries. Original features in the dining room include a beamed ceiling and an inglenook fireplace, while the full English breakfast, using local and home-grown produce, is certainly not to be hurried.

RECOMMENDED IN THE AREA

The Eden Project; The Lost Gardens of Heligan; Trelissick Garden (NT)

A selection of places to eat from the AA Restaurant & AA Pub guides

Restaurants

Drunken Duck Inn (British)
Barngates, Ambleside LA22 0NG
Tel 015394 36347

L'Enclume (French)
Cavendish Street, Cartmel LA11 6PZ
Tel 015395 36362

Queens Head Hotel (British, Mediterranean)
Main Street, Hawkshead LA22 0NS
Tel 015394 36271

The Castle Green Hotel in Kendal (Mediterranean)
Kendal LA9 6BH, Tel 01539 734000

Jambo (British)
7 Victoria Street, Windermere LA23 1AE
Tel 015394 43429

Jerichos (British, Mediterranean)
Birch Street, Windermere LA23 1EG
Tel 015394 42522

Pubs

The Royal Oak Inn
Bongate, Appleby-in-Westmorland
CA16 6UN, Tel 017683 51463

The Kings Head
Thirlspot, Keswick CA12 4TN
Tel 017687 72393

The Pheasant Inn
Casterton, Kirkby Lonsdale LA6 2RX
Tel 015242 71230

Three Shires Inn
Little Langdale LA22 9NZ
Tel 015394 37215

The Fat Lamb Country Inn
Crossbank, Ravenstondale CA17 4LL
Tel 015396 23242

Blackenrigg Inn
Watermillock CA11 0LP
Tel 017684 86206

Brathay Lodge ♦♦♦♦

Map ref 5 - NY30
Rothay Rd, AMBLESIDE, LA22 0EE
One-way system in town centre, Lodge on right opp church
T 015394 32000
E brathay@globalnet.co.uk
W www.brathay-lodge.com
21 rooms, S £40-£55, D £60-£135, No smoking

Combining traditional and contemporary styles, Brathay Lodge offers a chance to relax and indulge in impressive surroundings. The very spacious bedrooms are fitted with enormous beds, and decorated and furnished in smart fabrics and woods. Each room has a Jacuzzi spa bath, and some have balconies with stunning Lakeland views. The informal, atmosphere is conducive to unwinding, with the choice of enjoying an extensive continental breakfast in the privacy of your bedroom, or in the comfortable lounge. This immaculate property is over 110 years old, but offers accommodation to meet the most testing demands of the 21st century.

Recommended in the Area

Windermere cruises; Hill Top, Beatrix Potter's house,; Wordsworth's Dove Cottage

Elterwater Park ♦♦♦♦

Map ref 5 - NY30
Skelwith Bridge, AMBLESIDE, LA22 9NP
A593 from Ambleside to Coniston, 1m past Skelwith Bridge Hotel, layby on right fronts estate road to Elterwater Park, signed at gate

Ⓣ 015394 32227
Ⓕ 015394 31768
Ⓔ enquiries@elterwater.com
Ⓦ www.elterwater.com

5 rooms, D £64-£70, No smoking

Set high on the hills above Langdale, this stone house is full of traditional features and surrounded by wildlife and birds. All the attractive bedrooms are en suite and are furnished with radios, hairdryers, hospitality trays and fresh flowers - one room has easier access. Breakfast and dinner are served at individual tables in the spacious lounge-dining room. Your hosts hold a full residential licence with a wine list chosen for quality and value to go with the freshly prepared dinners. Packed lunches are available on request. There is a terrace for fine days - and a drying room for those other days.

RECOMMENDED IN THE AREA

Ambleside; Coniston Water; Cumbrian Way

Kent House ♦♦♦♦

Map ref 5 - NY30
Lake Rd, AMBLESIDE, LA22 0AD
From town centre, by Post Office on one-way system 300yds on left on terrace above main road

Ⓣ / Ⓕ 015394 33279
Ⓔ mail@kent-house.com
Ⓦ www.kent-house.com

5 rooms, S £45-£50, D £56-£86, No smoking, Closed 24-25 Dec

RECOMMENDED IN THE AREA

Lake Windermere; Wordsworth's Dove Cottage; World of Beatrix Potter

Gordon and Moira Cox have been sharing their charming stone house since 2002, offering a friendly welcome, a home-from-home atmosphere and delightful accommodation. You can relax on the terrace in fine weather, or in front of a blazing fire in the inviting lounge when it is cooler. The spacious bedrooms are en suite or have private facilities, and telephones and courtesy trays are among the extras (including plasters for sore feet) supplied. Home-baked bread, home-made preserves and marmalades are part of the lavish Lakeland breakfast served in the dining room.

Hall Croft ♦♦♦♦

Map ref 6 - NY62
Dufton, APPLEBY-IN-WESTMORLAND, CA16 6DB
Dufton signed from A66 near Appleby, B&B at bottom of village green
T 017683 52902
E r.walker@leaseholdpartnerships.co.uk
3 rooms, S £28, D £49, No smoking, Closed 24-26 Dec

This welcoming house is in a peaceful village at the foot of the Pennines, and has spectacular views in all directions. The gardens are a joy to explore, and the bedrooms and public areas are also delightful. Two of the traditionally furnished bedrooms are en suite while the third has a private bathroom. A wide range of home-cooked dishes is offered at breakfast, which is served in the lounge-dining room. Fully recharged, you can then explore one of the network of footpaths and walks from the village.

Recommended in the Area

North Pennines AONB; Northern Lake District; Appleby-in-Westmorland

---

Wheatsheaf Hotel ♦♦♦♦

Map ref 6 - SD47
BEETHAM, LA7 7AL
Off A6 into village centre, next to parish church
T 015395 62123
F 015395 64840
E wheatsheaf@beetham.plus.com
W www.wheatsheafbeetham.com
6 rooms, S £55, D £40-£85, No smoking, Closed 25-Dec

This country inn, originating from the 16th-century, is a tranquil retreat beside the church in the unspoiled village of Beetham. Family owned and run, the emphasis is on traditional service, comfort and quality accommodation. The en suite bedrooms are individually styled and have lots of thoughtful extras - the modern bathrooms are well equipped. The non-smoking bar is full of character, very much in keeping with the style and age of the building. Home-cooked dishes, using only the finest and freshest local produce, are available as bar meals or fine dining, served by the friendly and attentive staff.

Recommended in the Area

Walking, golfing & fishing; Leighton Moss RSPB; Lake District

Hazel Bank Country House ♦♦♦♦♦

Map ref 5 - NY21
Rosthwaite, BORROWDALE,
CA12 5XB
B5289 to Rosthwaite, signed opp village
T 017687 77248
F 017687 77373
E enquiries@hazelbankhotel.co.uk
W www.hazelbankhotel.co.uk
8 rooms, S £66-£95, D £132-£190,
No smoking

Set in the much-praised Borrowdale valley amid some of the Lake District's loveliest scenery, this Victorian house is an epitome of hospitality and comfort. Wander in the 4 acres of carefully-tended lawns and woodland, or relax in the well-proportioned sitting room where log fires cheer up colder days. Bedrooms, named after the surrounding fells, are fitted with four-poster, king-size or double beds, and smart bathrooms en suite. Glen and Brenda Davies have owned the house for eight years, and it has been completely refurbished in this time. Decor and the many thoughtful extras have been chosen to make you feel pampered and welcome. Imaginative four-course dinners with 'puddings to die for' are served in the delightful dining room, and equally tasty breakfasts are enjoyed with the views.

Recommended in the Area
Honister Slate Mine; Keswick Pencil Museum; Family of Ospreys, Bassenthwaite Lake

---

The Hill On The Wall ♦♦♦♦♦

Map ref 6 - NY56
Gilsland, BRAMPTON, CA8 7DA
A69 into Gilsland & follow brown tourist signs for Birdoswald, The Hill on the Wall 0.5m on right
T / F 016977 47214
E info@hadrians-wallbedandbreakfast.com
W http://hadrians-wallbedandbreakfast.com
3 rooms, S £40-£50, D £56-£66,
No smoking

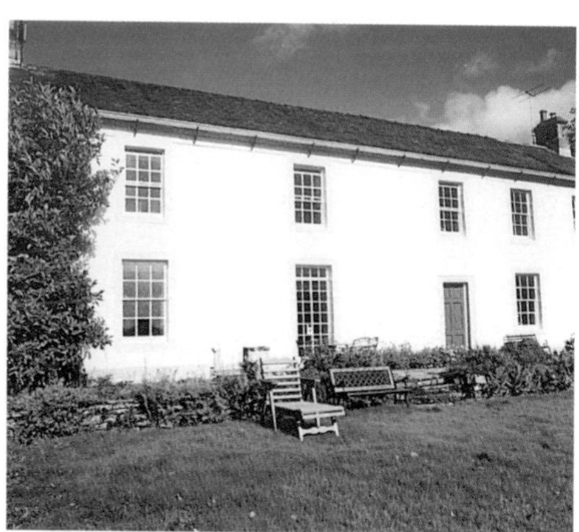

This elegant and upgraded farmhouse overlooks Hadrian's Wall. The Grade II listed former bastle (defended) house dates from the 16th century, and has impressive accommodation. The cosy Long Room lounge is comfortably furnished and well stocked with books and games, while the smart dining room is the setting for good home-cooked breakfasts and evening meals, using quality local produce whenever possible. The bedrooms, including one on the ground floor, are very large and have new bathrooms. Elaine and Dick Packer are friendly and obliging hosts who do their utmost to encourage you to feel at home.

Recommended in the Area
Hadrian's Wall; Birdoswald Roman Fort; Housesteads Roman Fort

Hullerbank ♦♦♦♦

Map ref 6 - NY56
Talkin, BRAMPTON, CA8 1LB
B6413 from Brampton for 2m, over railway & after golf club left to Talkin, onto Hallbankgate Rd & signs to Hullerbank

T / F 016977 46668
E info@hullerbank.freeserve.co.uk
W www.smoothhound.co.uk/hotels/huller.html

3 rooms, S £35-£40, D £56, No smoking, Closed Dec-Jan

RECOMMENDED IN THE AREA
Hadrian's Wall; Historic Carlisle; Lake District

The delightful Georgian farmhouse dates in part from the early 17th century. It stands in well-tended gardens and grounds adjoining a small holding for pedigree Suffolk sheep. This peaceful retreat has a home-from-home atmosphere, fostered by Sheila Stobbart who welcomes guests like old friends. In winter a fire burns in the inglenook fireplace, making the lounge a cosy place for a quiet read, or just to watch the television. Bedrooms are well proportioned and thoughtfully equipped, including one with a private bathroom and two with showers en suite. Expect to start the day with a hearty traditional breakfast, served in the dining room.

Swaledale Watch Farm House ♦♦♦♦

Map ref 5 - NY34
Whelpo, CALDBECK, CA7 8HQ
1m SW of Caldbeck on B5299

T / F 016974 78409
E nan.savage@talk21.com
W www.swaledale-watch.co.uk

4 rooms, S £25, D £44-£50, No smoking, Closed 24-26 Dec

This busy farm is set in idyllic surroundings, with open views of the fells and mountains. You are welcome to look round, a very special treat at lambing time. Just 1 mile away is the picturesque village of Caldbeck, once renowned for its milling and mining, or take a memorable walk through The Howk, a beautiful wooded limestone gorge with waterfalls. Nan and Arnold Savage work hard to make their hospitality seem effortless and to put you at ease. The converted farmhouse has exposed stonework and log fires for colder evenings. The lounges have televisions, books and games. The bedrooms are beautifully decorated and have bath and shower en suite - two rooms and a lounge are in the converted cowshed, ideal for a group of four. Nan's home-cooked dinners and hearty Cumbrian breakfasts are delicious.

RECOMMENDED IN THE AREA
100-acre nature reserve on site; Northern Fells; Howk Walk to Caldbeck village

Rose Cottage ♦♦♦♦

Map ref 5 - NY13
Lorton Rd, COCKERMOUTH,
CA13 9DX
A5292 from Cockermouth to Lorton/Buttermere, Rose Cottage on right
T / F 01900 822189
E bookings@rosecottageguest.co.uk
W www.rosecottageguest.co.uk
8 rooms, S £38-£45, D £55-£70, No smoking, Closed 7-28 Feb

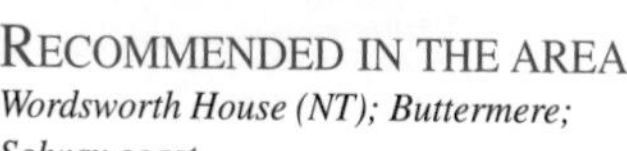

RECOMMENDED IN THE AREA
Wordsworth House (NT); Buttermere; Solway coast

This former inn on the edge of town has been refurbished to provide attractive, modern accommodation. John and Susan Graham maintain Rose Cottage to a high standard and offer genuine hospitality for visitors to the interesting and beautiful north Lakeland area. For the energetic there are opportunities to fish, play golf or tennis, go pony trekking or walk in the fabulous countryside. The local leisure centre offers swimming and badminton, while Cockermouth, the birthplace of William Wordsworth, has a medieval castle and the Castle Brewery that produces the excellent Jennings beer. The smart, well-equipped, centrally heated bedrooms with facilities en suite include a self-contained studio room with external access. There is a cosy lounge and a smart dining room where delicious home-cooked dinners are a highlight, accompanied by a good choice of wines. The full English breakfast is sure to please and most diets are catered for. Children are most welcome (cots are available), as are well-behaved dogs.

Uplands Hotel ♦♦♦♦♦

Map ref 5 - SD37
Haggs Ln, CARTMEL, LA11 6HD
Signed to Grange opp Pig & Whistle in Cartmel, 0.75m on left

T 015395 36248
F 015395 36848
E uplands@kencomp.net
W www.uplands.uk.com

5 rooms, No smoking in bedrooms or dining room, Closed Jan-Feb

Tom and Di Peter's country hotel is just outside the village, near Grange-over-Sands, on the southern edge of the Lake District. It stands in 2 acres of gardens with fine views, just 3 miles from Lake Windermere. Pre-dinner drinks and coffee are served in the bright lounge, where board games, books and magazines are provided. The spacious restaurant has two AA Rosettes for Tom's ambitious cooking. Bedrooms, named after Cumbrian rivers, are all en suite, with direct-dial telephones, radios, reading matter and toiletries. Also in residence are a couple of cats and a friendly Jack Russell.

Recommended in the Area

Cartmel antiques shops & 12th-century priory; Boating on Lake Windermere; Lake District & Yorkshire Dales

---

Wheelgate Country Guest House ♦♦♦♦♦

Map ref 5 - SD39
Little Arrow, CONISTON, LA21 8AU
1.5m S of Coniston, on W side of road

T 015394 41418
F 015394 41114
E enquiry@wheelgate.co.uk
W www.wheelgate.co.uk

5 rooms, S £36-£39, D £62-£78, No smoking

Recommended in the Area

Brantwood; Holker Hall & Motor Museum; Hill Top, Beatrix Potter's house

A quaint and charming house in a magical setting with views over the Coniston fells. The cosy atmosphere is immediately appealing, with oak beams, low ceilings, open fires and an intimate bar. Steve and Linda Abbott pursued a dream when they gave up busy careers in accountancy and engineering to open this 17th-century farmhouse and have never looked back. Praise in the visitors' book for the fabulous breakfasts, friendly service and delightful gardens prove that their venture has been worthwhile. The enchanting en suite bedrooms are thoughtfully designed, and some have king-size or four-poster beds. A warm welcome awaits you at this Lakeland retreat.

Crosthwaite House ♦♦♦♦

Map ref 6 - SD49
CROSTHWAITE, LA8 8BP
A590 onto A5074, 4m right to Crosthwaite, 0.5m turn left
T / F 015395 68264
E bookings@crosthwaitehouse.co.uk
W www.crosthwaitehouse.co.uk
6 rooms, S £22.50-£25, D £45-£50, No smoking, Closed mid Nov-mid Feb

A sturdy mid 18th-century house, this establishment stands in the village of Crosthwaite, at the northern end of the Lyth valley, famous for its damson orchards. You can see across the valley from the spacious lounge, and from the light and airy dining room, where an imaginative menu of traditional home cooking is is freshly cooked on the kitchen Aga. There is plenty of room in the bedrooms, and all have showers and toilets en suite, plus tea and coffee facilities. The owners have been looking after guests in Lakeland for many years now, and they create a relaxed atmosphere in which it is easy to feel at home. They know the surroundings extremely well and will be happy to provide you with any information.

Recommended in the Area

Lake Windermere; Sizergh Castle & Garden (NT); Three golf courses within 4 miles

---

Grizedale Lodge The Hotel in the Forest ♦♦♦♦

Map ref 5 - SD39
GRIZEDALE, LA22 0QL
From Hawkshead signs S to Grizedale, Lodge 2m on right
T 015394 36532
F 015394 36572
E enquiries@grizedale-lodge.com
W www.grizedale-lodge.com
8 rooms, S £40-£47.50, D £90-£95, No smoking

Recommended in the Area

Windermere cruises; Hawkshead; Grizedale Forest

Anyone seeking seclusion and tranquility will love this sprawling, white-painted old building with friendly hosts. Set in the heart of the historic Grizedale Forest, the lodge has superb views of the surrounding countryside from the balcony and patio. The particularly well-appointed bedrooms are elegant, some very spacious with four-poster beds, and including one suite with private access to a balcony. Hearty breakfasts are served in the attractive breakfast room that overlooks the forest. Evening meals are not available, but guests can order sandwiches until the late evening.

Sawrey Ground ♦♦♦♦

Map ref 5 - SD39
Hawkshead Hill,
HAWKSHEAD, LA22 0PP
B5285 from Hawkshead, 1m to Hawkshead Hill, sharp right after Baptist chapel, signs to Tarn Hows for 0.25m. Sawrey Ground on right

T 015394 36683
E mail@sawreyground.com
W www.sawreyground.com

3 rooms, D £58-£68, No smoking

RECOMMENDED IN THE AREA

Great walks from the front door; Blackwell (The Arts & Crafts House), Bowness-on-Windermere; Brantwood (Ruskin's house), Coniston

Built by Anthony Sawrey in 1627, this picturesque oak-beamed farmhouse has a magical setting on the edge of the Tarn Hows Forest, a peaceful location in the centre of the Lake District just above Hawkshead village. Mike and Gill O'Connell offer a warm welcome to their home, with its friendly, relaxed atmosphere and popular home-made bread and cakes. They will do all they can to make your stay enjoyable and memorable. The centuries have created a comfortable and lived-in feeling, from the entrance hall, lounge and dining room, to the attractive south-facing bedrooms. Many walks are possible from the front door, to Coniston, Windermere and Langdale, and including the beautiful lake of Tarn Hows. The area is good for birdwatching and wildlife, and also for cycling and fishing. The central location is ideal for touring the Lakeland region, and there are some excellent places to eat within easy driving distance. Gill was a runner up for AA Landlady of the Year 2005.

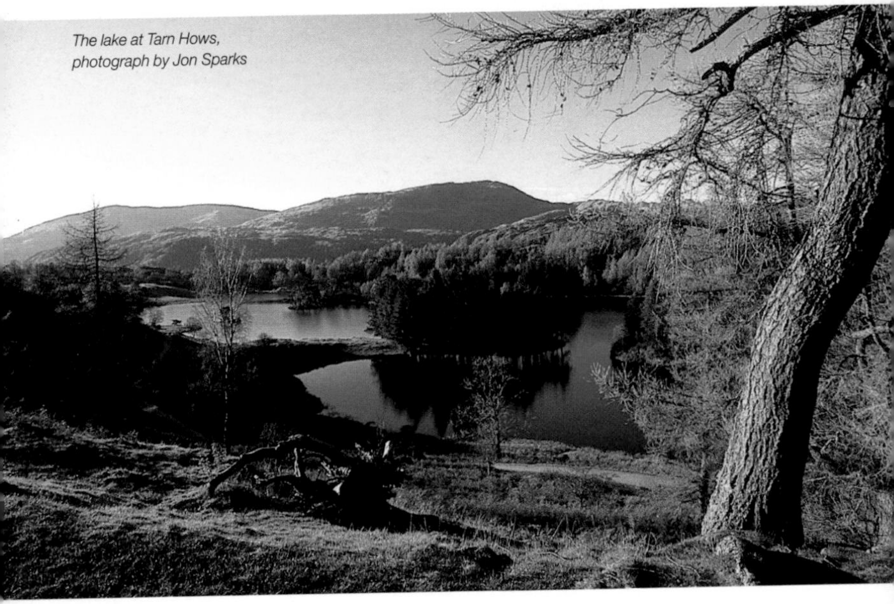

The lake at Tarn Hows, photograph by Jon Sparks

West Vale Country House ♦♦♦♦♦  

Map ref 5 - SD39

Far Sawrey, HAWKSHEAD, LA22 0LQ

Cross Windemere by car ferry at Bowness, B5285 for 1.25m to Far Sawrey, West Vale on left leaving village

T 015394 42817
F 015394 45302
E enquiries@westvalecountryhouse.co.uk
W www.westvalecountryhouse.co.uk

7 rooms, S £63-£80, D £96-£144, No smoking

RECOMMENDED IN THE AREA

Hill Top, Beatrix Potter's home; Brantwood; Dove Cottage

West Vale is a lovely country house where you can forget all your cares. It is surrounded by countryside on the edge of the pretty village of Far Sawrey, with views of Grizedale Forest and the Old Man of Coniston beyond the vale. Beautiful gardens have been cultivated around the property, and the large pond is a delightful spot to sit and soak up the sun. Yours hosts Dee and Glynn Pennington have left nothing to chance in their desire to create a perfect retreat. Bedrooms are impeccably decorated, furnished and equipped, and the bathrooms are stylish. After a long journey you can anticipate a welcoming decanter of sherry in the bedroom. Elegant lounges further help you to unwind, and excellent dinners are served in the dining room. The traditional breakfasts are equally delicious.

Dalegarth House Country Hotel ♦♦♦♦

Map ref 5 - NY22
Portinscale, KESWICK, CA12 5RQ
Off A66 to Portinscale, pass Farmers Arms, 100yds on left

T / F 017687 72817
E allerdalechef@aol.com
W www.dalegarth-house.co.uk

10 rooms, S £33-£35, D £66-£70, No smoking

Recommended in the Area

Rum Story, Whitehaven; Cars of the Stars; Mirehouse

Dalegarth is a spacious Edwardian house set in 1 acre of grounds, with superb views of Derwentwater and the surrounding hills. It occupies a sunny elevated spot in the pretty village of Portinscale, and is ideally situated for walking and touring. Friendly owners Pauline and Bruce Jackson offer attractive and well-equipped en suite bedrooms, each with a radio and a hospitality tray - two rooms are on the ground floor. There are a couple of lounges and a bar well stocked with malt whiskies. Delicious five-course dinners with wine are prepared with much imagination and skill and served in the Dorothy Well Restaurant, giving a true taste of the Lake District. After one of these super evening meals, the quality of the hearty, well-cooked breakfasts will come as no surprise. Free transport is provided from Penrith station for longer staying guests. The hotel is completely non-smoking.

Sunnyside Guest House ♦♦♦♦

Map ref 5 - NY22
25 Southey St, KESWICK,
CA12 4EF

200yds E of town centre. Off A5271 Penrith Rd onto Southey St, Sunnyside on left

T 017687 72446
E enquiries@sunnysideguesthouse.com
W www.sunnysideguesthouse.com

7 rooms, No smoking

This Victorian house is in a quiet location just a stroll from the town centre with its pubs and restaurants. Each of the en suite bedrooms has its own character and a loyal following of regular guests. All rooms are decorated to a high standard and one bedroom is especially suitable for families - a cot and high chair are readily available. Plan your next day in the spacious lounge, with its library of guide books and maps. Gill and Mike Brown pride themselves on serving a top-quality breakfast. They use Cumbrian produce wherever possible, to support local farmers and to ensure that what goes on your plate will taste delicious - choose from a wide range of cereals, fresh home-made yogurt, fruit salad and traditional cooked English fare, all topped off with free-range eggs, of course.

Recommended in the Area

Theatre by the Lake; Trotters World of Animals; Borrowdale

The Grange Country House ♦♦♦♦♦

Map ref 5 - NY22
Manor Brow, Ambleside Rd,
KESWICK, CA12 4BA
A591 from Keswick for Windermere, 0.5m 1st right, house 200yds on right
T 017687 72500
E info@grangekeswick.com
W www.grangekeswick.com
10 rooms, S £35.50-£49.50, D £71-£89, No smoking, Closed 2 Nov-5 Mar

Jane and Duncan Miller welcome returning and new guests to their spacious Victorian property set in lovely gardens. The panoramic views from the stone house of the Lakeland fells and mountains are just part of its attraction, while the town centre is only a stroll away. Also appealing are the spacious en suite bedrooms with pretty soft furnishings, and there is a stylish lounge. The extensive and tasty breakfast menu guarantees a filling start to your day. The Millers are very familiar with the surrounding area and are happy to assist with meal bookings, and walking or tourist information.

RECOMMENDED IN THE AREA
Theatre by the Lake; Lakeland fells; Keswick outdoor clothing shops

---

Howe Keld Lakeland Hotel ♦♦♦♦

Map ref 5 - NY22
5-7 The Heads, KESWICK,
CA12 5ES
From town centre towards Borrowdale, right opp main car park, 1st on left
T / F 017687 72417
E david@howekeld.co.uk
W www.howekeld.co.uk
15 rooms, S £33-£35, D £65-£70, No smoking, Closed Xmas, Jan

Howe Keld is a splendid location for easy access to the facilities in Keswick and to Derwentwater and the fells. This friendly, well-run, non-smoking establishment has a cosy first-floor lounge with spectacular fell views. Local, homemade and organic produce make breakfast a highlight in the spacious dining room, whether you stick to the impressive buffet or order from the varied cooked selection. The colourful bedrooms are all en suite and smartly decorated - particularly popular are the two spacious rooms on the ground floor.

RECOMMENDED IN THE AREA
Keswick; Walking in the fells; Castlerigg Stone Circle

New House Farm ♦♦♦♦♦

Map ref 5 - NY12
LORTON, CA13 9UU
6m S of Cockermouth on B5289 between Lorton & Loweswater
T 01900 85404
F 01900 85478
E hazel@newhouse-farm.co.uk
W www.newhouse-farm.co.uk
5 rooms, D £130-£134, No smoking

RECOMMENDED IN THE AREA
Keswick; Cockermouth; Buttermere lake

Hazel Thompson bought New House Farm in 1990 and completely renovated to its present de luxe standard. Located in the north-west corner of the Lake District National Park, this Grade II listed house dates from 1650. The restoration discovered original oak beams and rafters, flagstone floors, and fireplaces where log fires now crackle on colder days. There are lovely views from all the stylish rooms, which can also be enjoyed by taking a relaxing Hot Spring Spa in the beautifully maintained garden. The appealing en suite bedrooms are richly furnished and equipped with many thoughtful extras including home-baked biscuits or a champagne tray and flowers for special occasions - two rooms have an oak four poster. The delicious five-course dinner menu uses local ingredients whenever possible and changes daily - traditional puddings are a speciality. Hearty breakfasts are another highlight. Stabling is available, and guests' dogs and horses are welcome to wander around the 15 acres of open fields, woods, streams and ponds.

Loweswater, near Lorton

*T*he Old Vicarage ♦♦♦♦ 

Map ref 5 - NY12
Church Ln, LORTON, CA13 9UN
B5292 onto B5289 N of Lorton. 1st left signed Church, house 1st on right
T 01900 85656
E enquiries@oldvicarage.co.uk
W www.oldvicarage.co.uk
8 rooms, S £44-£58, D £88-£116, No smoking

RECOMMENDED IN THE AREA
Cockermouth, Wordsworth's birthplace; Buttermere; Crummock Water

Stunning views, log fires and historic charm - this elegant country house is a relaxing base with and an unhurried and peaceful ambience. It offers spacious accommodation in the Lorton valley, in the heart of the Lake District National Park. High standards are carried through to the well-appointed bedrooms with facilities en suite and excellent views of distant mountains. A converted barn has two rooms with exposed stone walls, and is ideal for families with young children. Breakfasts and dinner are prepared freshly from the best local produce available and served in the bright dining room. So, relax, unwind and let your hosts do the rest.

Winder Hall Country House ♦♦♦♦♦ 

Map ref 5 - NY12
LORTON, CA13 9UP
A66 W from Keswick, at Braithwaite onto B5292 to Lorton, left at T-junct signed Buttermere, Winderhall 0.5m on right

T 01900 85107
F 01900 85479
E nick@winderhall.co.uk
W www.winderhall.co.uk

7 rooms, S £100-£110, D £120-£170, No smoking, Closed 2-31 Jan

RECOMMENDED IN THE AREA

Buttermere; Keswick; Beaches of west Cumbria

Winder Hall an impressive former manor house, set in a peaceful valley. It is now home to Ann and Nick Lawler and their two young children who are only too happy to share their home and the delightful Lakeland countryside. The smart, individually styled bedrooms are thoughtfully equipped, and all are furnished with fine antiques or pine and have stunning fell views. Two rooms have beautiful four-poster beds. You can take afternoon tea in the luxurious lounge in front of a log fire in winter, or in the garden during summer. The oak-panelled dining room is the perfect venue for skilfully prepared meals using local seasonal produce - dishes such as Lakeland lamb, cooked in red wine, rosemary and balsamic vinegar, or wild mushroom tart are among the temptations.
An extensive breakfast menu sets you up for the day. A complimentary pass to leisure facilities at a nearby hotel is available, and small intimate weddings or any special anniversaries are caringly catered for.

Ees Wyke Country House ♦♦♦♦♦ 

Map ref 5 - SD39
NEAR SAWREY, LA22 0JZ
On B5285 on W side of village

T 015394 36393
F 015394 36740
E mail@eeswyke.co.uk
W www.eeswyke.co.uk

8 rooms, D £144-£170, No smoking

RECOMMENDED IN THE AREA
Hill Top Farm (NT home of Beatrix Potter); Blackwell, The Arts & Crafts House; Brantwood (Ruskin's House)

A warm welcome awaits you at Ees Wyke, once the holiday home of Beatrix Potter. The Georgian house has a reputation for fine food, and the thoughtfully equipped bedrooms - most with stunning Lakeland views - have been carefully furnished and come with all comforts plus tea and coffee facilities. After a day walking, fishing, sailing or riding in the surrounding countryside, come back to Ees Wyke to relax. The charming lounge has an open fire, and carefully prepared five-course dinners are served in the splendid dining room to guests and non-residents. Breakfasts are the result of the skilful use of local produce - feast on Cumberland sausage, bacon and eggs, or choose a lighter option of fresh fruit, yoghurt and cereals.

Sawrey House Country Hotel & Restaurant ♦♦♦♦♦ 

Map ref 5 - SD39
NEAR SAWREY, LA22 0LF
On B5285 in village

T 015394 36387
F 015394 36010
E enquiries@sawrey-house.com
W www.sawrey-house.com

12 rooms, S £50-£65, D £100-£150, No smoking, Closed Jan

Built around 1830 of Lakeland stone, the house retains many original features including the stained-glass window in the spacious hall. There is an elegant lounge with deep sofas, and a log fire burns on chilly nights. Bedrooms are en suite and many have views of the lake. Sawrey House has been awarded an AA rosette for its food, which is imaginatively and stylishly presented, helped along with a varied larder. Breakfast is in the traditional style with a choice of lighter alternatives, such as smoked haddock, or mushrooms on toast with thyme.

RECOMMENDED IN THE AREA
Hilltop, Beatrix Potter's house; Windermere; Many walks from hotel

The Knoll Country House ♦♦♦♦♦

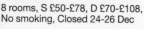

Map ref 5 - SD38
Lakeside, NEWBY BRIDGE, LA12 8AU
A590 W to Newby Bridge, over rdbt, signed right for Lake Steamers, house 0.5m on left
T 015395 31347
F 015395 30850
E info@theknoll-lakeside.co.uk
W www. theknoll-lakeside.co.uk
8 rooms, S £50-£78, D £70-£108, No smoking, Closed 24-26 Dec

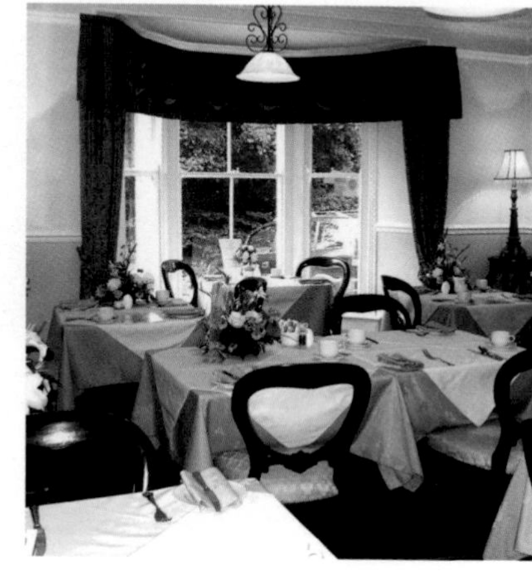

ꞦECOMMENDED IN THE AREA

.quarium of the Lakes; World of Beatrix Potter; Iolker Hall & Gardens

Jenny Meads and Tracey Watson escaped from the daily commute and corporate life in 001 and found the Knoll, a small Victorian ountry house set in a leafy dell on the west side f Windermere. They knew this was the place to reate a tranquil oasis offering fabulous food nd quality accommodation. All rooms have een refurbished, including new bathrooms, nd some are de luxe. They are all well quipped, and hospitality trays provide fruit and eaf teas, coffee and hot chocolate, and hand-aked biscuits. Food is the real feature here. he girls passionately support local businesses, using excellent Cumbrian produce including daily fresh fish and meat. Hot breakfast is a hearty traditional affair complemented by a healthy buffet option and home-made preserves. Jenny and Tracy also actively support local conservation. Their formula for the Knoll clearly works - more than half of the bookings come from people who have stayed before.

*B*rooklands Guest House ♦♦♦♦

Map ref 6 - NY53
2 Portland Place, PENRITH, CA11 7QN
From town hall onto Portland Place, 50yds on left
T 01768 863395
E enquiries@brooklandsguesthouse.com
W www.brooklandsguesthouse.com
7 rooms, S £35-£40, D £60-£70, No smoking

Charming and elegant, Brooklands Guest House is situated in the heart of historic Penrith. This beautiful, refurbished Victorian terrace house is an excellent base for exploring the many delights of the Lake District National Park while convenient for the attractive Eden valley. Debbie and Leon ensure you have a most enjoyable stay and that you will be keen to make a return visit. The hearty breakfast satisfies the largest of appetites. For a romantic escape with a touch of luxury, the Brooklands' suite has a locally handcrafted four-poster bed, a sofa, television, DVD, radio-alarm clock, hairdryer and a choice of light refreshments.

RECOMMENDED IN THE AREA

Penrith; Coast to Coast cycle route; Ullswater lake

Cumbrian Lodge Hotel ♦♦♦♦

Map ref 5 - NY00
Gosforth Rd, SEASCALE, CA20 1JG
Off A595 at Gosforth onto B5344 signed Seascale, B&B 2m on left
T 019467 27309
F 019467 27158
E cumbrianlodge@btconnect.com
W www.cumbrianlodge.com
6 rooms, S £62.50, D £70,
No smoking in bedrooms or dining room

The Cumbrian Lodge is a very pleasant house run by enthusiastic hands-on owners. Its contemporary interior design creates a relaxed and friendly atmosphere and the modern bedrooms are spacious and well-equipped. The restaurant is a popular local attraction by itself and offers well-prepared tasty dinners well worthy of the AA Rosette and also a good wine list. Luxury items in the bedrooms include opulent Siberian goose down duvets, flat-screen televisions, thick fluffy towels and fine complementary toiletries.

Recommended in the Area
Wast Water; St Bees Head; Muncaster Castle & Gardens

Brookfield House ♦♦♦♦

Map ref 6 - NY51
SHAP, CA10 3PZ
M6 junct 39, A6 towards Shap, 1st accommodation off motorway
T / F 01931 716397
E info@brookfieldshap.co.uk
W www.brookfieldshap.co.uk
4 rooms, S £25-£30, D £46-£55,
No smoking, Closed Xmas, New Year

Recommended in the Area
Shap Abbey; Kendal; Penrith

Brookfield is a very well-maintained property, where refreshments on arrival are just part of the warm welcome. The pretty garden enhances the peaceful atmosphere, even though the motorway is just a short drive away. Home cooking is a speciality - substantial and enjoyable dinners and breakfasts are freshly prepared and served in the pleasant dining room. The en suite bedrooms are extremely well-appointed, and home comforts include radio alarms, hospitality trays and hairdryers. There is a wide choice in the small bar, and the traditional lounge is ideal for relaxation after touring the northern lakes. No children under 12 years and no pets. Parking is available.

Queens Head Hotel ♦♦♦♦

Map ref 6 - NY40
Town Head, TROUTBECK (NEAR WINDERMERE), LA23 1PW
A592 from Windermere for Penrith/Ullswater, Queens Head 2m on right

T 015394 32174
F 015394 31938
E enquiries@queensheadhotel.com
W www.queensheadhotel.com

14 rooms, S £67.50-£77.50, D £100-£120, No smoking in bedrooms, Closed 25-Dec

This 17th-century coaching inn stands at the head of the Troutbeck valley and has stunning views to Garburn Pass. The master bedroom has a four-poster bed, and all the rooms are traditionally furnished and equipped with modern facilities. Oak beams, flagstone floors, and a bar that was once an Elizabethan four-poster provide an atmospheric setting in which to enjoy imaginative food, a splendid choice of real ales, and fine wines. The attractive seating area outside is paved with Kirkstone slate and takes full advantage of the views.

Recommended in the Area

Windermere Steamboats & Museum; Troutbeck (NT); Lake District Visitor Centre, Brockhole

---

The Coach House ♦♦♦♦

Map ref 6 - SD49
Lake Rd, WINDERMERE, LA23 2EQ
A591 into Windermere & towards Bowness, House 0.5m on right opp St Herbert's Church

T 015394 44494
E enquiries@lakedistrictbandb.com
W www.lakedistrictbandb.com

5 rooms, S £33-£47, D £50-£70, No smoking, Closed 24-26 Dec

The property was originally a Victorian coach house, but now the interior is more chic and minimalist, achieved through the bold use of bright colours and contemorary furnishings. The modern decor continues in the en suite bedrooms, including one pretty room in fuchsia pink, and another in duck-egg blue. Stylish iron beds, showers, and a host of amenities such as radios, alarm clocks and hairdryers ensure your well-being. The freshly prepared breakfasts made from local produce are another special feature.

Recommended in the Area

Windermere lake cruises; Blackwell, The Arts & Crafts House; Holehird Gardens

Lake Windermere

The Fairfield Garden Guest House ♦♦♦♦

Map ref 6 - SD49
Brantfell Rd,
Bowness-on-Windermere,
WINDERMERE, LA23 3AE

Into Bowness town centre, turn opp St Martin's Church & left again by Spinnery restaurant, house 200yds on right

T / F 015394 46565
E tonyandliz@the-fairfield.co.uk
W www.the-fairfield.co.uk

10 rooms, S £27-£49, D £54-£78, No smoking

Genuine hospitality in a Lakeland country house - Tony and Liz Blaney offer a high standard of personal service at their 200-year-old home. Situated just above Bowness, with its restaurants and pubs, and Windermere lake, the Fairfield is perfect for a tranquil break or for Dales Way walkers. The bedrooms have lovely views of the garden and surrounding hills, and are well furnished with a host of thoughtful extras. Special attention is paid to accommodating visitors with mobility requirements. Choose from either the hearty or the healthy breakfast options, both using the best of ingredients. Porridge is a highlight, and a drizzle of Scottish whisky can be added if desired. Well-behaved children are very welcome.

Recommended in the Area

Blackwell Arts & Crafts House; Windermere lake steamers; Wordsworth House (NT)

The Howbeck ♦♦♦♦♦

Map ref 6 - SD49
New Rd, WINDERMERE, LA23 2LA
A591 through Windermere town centre & towards Bowness
T 015394 44739
E relax@howbeck.co.uk
W www.howbeck.co.uk
10 rooms, D £31.50-£71.50, No smoking

RECOMMENDED IN THE AREA
Windermere Steamboats & Museum; World of Beatrix Potter; Lake cruises

The Howbeck, a delightful Victorian villa convenient for the town and lake, is once discovered, never forgotten. Hazel and Richard create the atmosphere of a friendly luxurious hotel combined with an elegant private home. The bedrooms are well appointed with lovely soft furnishings and some have luxurious spa baths. Each room is named after a Cumbrian beck (stream) and those in the luxury class come with a decanter of sherry, fresh fruit and mineral water as additional touches. Attention to detail is the key and everywhere is spotless. The bright lounge has Internet access, and home-prepared dinners and hearty Cumbrian breakfasts are served at individual tables in the attractive dining room.

Newstead ♦♦♦♦

Map ref 6 - SD49
New Rd, WINDERMERE, LA23 2EE
0.5m from A591 between Windermere & Bowness
T 015394 44485
F 015394 88904
E info@newstead-guesthouse.co.uk
W www.newstead-guesthouse.co.uk
7 rooms, S £40-£60, D £50-£90, No smoking

This charming house has been stylishly refurbished to blend Victorian elegance with modern comforts. The spacious bedrooms have bathrooms en suite, and coordinated decor and soft furnishings. Original fireplaces and woodwork, and tea and coffee trays enhance the comfortable atmosphere. There is a fine mahogany staircase and a lounge with a coal fire on cooler days. Delicious breakfasts include a vegetarian choice, and are served at separate tables in the large dining room. Ask about free use of the local private leisure facilities.

RECOMMENDED IN THE AREA
Hill Top, Beatrix Potter's home (NT); Wrynose Pass spectacular drive; Windermere lake steamers

*T*he Willowsmere ♦♦♦♦

Map ref 6 - SD49

Ambleside Rd, WINDERMERE, LA23 1ES

On A591, 500yds on left after Windermere station, towards Ambleside

Ⓣ 015394 43575
Ⓕ 015394 44962
Ⓔ info@thewillowsmere.com
Ⓦ www.thewillowsmere.com

12 rooms, S £35-£45, D £56-£100, No smoking

RECOMMENDED IN THE AREA

Windermere lake cruises; Windermere Steamboats & Museum; Natiional Park Visitor Centre

The imposing 1850s house offers a home from home atmosphere in the heart of the Lake District and within easy walking distance of Windermere centre. Owners Martin and Sue have done lots of refurbishment at this large Lakeland stone building, set in a colourful, well-tended garden, with a patio and water feature to the rear. The large bedrooms have been upgraded, with new pocket-sprung beds and headboards in all rooms, as well as thoughtful extras including tea and coffee facilities. One ground floor-room has easier access. There is a choice of inviting lounges, a well-stocked bar, and a stylish dining room where delicious breakfasts are served at individual tables. The large private car park can accommodate boat or glider trailers with ease. An added bonus to your stay at Willowsmere is the free use of the leisure facilities at nearby Windermere Manor Hotel. No children under 12.

A selection of places to eat from the AA Restaurant & AA Pub guides

Restaurants

Bramhall's (British)
6 Buxton Road, Ashbourne DE6 1EX
Tel 01335 346158

Renaissance Restaurant (French)
Bath Street, Bakewell DE45 1BX
Tel 01629 812687

Fischer's Baslow Hall (European)
Calver Road, Baslow DE45 1RR
Tel 01246 583259

Best Western Lee Wood Hotel (European)
The Park, Buxton SK17 6TQ
Tel 01298 23002

Darleys Restaurant (European)
Darley Abbey Mill, Darley Abbey DE22 1DZ
Tel 01332 364987

The Old Vicarage (British)
Ridgeway Moor, Ridgeway S12 3XW
Tel 0114 2475814

Pubs

The Monsal Head Hotel
Monsal Head, Bakewell DE45 1NL
Tel 01629 640250

Yorkshire Bridge Inn
Ashopton Road, Bamford S33 0AZ
Tel 01433 651361

The Devonshire Arms
The Square, Beeley DE4 2NR
Tel 01629 733259

The Waltzing Weasle Inn
New Mills Road, Birch Vale SK22 1BT
Tel 01663 743402

The Maynard Arms
Main Road, Grindleford S32 2HE
Tel 01433 630321

The Red Lion Inn
Main Street, Hognaston DE6 1PR
Tel 01335 370396

The Courtyard ♦♦♦♦

Map ref 7 - SK13
Dairy House Farm, ALKMONTON, DE6 3DG
1.5m SE of Alkmonton. Off A50 at Foston, 3.5m up Woodyard Ln & Ashbourne Rd
T / F 01335 330187
E michael@dairyhousefarm.org.uk
W www.dairyhousefarm.org.uk/
7 rooms, S £35, D £52-£54, No smoking, Closed Xmas

The Courtyard is surrounded by the Derbyshire dales and is close to the Peak District National Park. The converted Victorian cowsheds provide a base for a range of outdoor activities including hill walking and mountain biking, though others may prefer the historic houses or craft and pottery shops in the vicinity. Michael and Charlotte offer a warm welcome to all and have carefully furnished the buildings throughout. The bedrooms, which are all on the ground floor, are thoughtfully equipped and all come with hospitality trays. Two rooms have been especially designed for easier access. A substantial breakfast is provided in the bright dining room and dinner is available by arrangement. Children welcome but no pets.

Recommended in the Area

Kedleston Hall (NT); Sudbury Hall (NT, museum of childhood); Alton Towers

Omnia Somnia ♦♦♦♦♦

Map ref 7 - SK14

The Coach House, The Firs,
ASHBOURNE, DE6 1HF

200yds S of town centre. Off station St onto Old Hill, 1st left onto The Firs & signed

T 01335 300145
F 01335 300958
E alan@omniasomnia.co.uk
W www.omniasomnia.co.uk

2 rooms, D £90-£100, No smoking

RECOMMENDED IN THE AREA

'eak District National Park; Alton Towers; 'hatsworth

Paula and Alan Coker Mayes began B&B as an experiment with just one oom. Since then the business has grown nd they now run Omnia Somnia full time. he house is within easy walking distance f the town and is beautifully furnished to ffer every comfort. The ground-floor en uite guest rooms vary in design, one with valls full of pictures and a double-size bath n suite, the other with its own sitting room nd stairs to a romantic hideaway. Home-nade dinners and substantial breakfasts re served in the upstairs dining room, verlooking the garden and hillside beyond, nd white linen, silver cutlery, cut glass and one china are all part of the experience. For the less mobile, breakfast can be brought to the room. Prepare to be pampered, with ample reading material in the cosy lounge and secret chocolates in the rooms. Paula and Alan are always happy to rise to special occasions with extra touches.

The Peak District near Hathersage

The Outpost ♦♦♦♦

Map ref 7 - SK28
Shatton Ln, BAMFORD, S33 0BG
Off A6187 between Bamford & Hope opp High Peak Garden Centre, then 200yds on right
Ⓣ 01433 651400
Ⓔ aabest.enquires@theoutpost.info
Ⓦ www.bkmworld.com/theoutpost
3 rooms, S £35-£45, D £50-£60, No smoking, Closed 24 Dec-2 Jan

Lovely gardens with plenty of trees surround this large family home, set opposite a garden centre in the heart of the Peak District. The Outpost offers genuine hospitality and high standards of comfort. Bedrooms are cosily equipped with tea and coffee facilities , and there is a four-poster bed for special occasions. Breakfast is a memorable feast with home-made bread and preserves, and can be enjoyed in the dining room or conservatory. The garden lounge with its delightful outlook is a favourite with guests.

Recommended in the area

Blue John Cavern & Mine; Eyam Hall; Chatsworth

Dannah Farm Country House Ltd ♦♦♦♦♦

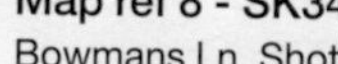

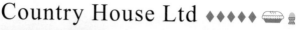

Map ref 8 - SK34

Bowmans Ln, Shottle, BELPER, DE56 2DR

A517 from Belper towards Ashbourne, 1.5m right into Shottle after Hanging Gate pub on right, over x-rds & right

T 01773 550273
F 01773 550590
E reservations@dannah.demon.co.uk
W www.dannah.co.uk

8 rooms, S £65-£85, D £85-£160, No smoking in bedrooms or dining room, Closed 24-26 Dec

Recommended in the Area

Chatsworth; Dovedale; Alton Towers

Dannah is a Georgian farmhouse on a working farm on the Chatsworth Estate, and is home to Joan and Martin Slack and their collection of pigs, hens and cats, and Cracker the very good-natured English setter. The house is being upgraded to even higher standards while keeping many original features. Each bedroom has individual character, beautifully furnished with antiques and old pine and filled with a wealth of thoughtful extras. Some rooms have private sitting rooms, four-poster beds and amazing bathrooms featuring a double spa bath or Japanese-style tubs - the Studio Hideaway suite even has its own private terrace with hot tub. The two delightful sitting rooms have open fires on a chilly evening and views over the gardens. Farmhouse breakfasts are a true delight, served in relaxed and elegant surroundings; dinner is available by arrangement. Footpaths criss-cross the surrounding area making it an ideal location for walking enthusiasts.

Buxton's Victorian Guest House ♦♦♦♦♦

Map ref 7 - SK07
3A Broad Walk, BUXTON, SK17 6JE
Signs to Opera House, proceed to Old Hall Hotel, right onto Hartington Rd, car park 100yds on right

T 01298 78759
F 01298 74732
E buxtonvictorian@btconnect.com
W www.buxtonvictorian.co.uk

9 rooms, S £43-£71, D £61-£85, No smoking

This Grade II listed house is only minutes from the famous Opera House and the town's amenities, and has great views over Buxton's renowned Pavilion Gardens. Attention to detail and high quality accommodation are hallmarks at this refurbished Victorian house, and the hosts ensure your stay will be memorable. Luxury bedrooms are individually themed and have many thoughtful extras - flowers, chocolates and champagne can be ordered for that special occasion. A complimentary tray of tea or coffee and biscuits awaits you in the tranquil drawing room on arrival. Excellent breakfasts are served in the Oriental breakfast room and hospitality is first class.

RECOMMENDED IN THE AREA
Poole's Cavern (Buxton Country Park); Peak District National Park; Chatsworth

---

Grendon Guest House ♦♦♦♦♦

Map ref 7 - SK07
Bishops Ln, BUXTON, SK17 6UN
0.75m from Buxton centre, just off A53, St Johns Rd, turn before Duke of York pub & lights leaving town

T 01298 78831
F 01298 79257
E grendonguesthouse@hotmail.com
W www.grendonguesthouse.co.uk

4 rooms, S £29-£35, D £58-£79, No smoking, Closed 5-29 Jan

Spaciousness distinguishes this detached property set in attractive gardens with views to the Peak District. The house stands in a country lane within easy walking distance of the centre of Buxton. The committed proprietors, Colin and Hilary Parker, love to have people to stay in their delightful home. Coordinated design and antique furnishings characterise the interior, and the en suite accommodation comprises a twin, a double, and a four-poster suite. All rooms have easy chairs and hospitality trays. Memorable breakfasts, including home-baked bread, are served in the elegant dining room, and dinner is available by arrangement. The lounge opens onto a large balcony with glorious views.

RECOMMENDED IN THE AREA
Walks to the Goyt Valley from the door; Chatsworth; Castleton Caverns

The Crescent, Buxton

Oldfield Guest House ♦♦♦♦

Map ref 7 - SK07
8 Macclesfield Rd, BUXTON,
SK17 9AH
On B5059 0.5m SW of town centre
Ⓣ 01298 78264
Ⓔ avril@oldfieldhousebuxton.co.uk
Ⓦ www.oldfieldhousebuxton.co.uk
4 rooms, D £64-£74, No smoking, Closed Xmas, New Year

A warm welcome awaits you at this Victorian stone house in a leafy residential avenue not far from Buxton's attractions. The large, carefully furnished bedrooms have luxurious king- or queen-size beds with crisp linens, are equipped with tea and coffee facilities, and have modern bath-shower rooms en suite. Choose between a full English or continental breakfast complimented by an array of cereals, fruit juices and fruits, served in the bright, attractive dining room. The cosy lounge has French doors opening onto a patio and very pleasant grounds with ponds and a stream. Off-street parking is available.

Recommended in the Area

Buxton Opera House & Pavilion Gardens; Chatsworth ; Peak District National Park

Roseleigh Hotel ♦♦♦♦

Map ref 7 - SK07
19 Broad Walk, BUXTON, SK17 6JR
A6 to Safeway rdbt, onto Dale Rd, right at lights, 100yds left by Swan pub, down hill & right onto Hartington Rd

T / F 01298 24904
E enquiries@roseleighhotel.co.uk
W www.roseleighhotel.co.uk

14 rooms, S £30-£78, D £64-£78, No smoking, Closed 16 Dec-10 Jan

When Gerard and Maggi Heelan bought the Roseleigh in 1998 they put all their enthusiasm and energy as seasoned travellers into the enterprise. The result is stylish accommodation with quality furnishings and decoration highlighting the original features. The elegant Victorian property is in the centre of Buxton overlooking the lake in the 23-acre Pavilion Gardens, with the hills of the Peak District National Park forming a backdrop. The thoughtfully furnished bedrooms have smart modern shower rooms and come with considerate extras including tea and coffee facilities. The warmly decorated lounge, complete with a large collection of travel guides, maps, history and lifestyle books, has a relaxing atmosphere. The excellent breakfast, using local produce, is served in the attractive yellow dining room. Gerard and Maggi can suggest plenty of places to visit in this glorious part of Britain.

RECOMMENDED IN THE AREA

Buxton Opera House; Chatsworth; Peak District National Park

The Rising Sun Hotel ♦♦♦♦

Map ref 7 - NZ60
Thornhill Moor, Bamford,
CASTLETON, S33 0AL
On A625 from Sheffield to Castleton
T 01433 651323
F 01433 651601
E info@the-rising-sun.org
W www.the-rising-sun.org
12 rooms, S £49.50-£69.50, D £60-£140, No smoking in bedrooms

arefully restored and lovingly presented by Carole and Graham /alker, the 18th-century Rising Sun at hornhill Moor lies within the Hope Valley the heart of the Peak District. The ımily-run inn offers spacious luxury edrooms with quality furnishings and fficient modern bathrooms. Some ooms have stunning country views, and ice touches include fresh flowers and ntique furniture. The friendly staff attend your every need in an efficient manner naking any stay here truly memorable. highlight is the excellent and imaginative food served in the pleasant public areas. The lunch and dinner menus are created daily, a choice of traditional dishes with modern European and Far Eastern influences. Choose from buffet-style menus or individually prepared dishes such as lamb shank braised in onion, soya and red wine gravy. The good food is complemented by an equally good selection of real ales and fine wines.

Recommended in the Area

Chatsworth; Castleton Caverns; Bakewell market town

Hornbeam House ♦♦♦♦

Map ref 8 - SK37
Mile Hill, Mansfield Rd, Hasland, CHESTERFIELD, S41 0JN
M1 junct 29, A617 towards Chesterfield, 1.5m 1st exit turn left at top of slip road, 200yds turn right towards Hasland. Hornbeam House 0.75m on right

T 01246 556851
F 0870 0521647
E enquiries@hornbeamhouse4t.demon.co.uk
W www.hornbeamhouse.4t.com

2 rooms, S £35-£43, D £55-£71, No smoking

Convenient for the M1, Chesterfield and for touring, this large detached Victorian house stands in substantial grounds with ample parking. It is a great location for golfers with an 18-hole course and floodlit driving range just minutes away. The carefully renovated bedrooms are light and airy. On the ground floor there is a magnificent lounge with views to the front and rear gardens. Attentive service is always evident here, and fresh and healthy cooking is enjoyed at breakfast (and excellent dinners by arrangement). A cottage-style annexe is also available. No pets.

RECOMMENDED IN THE AREA
Hardwick Hall (NT); Matlock; Chatsworth

The Bulls Head Inn ♦♦♦♦

Map ref 7 - SK17
FOOLOW, S32 5QR
Off A623 into Foolow

T 01433 630873
F 01433 631738

3 rooms, S £50, D £70, No smoking in bedrooms or dining room

This quiet village pub is popular with locals and the many walkers who enjoy the splendid countryside of the Peak District National Park. Many of the inn's original features survive, and it offers well-equipped bedrooms with quality fittings and furnishings. A very good choice of imaginative bar meals as well as more formal dishes are served in the traditional dining room or the cosy bar areas. Local and guest ales are also a feature of the bar. Breakfast is a comprehensive selection of hot and cold dishes.

RECOMMENDED IN THE AREA
Chatsworth; Castleton Caverns; Haddon Hall

Underleigh House ♦♦♦♦♦

Map ref 7 - SK18
Off Edale Rd, HOPE, S33 6RF
From village church on A6187 onto Edale Rd, 1m left onto lane
T 01433 621372
F 01433 621324
E info@underleighhouse.co.uk
W www.underleighhouse.co.uk
6 rooms, S £50, D £72-£85, No smoking, Closed Xmas, New Year

RECOMMENDED IN THE AREA
Castleton Caverns; Chatsworth; Eyam

Walkers and others visitors to the Peak District National Park will find this creeper-clad cottage a charming and convenient base. Vivienne and Philip Taylor are convivial and entertaining hosts who provide thoughtfully furnished bedrooms with facilities en suite, each equipped with a hairdryer, radio alarm, and tea and coffee facilities. Some rooms have direct access to the gardens, while one room comes with its own lounge. Enjoy an evening drink on the terrace overlooking marvellous scenery in summer, or by the log fire in the lounge in cooler weather. Home-made and local specialities feature on the breakfast menu, and are served around one large table in the dining room.

Hodgkinsons Hotel ♦♦♦♦

Map ref 7 - SK35
150 South Parade, Matlock Bath, MATLOCK, DE4 3NR
On A6 in village centre
T 01629 582170
F 01629 584891
E enquiries@hodgkinsons-hotel.co.uk
W www.hodgkinsons-hotel.co.uk
8 rooms, S £40-£75, D £75-£120, Closed 24-26 Dec

RECOMMENDED IN THE AREA
Heights of Abraham; Matlock Bath; Chatsworth

You will receive a warm welcome at this fine Grade II listed Georgian hotel with many interesting and unusual features. Hodgkinsons has loads of character and the hotel is perfect for visiting the lovely Derbyshire countryside with its many historic houses. The bedrooms are equipped with fine antique furniture, sumptuous furnishings and a wealth of thoughtful extras. The elegant dining room is the venue for imaginative European cuisine using fresh local produce. Relax in the lounge, beside a real fire, or in summer in the terraced garden overlooking the steep wooded valley. Children and pets are welcome.

Hearthstone Farm ♦♦♦♦

Map ref 7 - SK35

Hearthstone Ln, Riber, MATLOCK, DE4 5JW

A615 at Tansley 2m E of Matlock, turn opp Royal Oak towards Riber, at gates to Riber Hall left onto Riber Rd and 1st left onto Hearthstone Ln, farmhouse on left

T 01629 534304
F 01629 534372
E enquiries@hearthstonefarm.co.uk
W www.hearthstonefarm.co.uk

3 rooms, S £40, D £60, No smoking, Closed Xmas, New Year

Recommended in the Area

Chatsworth; Haddon Hall; Dovedale & Manifold Valley

Set high on the hill above Matlock, this traditional farmhouse is a welcoming home in a lovely rural area. The farm has unrivalled views of the historic village of Riber, dominated by Riber Castle. Beautifully decorated in keeping with its age and character, the stone house has original exposed stone walls and oak beams. The charming bedrooms are equipped with a host of extras for that home-from-home feel, and all rooms are en suite with modern bathrooms. Unwind in the inviting sitting room after a day exploring the area, while the elegant dining room is a stylish setting for breakfast. As a working farm producing organic meat and other produce, Hearthstone can offer delicious fresh food for this meal, particularly the sausages and bacon that are prepared on the premises.

Pear Tree Farm ♦♦♦♦

Map ref 7 - SK35

Lea Main Rd, Lea Bridge, MATLOCK, DE4 5JN

M1 junct 28, A38 S, A610 Ambergate, A6 Cromford. Turn right at lights, after 2m turn left at John Smedley Mills, 0.5m on left

T 01629 534215
F 01629 534060
E sue@derbyshirearts.co.uk
W www.derbyshirearts.co.uk

8 rooms, S £45, D £60, No smoking

Recommended in the Area

Chatsworth; Carsington Water; Crich Tramway Village

Set in 76 acres of woodland and pasture overlooking Lea Brook, this renovated traditional farmhouse offers the perfect rural retreat. It provides a range of thoughtfully furnished bedrooms, two of which have easier access. All bedrooms have facilities en suite and are of a good size. Comprehensive breakfasts are served in the oak-furnished dining room, and dinner can be provided by arrangement. There is spacious, cosy lounge with wood-burning stove, a large television and DVD player and a selection of books. Pear Tree Farm has a well-equipped separate studio offering varied and interesting art and craft courses which are open to guests.

Yew Tree Cottage ♦♦♦♦

Map ref 7 - SK35

The Knoll, Tansley, MATLOCK, DE4 5FP

A615 from Matlock to Tansey, 1.5m left onto Church St, 0.25m fork left, onto The Knoll, 2nd entrance on right

T 01629 583862, 07799 541903
E enquiries@yewtreecottagebb.co.uk
W www.yewtreecottagebb.co.uk

3 rooms, D £60-£70, No smoking

Yew Tree Cottage is a true home from home, a renovated 18th-century cottage full of original character set in pretty gardens in the village of Tansley. Jeanie and Richard Dornan are a well-travelled couple who use their experience of staying in hotels to provide outstanding hospitality. They provide elegantly furnished and decorated bedrooms fitted with well-stocked refreshment trays and clock radios. Breakfast is a memorable feast of home-made produce, and snacks and light refreshments are offered on arrival. Log fires cheer up the cooler days.

Recommended in the Area

Chatsworth; Crich Tramway Village; Heights of Abraham cable cars

The Smithy ♦♦♦♦♦

Map ref 7 - TQ40
NEWHAVEN, SK17 0DT
On A515 10m S of Buxton. Adjacent to Biggin Ln, entrance via private driveway opp Ivy House
T / F 01298 84548
E thesmithy@newhavenderbyshire.freeserve.co.uk
W www.thesmithybedandbreakfast.co.uk
4 rooms, S £45-£50, D £60-£75, No smoking in bedrooms or dining room

Lynn and Gary Jinks-Lowe enthusiastically provide the simple pleasures for their guests - good food, comfortable surroundings, cosy fires in winter and walks for the dog. They have restored this drovers' inn and blacksmith's shop to a high standard with all modern comforts and offer a personal service. The well-decorated family-size bedrooms are all en suite and come with hospitality trays. Tasty breakfasts including free-range eggs and home-made preserves are served in the forge, which still has its vast open hearth, and there is a cosy lounge. The pleasant gardens are set within 3 acres of meadow and are enclosed by the Peak District National Park.

Recommended in the area

Chatsworth; Tissington & High Peak Trail (walking distance); Peak District National Park

Devon

A selection of places to eat from the AA Restaurant & AA Pub guides

Restaurants

@@ Dartmoor Inn (British)
Lydford EX20 4AY, Tel 01822 820221

@ Hotel Barcelona (British, Mediterranean)
Magdalen Street, Exeter EX2 4HY
Tel 01392 281010

@@ Rising Sun Hotel (British, French)
Harbourside, Lynmouth EX35 6EG
Tel 01598 753223

@ The Sea Trout (British)
Staverton TQ9 6PA, Tel 01803 762274

@@ Tanners Restaurant (European)
Prysten House, Finewell Street, Plymouth PL1 2AE, Tel 01752 252001

@@ Pophams
Castle Street, Winkleigh EX19 8HQ
Tel 01837 83767

Pubs

The Masons Arms
Branscombe EX12 3DJ
Tel 01297 680300

The Tuckers Arms
Dalwood EX13 7EG, Tel 01404 881342

The Drewe Arms
The Square, Drewsteignton EX6 6QN
Tel 01647 281224

The Fox & Goose
Parracombe EX31 4PE, Tel 01598 763239

The Victoria Inn
Fore Street, Salcombe TQ8 8BU
Tel 01548 842604

The Tower Inn
Church Road, Slapton TQ7 2PN
Tel 01548 580216

Gages Mill Country Guest House ♦♦♦♦

Map ref 2 - SX77
Buckfastleigh Rd, ASHBURTON, TQ13 7JW
Off A38 at Peartree junct, turn right then left at filling station, Gages Mill 500yds on left
Ⓣ 01364 652391
Ⓕ 01364 652641
Ⓔ richards@gagesmill.co.uk
Ⓦ www.gagesmill.co.uk
7 rooms, S £26-£34, D £52-£68, No smoking in bedrooms or dining room, Closed 23 Oct-Feb

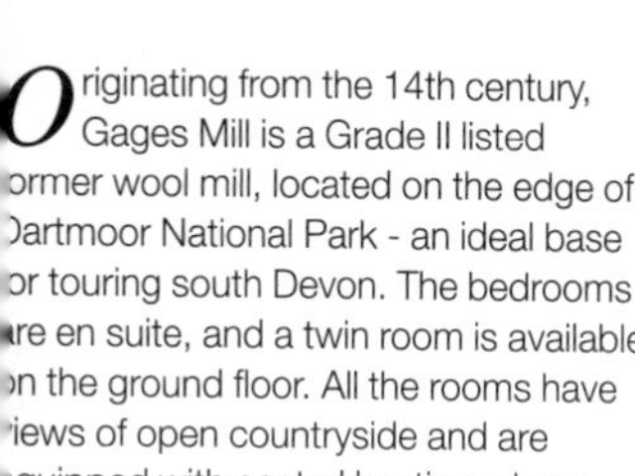

Originating from the 14th century, Gages Mill is a Grade II listed former wool mill, located on the edge of Dartmoor National Park - an ideal base for touring south Devon. The bedrooms are en suite, and a twin room is available on the ground floor. All the rooms have views of open countryside and are equipped with central heating, alarm clocks and radios, hairdryers, and tea and coffee facilities. The large dining room has a well-stocked corner bar, and stone archways lead through to the cosy sitting room with a television. There is over 1 acre of gardens to enjoy.

Recommended in the Area

Buckfast Abbey; Dartmoor National Park; South Devon Steam Railway

---

Greencott ♦♦♦♦

Map ref 2 - SX77
Landscove, ASHBURTON, TQ13 7LZ
3m SE of Ashburton. Off A38 at Peartree junct, at top of slip road sharp left to Landscove, village green 2m on right, opp village hall
Ⓣ 01803 762649
2 rooms, S £19-£20, D £38-£40, No smoking in bedrooms or dining room, Closed 25-26 Dec

Recommended in the Area

Dartington; Buckfast Abbey; Riding, fishing & golf nearby

Modern facilities in a traditional atmosphere are offered at this renovated house in the village of Landscove, which is just 3 miles from Ashburton. Greencott stands in a garden with lovely country views. The bedrooms are carefully furnished and well equipped with baths and showers en suite, central heating, and tea and coffee amenities. Television, books, maps and local information are provided in the comfortable sitting room, and traditional country cooking is served around the oak dining table. The full English breakfast includes home-made bread, and dinner is available on request. Older children are welcome, but pets cannot be accommodated, with the exception of guide dogs. Tarmac off-road parking is provided.

The Rising Sun ♦♦♦♦

Map ref 2 - SX77
Woodland, ASHBURTON, TQ13 7JT
Off A38 signed Woodland & Denbury, Rising Sun 1.5m on left
T 01364 652544
F 01364 654202
E mail@risingsunwoodland.co.uk
W www.risingsunwoodland.co.uk
6 rooms, S £38-£45, D £60-£70, No smoking in bedrooms or dining room

RECOMMENDED IN THE AREA
Dartmoor; Buckfast Abbey; South Devon Steam Railway, Buckfastleigh

Home-made food using fresh local produce - much of it organic - make this inn with restaurant and rooms an enticing prospect. Its position in glorious countryside on the edge of Dartmoor appeals to passers-by as well as visitors who choose to stay longer. The attractive bedrooms are furnished to make the most of limited space, and each has a bathroom en suite and a hospitality tray. Breakfast is an impressive start to the day with its variety and emphasis on quality, and the interesting dinner menus include the inn's famous home-made pies (available to take home), washed down with real ales, local cider, apple juice or wine.

Kerrington House ♦♦♦♦♦

Map ref 2 - SY29
Musbury Rd, AXMINSTER, EX13 5JR
0.5m from Axminster on A358 towards Seaton, house on left
T 01297 35333
F 01297 35345
E jreaney@kerringtonhouse.com
W www.kerringtonhouse.com
5 rooms, S £69-£75, D £90-£110, No smoking

RECOMMENDED IN THE AREA
Lyme Regis; Dorchester; East Devon Heritage Coast

Be prepared for a very warm welcome and some genuine pampering at this lovingly-restored period house, set in landscaped gardens. Bedrooms are beautifully decorated and feature quality furniture and coordinated fabrics. Many thoughtful extras and soft neutral colours make you feel at home, and all rooms have showers or bathrooms en suite equipped to a very high standard. Antique pieces and well-loved treasures create a very personal atmosphere in the light and airy drawing room, and Kerrington is renowned for its delicious food at dinner and breakfast. Groups of families and friends are welcome to use the accommodation for small house parties.

*H*almpstone Manor ♦♦♦♦♦

Map ref 2 - SS53
Bishop's Tawton, BARNSTAPLE, EX32 0EA
3m SE of Barnstaple, off A377 E of river & rail bridges
T 01271 830321
F 01271 830826
E jane@halmpstonemanor.co.uk
W www.halmpstonemanor.co.uk
5 rooms, S £70, D £100-£140, No smoking in bedrooms or dining room, Closed Xmas, New Year

A place to seriously relax, this gracious 1700s house has its origins in the 12th century. It has been ʼaised for its hospitality for hundreds of years, a adition that entertainment-loving owners Jane and ʼharles Stanbury happily continue. The country house ands in tranquil grounds, and offers a memorable stay ith squashy sofas, crackling fires and quality ɔdrooms. One room has a four-poster bed - just the ing for a luxury break. Food is another high point, the excellent five-course dinner menu offering fine cuisine based on the produce of Devon.

Recommended in the Area
RHS Rosemoor & Marwood Hill; North Devon Heritage Coast; Tarka Trail

---

*T*he Pines at Eastleigh ♦♦♦♦

Map ref 1 - SS42
The Pines, Eastleigh, BIDEFORD, ΞX39 4PA
A39 onto A386 signed East-The-Water. 1st left signed Eastleigh, 500yds next left, 1.5m to village, house on right
T 01271 860561
E pirrie@thepinesateastleigh.co.uk
W www.thepinesateastleigh.co.uk
6 rooms, S £35-£60, D £70-£90, No smoking

From its magnificent hilltop position overlooking the Torridge estuary d Lundy Island, this Georgian mhouse is perfect for a relaxing break. stands in 7 acres of pleasant gardens at guarantee peace and seclusion. ɔst of the bedrooms, all en suite, are in nverted stables around a charming urtyard, each having independent ɔund-floor access - there are also two ɔms in the main house. Comfort is ramount and each room has teletext evision, a telephone and a hairdryer. Widely travelled in the US, the proprietors have taken inspiration from the quality and hospitality provided in American country inns for their approach at the Pines. The tasty breakfasts are made from local and home-made produce.

Recommended in the Area
Unspoiled coastal villages of Instow & Clovelly; Biking & hiking on The Tarka Trail; Hartland Heritage Coast

Easton Court ♦♦♦♦

Map ref 2 - SX78
Easton Cross, CHAGFORD,
TQ13 8JL
Off A30 at Whiddon Down rdbt onto A382 signed Moretonhampstead. House 3.5m on left at x-rds for Chagford

T 01647 433469
F 01647 433654
E stay@easton.co.uk
W www.easton.co.uk

5 rooms, S £45-£49, D £58-£72, No smoking

In 2001 Debra and Paul Witting's dream of running a guesthouse came true, and you can share the peace and beauty of their corner of Dartmoor. The thatched Tudor farmhouse stands in acres of gardens and paddocks in the Teign valley. Evelyn Waugh was charmed by the place and wrote Brideshead Revisited here, and you too should find it inspiring. An Edwardian extension houses the en suite bedrooms with fabulous views of the countryside - four rooms are de luxe, and there is a mixture of showers and bathrooms. The open house policy allows visitors to come and go as they please.

RECOMMENDED IN THE AREA
Castle Drogo (NT); Fingle Bridge; Dartmoor National Park

Parford Well ♦♦♦♦♦

Map ref 2 - SX78
Sandy Park, CHAGFORD,
TQ13 8JW
A30 onto A382, after 3m left at Sandy Park towards Drewsteignton, house 50yds on left

T 01647 433353
E tim@parfordwell.co.uk
W www.parfordwell.co.uk

3 rooms, S £35-£75, D £60-£75, No smoking, Closed Xmas

Set in delightful grounds on the edge of Dartmoor, this attractive house is a restful and very friendly home. Quality and style describe the bedrooms, two of which are have facilities en suite, the third, a smaller double, having its own private bathroom. The lounge overlooks well-tended walled gardens, and a hearty breakfast is served at tables laid with silver and crisp linen in one of two dining rooms. Carefully cooked using top local ingredients, the breakfast is the perfect preparation for exploring the moors. There are wonderful walks on the doorstep and Parford is well placed for touring Devon and Cornwall. No children under eight and no pets.

RECOMMENDED IN THE AREA
Chagford village; Castle Drogo (NT); Dartmoor National Park

Tor Cottage ♦♦♦♦♦

Map ref 1 - SX48
CHILLATON, PL16 0JE
A30 Lewdown exit through Chillaton towards Tavistock, 300yds after Post Office right signed Bridlepath No Public Vehicular Access to end

T 01822 860248
F 01822 860126
E info@torcottage.co.uk
W www.torcottage.co.uk

4 rooms, S £89,
D £130-£140, No smoking,
Closed 17 Dec-7 Jan

This romantic cottage offers tranquillity and seclusion in 18 acres of grounds. Nothing is o much trouble for Maureen Rowlatt, who has uipped the en suite bed-sitting rooms with erything you could desire. Each one is lividually designed, from the warmth and style the Art Deco Room to the blue and cream gance of The Craftman's Room. One room is the cottage wing and the others are in nverted barns - each has a private race/garden and a log fire. Breakfast is an aginative range of dishes, and can be taken in conservatory-style dining room or on the race in fine weather. The gardens are a feature in their own right with many private corners, a stream, and in summer a heated swimming pool. Children cannot be accommodated. Autumn/spring breaks are available - 3 nights for the price of 2.

Recommended in the Area

Dartmoor; The Eden Project; National Trust houses & gardens

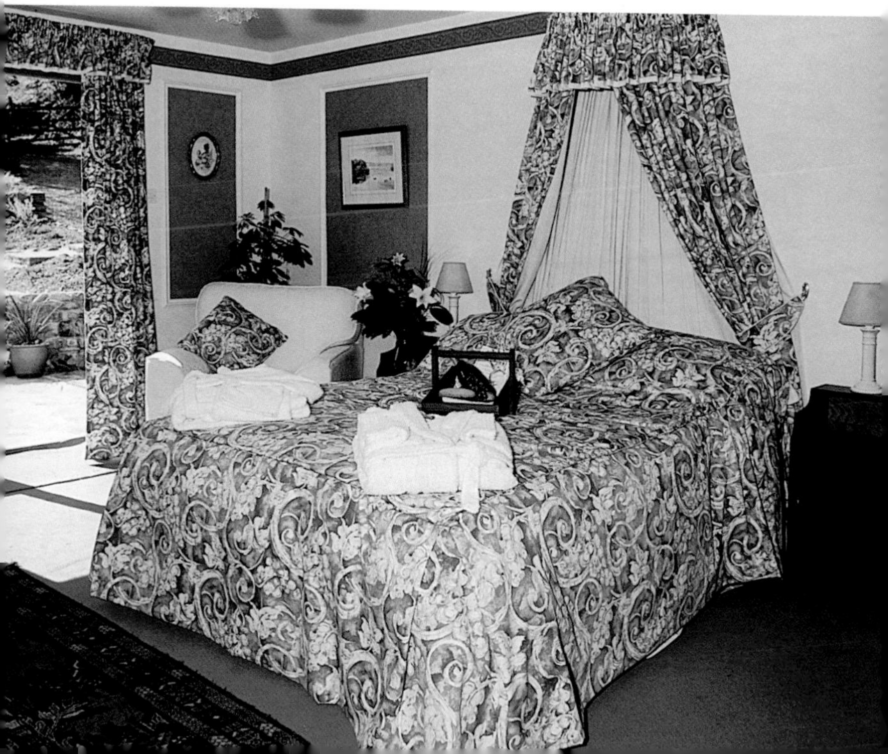

Lower Orchard ♦♦♦♦

Map ref 2 - SY29
Swan Hill Rd, COLYFORD,
EX24 6QQ
On A3052 in Colyford, between Lyme Regis & Sidmouth
T 01297 553615
2 rooms, S £40-£45, D £50-£55,
No smoking

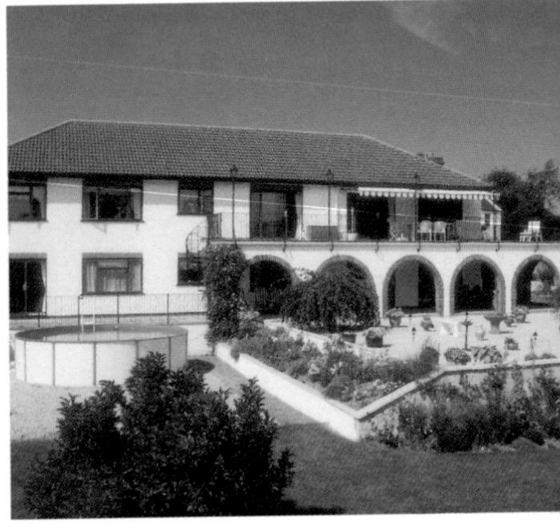

The modern ranch-style family house has uninterrupted rural views across the Axe Valley. The two very spacious bedrooms are on the ground floor, one with a bathroom en suite and the other with adjacent private shower facilities. Breakfast is served in the lounge-dining room with patio doors leading to a sun terrace. A splash pool in the garden is tempting in warm weather. Lyme Regis only 6 miles away, and the unspoiled towns of Honiton and Sidmouth are also within easy reach. Owner Lorrie Barnard breeds Tibetan Terriers, so the establishment pet friendly.

RECOMMENDED IN THE AREA
Forde Abbey & Gardens; Seaton Tramway; Jurassic Coa World Heritage Site

---

Nonsuch House ♦♦♦♦♦

Map ref 2 - SX85
Church Hill, Kingswear,
DARTMOUTH, TQ6 0BX
A3022 onto A379 2m before Brixham. Fork left onto B3205. Left up Higher Contour Rd, down Ridley Hill, house on bend
T 01803 752829
F 01803 752357
E enquiries@nonsuch-house.co.uk
W www.nonsuch-house.co.uk
3 rooms, S £75-£95, D £95-£120,
No smoking

Wonderful views of the sea and harbour are the prospect from every room at this welcoming guesthouse. The Dart estuary below and Dartmouth opposite are a joy to watch, especially in the evening when the lights come on. The spacious bedrooms are superbly appointed and the thoughtful extras show that guests are foremost here. Meals are unforgettable - generous breakfasts and super dinners cooked from quality produce, served in the conservatory-dining room. Log fires make a cheerful blaze the lounge, or linger in the conservatory and on the terraces on a summer's evening.

RECOMMENDED IN THE ARE
Coleton Fishacre House & Garden; Dartmouth Castle; Greenway (NT)

*B*arrington House ♦♦♦♦♦

Map ref 2 - SX85

Mount Boone, DARTMOUTH, TQ6 9HZ

A3122 pass BP garage after 0.5m turn right onto Townstal Rd, at x-rds turn left into Mount Boone. Barrington House 3rd on left

Ⓣ 01803 835545
Ⓔ enquiries@barrington-house.com
Ⓦ www.barrington-house.com

3 rooms, S £65-£105, D £95-£135, No smoking

ꓤECOMMENDED IN THE AREA

'team train to Paignton; Dartmouth Golf Club; ;reenway (NT)

*O*ne of the area's best-kept secrets, this elegant house is a tranquil haven on a hill ›verlooking the spectacular Dartmouth harbour.)ramatic high ceilings give feeling of space, ›nhanced by a wonderful hall with a sweeping ;tairway, and quintessential English-country ;tyle furnishings are perfectly complimented ›ith antique Chinese pieces. Whether you ›hoose a superior room or luxury suite, each ›as breathtaking views, facilities en suite and ┤arrods teddies to cuddle up with. The cosy drawing room is just the place for a welcoming pot of tea, or perhaps a glass of sherry and nibbles before dinner (available on request). An interesting buffet breakfast is sourced from local produce and served in the smart dining room. Ample parking is provided within the grounds, and the centre of town is just a stroll away. But best of all are the unrivalled views from the front of the house, over Dartmouth to the sea beyond.

Galley Fish & Seafood Restaurant with Rooms ◆◆◆◆◆ 

Map ref 2 - SX99
41 Fore St, Topsham, EXETER, EX3 0HU
M5 junct 30, follow signs for Topsham, then signs to Quay. Restaurant behind Lighter Inn overlooking river

Ⓣ 0845 602 6862
Ⓔ fish@galleyrestaurant.co.uk
Ⓦ www.galleyrestaurant.co.uk

4 rooms, S £67.50-£87.50, D £99.90-£175, No smoking, Closed Xmas-New Year

RECOMMENDED IN THE AREA

Historic Exeter; Dawlish Warren; Exmouth Beach

Quirky yet quaint, this part-restaurant part-guesthouse overlooking the Exe estuary is a magical experience. You are greeted with genuine courtesy and a desire to make your stay as enjoyable as possible. Reached by steep stairs, the bedrooms are in a 17th-century cottage with original brickwork, beams, slate flooring and log fires, and these so-called cabins have a maritime theme. The stylish suite and double or twin rooms perfectly fit the period property, while modern facilities include minibars, Internet access and private bathrooms. Breakfast is an extensive continental variety, though a very good cooked alternative is available by request at an extra charge. A high point is dinner, when the nautical themed restaurant displays its skills in preparing imaginative fish and seafood dishes. Jacuzzi, hot tub and spa facilities are available on site. This certainly is characterful accommodation with a contemporary twist.

he River Exe near Bickleigh

Fairwinds Village House Hotel ♦♦♦♦

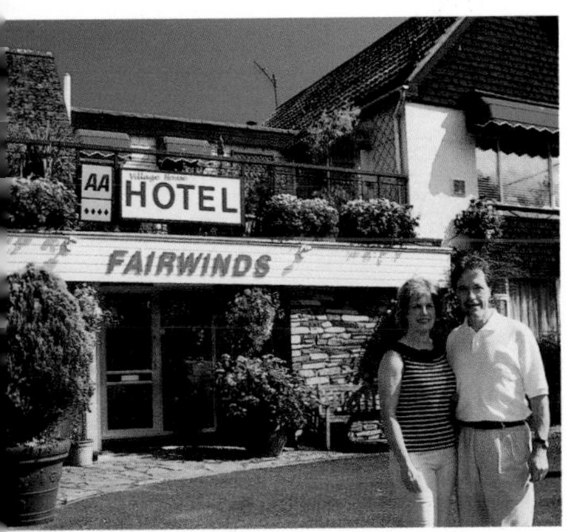

Map ref 2 - SX99
Kennford, EXETER, EX6 7UD
4m S of Exeter. M5 junct 31, A38, 2m left for Kennford, 1st hotel on left
Ⓣ 01392 832911
Ⓔ fairwindshotbun@aol.com
Ⓦ www.hotbun.co.uk
6 rooms, S £48, D £64, No smoking, Closed mid Nov-early Jan

Exclusively for non-smokers, this house lies on the edge of Kennford village just below Haldon forest ills. Inside you can expect a warm welcome and high tandards of housekeeping. Well suited for business nd leisure, Fairwinds is convenient for the coast, the noors, Exeter and Plymouth, and it is only 2 miles from ne M5 motorway. The en suite bedrooms are well quipped and are continually upgraded. A variety of njoyable home-cooked food is served in the bright dining room next to the cosy bar. Private parking is available.

RECOMMENDED IN THE AREA

Powderham Castle; Dartmoor National Park; Exeter city

Mill Farm ♦♦♦♦

Map ref 2 - SX99
Kenton, EXETER, EX6 8JR
A379 from Exeter towards Dawlish, over minirdbt by Swans Nest, farm 1.75m on right
Ⓣ 01392 832471
5 rooms, S £30, D £46,
Closed Xmas

Just a short drive from the Powderham estate and outside the pretty village of Kenton, this charming working farmhouse is surrounded by peaceful pastureland and streams. Inside the decor is carefully coordinated, with stencil designs on the walls and lots of antique furniture. Bedrooms are sunny with spacious en suites and have wide country views. Hearty farmhouse breakfasts in the bright dining room are an appetising start to the day, and there are plenty of local places serving evening meals. There is also a lounge. The owner is very friendly and keen to welcome you to her well-managed home.

RECOMMENDED IN THE AREA

Powderham Castle; Dartmoor; Exe Estuary Nature Reserve

St Andrews Hotel ♦♦♦♦

Map ref 2 - SX99
28 Alphington Rd, EXETER,
EX2 8HN
M5 junct 31, signed Exeter, follow signs for city centre & Marsh Barton along Alphington road A377. Hotel on left
Ⓣ 01392 276784
Ⓕ 01392 250249
Ⓔ standrewsexeter@aol.com
Ⓦ www.standrewsexeter.co.uk
17 rooms, S £45-£58, D £65-£76,
Smoking in bar only,
Closed 24 Dec-1 Jan

This friendly and long-established family-run hotel provides a high standard of comfort within walking distance of the city centre. The elegant former Victorian residence has a range of en suite bedrooms to suit your needs - some are suitable for families, while one room on the ground floor (double/twin) has level access and allocated parking in the ample rear car park. All rooms have telephones, 6-channel televisions, hairdryers, tea and coffee facilities, and most have trouser presses. For relaxing there are two sitting rooms and a well-stocked bar. Delicious home-cooked evening meals served in the dining room (weekdays) are a highlight of a stay here.

RECOMMENDED IN THE AREA

Cathedral city of Exeter; Exeter quayside, river & canal; Dartmoor National Park

The Devoncourt Hotel ♦♦♦♦

Map ref 2 - SY08
16 Douglas Av, EXMOUTH, EX8 2EX
A376 to Exmouth, follow seafront to Maer Rd, right at T-junct
T 01395 272277
F 01395 269315
E enquiries@devoncourt.com
W www.devoncourt.com
10 rooms, S £40-£65, D £60-£95

Subtropical gardens sloping gently towards the sea and sandy beaches give an ppealing Mediterranean character to this aside hotel. The smart Devoncourt has an utdoor pool with sun terrace and loungers, therwise explore the landscaped grounds and nd the private access to the beach, tennis ourts, croquet, putting greens and golf nets. If does rain, the leisure complex offers an indoor ool, spa, sauna, steam room, solariums and ness centre. The various, well-equipped edrooms are light and simple, decorated in astel tones and patterned fabrics. Choose between eating in the informal bar or in Avenues restaurant, where picture windows frame the sea and the cuisine satisfies all tastes. Among the spacious public areas, the sun lounge is a particularly lovely spot to enjoy a pot of tea and while away the day. Or you may even venture out along the seafront to the mouth of the River Exe.

RECOMMENDED IN THE AREA

Bicton Park Botanical Gardens; Crealy Adventure Park; Roman Exeter

Leworthy Farm House ♦♦♦♦

Map ref 1 - SS30
Lower Leworthy, Nr Pyworthy,
HOLSWORTHY, EX22 6SJ
From Holsworthy onto Bodmin St towards North Tamerton, 4th left signed Leworthy/Southdown
T / F 01409 259469
E leworthyfarmhouse@yahoo.co.uk
W www.leworthyfarmhouse.co.uk
7 rooms, S £35-£45, D £55-£65,
No smoking

RECOMMENDED IN THE AREA

Rosemoor Gardens; South West Coast Path; Dartington Glass

Pat and Phil Jennings' passions for the countryside, collecting books, curios and classical music, and meeting new people come together wonderfully at Leworthy Farmhouse. Spacious public rooms include a softly lit dining room with an oak parquet floor and colourful displays of old china, a drawing room with comfortable old sofas and armchairs and more displays of pictures and china, and a warmly decorated conservatory. Bedrooms, some with window seats, are beautifully furnished with pine or antique pieces and thoughtfully equipped with radio alarms, hairdryers, electric blankets, books and magazines. Hospitality trays are set with bone china, fresh milk, a selection of teas, coffees and chocolate, biscuits and fresh flowers. All the rooms are en suite and have ample supplies of towels and toiletries. A good choice of dishes is served at breakfast, and picnics are available by arrangement. There are plenty of cafés, pubs and restaurants in the area. No pets, please.

Courtmoor Farm ♦♦♦♦

Map ref 2 - ST10
Upottery, HONITON, EX14 9QA
4m NE of Honiton. Off A30, 0.5m W of junct A30 & A303
T 01404 861565
E courtmoor.farm@btinternet.com
W www.courtmoor.farm.btinternet.co.uk
3 rooms, S from £33, D from £50, No smoking, Closed 20 Dec-1 Jan

Rosalind and Bob Buxton welcome you to their spacious farmhouse vith marvellous views over the Otter alley. The extensive grounds are home) a flock of sheep and three ponies. ccommodation is provided in a family oom, double room and twin, all with hower en suite and equipped with igital televisions, hairdryers, electric lankets, clock radios and tea and offee facilities. A freshly cooked dinner f local produce is available by rrangement on weekdays. The full English breakfast should easily satisfy but special diets can be catered for. Additional facilities include a conservatory-lounge with glorious views and a gym and sauna. Self-catering cottages are also available.

Recommended in the Area

Honiton antiques shops & Lace Museum; Lyme Regis; Forde Abbey & Gardens

---

West Colwell Farm ♦♦♦♦♦

Map ref 2 - ST10
Offwell, HONITON, EX14 9SL
2m E of Honiton. Off A35 to village, at church go downhill, farm 0.5m on right
T 01404 831130
F 01404 831769
E stay@westcolwell.co.uk
W www.westcolwell.co.uk
3 rooms, S £45, D £70-£75, No smoking, Closed Xmas

Recommended in the Area

East Devon Heritage Coast; Shute Barton (NT); Honiton

The Hayes are enthusiastic hosts who obviously enjoy welcoming guests. Their farm has a glorious etting down a peaceful country lane, in an Area of)utstanding Natural Beauty. The stylish, spacious edrooms are in converted stone barns beside a obbled yard, and two rooms on the ground floor open n to their own terraces. Breakfast of home-baked read, fresh coffee and the best local produce is taken overlooking a wooded valley and fields in the split-level dining room, with its roaring log-burning stove in the cooler months. Country walks start right at your door - ask Frank and Carol for the farm's own Walks Guide.

Beechwood Hotel ♦♦♦♦

Map ref 2 - SS54
Torrs Park, ILFRACOMBE, EX34 8AZ
A361 to Ilfracombe, signs to Tunnels Beaches, left into Torrs Park, hotel 0.5m on right

T 01271 863800
F 0871 242 8179
E info@beechwoodhotel.co.uk
W www.beechwoodhotel.co.uk

7 rooms, S £40-£45, D £60-£90, No smoking, Closed Nov-Feb

RECOMMENDED IN THE AREA

South West Coast Path; Ilfracombe Harbour; Woolacombe Beach

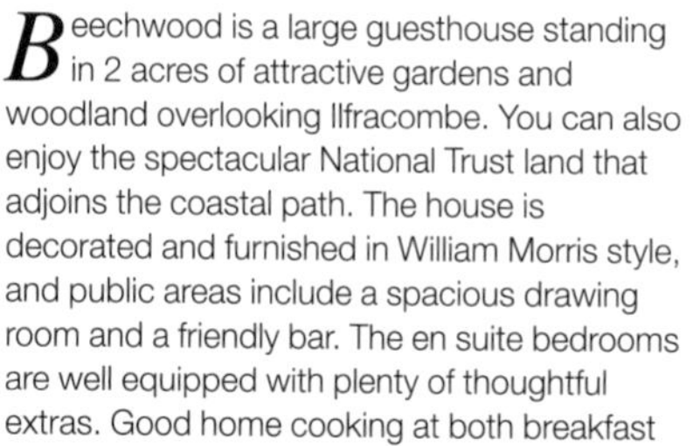

Beechwood is a large guesthouse standing in 2 acres of attractive gardens and woodland overlooking Ilfracombe. You can also enjoy the spectacular National Trust land that adjoins the coastal path. The house is decorated and furnished in William Morris style, and public areas include a spacious drawing room and a friendly bar. The en suite bedrooms are well equipped with plenty of thoughtful extras. Good home cooking at both breakfast and dinner is a particular feature of this friendly hotel - everything from soups and breads to puddings and pies is made on the premises. The town is just a 15-minute walk away, and there is ample private parking. The Beechwood does not accommodate children or pets.

Norbury House ♦♦♦♦

Map ref 2 - SS54
Torrs Park, ILFRACOMBE,
EX34 8AZ
A361 from Barnstaple, 1st lights turn left, over 2nd lights & left into Torrs Park, Norbury House on right
T 01271 863888
E info@norburyhouse.co.uk
W www.norburyhouse.co.uk
6 rooms, S £31, D £54-£78,
No smoking

Norbury House, built in 1870, stands on a quiet elevated position with views over the town and the sea in the distance. Andy and Carole Walters have transformed the property, bringing contemporary style to this traditional Victorian residence. There are light room colours and fabrics throughout, enhanced by their collection of art, ceramics, glass and sculpture. The well-equipped bedrooms have generous hospitality trays, and there is a choice of suites, family and double rooms. Relax in the conservatory or lounge, or outside in the attractive terraced gardens. Breakfast is served in the pleasant dining room and dinner is available by arrangement. All meals are freshly prepared, using local Devon produce whenever possible. Suites and family rooms are available, and pets are welcome.

Recommended in the Area
Marwood Hill Gardens; Arlington Court (NT); Lundy Island

Staunton Lodge ♦♦♦♦

Map ref 2 - SX74
Embankment Rd, KINGSBRIDGE,
TQ7 1JZ
A381 from Kingsbridge centre along estuary signed Dartmouth, Lodge 0.25m on left
T 01548 854542
F 01548 854421
E miketreleaven@msn.com
W www.stauntonlodge.co.uk
2 rooms, D £60, No smoking,
Closed Dec-Feb

Recommended in the Area
Salcombe; Dartmouth; The Eden Project

This idyllic waterside property is in the busy market town of Kingsbridge and within easy walking distance of a host of pubs and restaurants. The caring hosts at this small guesthouse provide thoughtful little touches throughout the house and attentive service. Comfort is a priority here and the stylish bedrooms are equipped to ensure a relaxing stay - the twin has a private bathroom and the double has a bathroom en suite . The lovely views over the estuary are even better while tucking into an excellent breakfast, where freshly cooked choices using local produce are a memorable start to the day. Unsuitable for children under 8-years-old.

Moor View House ♦♦♦♦♦

Map ref 2 - SX58

Vale Down, LYDFORD, EX20 4BB

Off A30 at Sourton Cross onto A386 Tavistock road, hotel drive 4m on right

T / F 01822 820220

4 rooms, S £50-£60, D £65-£85, No smoking

RECOMMENDED IN THE AREA

Lydford Gorge (NT); The Garden House; Castle Drogo (NT)

Moor View is a substantial Victorian house set in 2 acres of gardens with direct access to Dartmoor. The house was built in 1869 to face the wild moor, while to the west there are magnificent views towards Cornwall. Many original features survive, and the rooms are stylishly furnished with interesting family antiques. The en suite bedrooms are all decorated in Victorian style. Good food is one of the proud boasts at this hospitable establishment, and dinner is available by arrangement. Wendy Sharples' four-course menu is based on traditional country recipes. Only the best local meat, game and fish are used, and the table settings in the dining room are exquisite. Dinner is served family style or at individual tables if preferred. The bright and inviting sitting room has family photographs on top of a grand piano, and an open fire in winter.

*T*he Heatherville ♦♦♦♦♦

Map ref 2 - SS74
Tors Park, LYNMOUTH, EX35 6NB
Off A39 onto Tors Rd, 1st left fork into Tors Park
T 01598 752327
F 01598 752634
W www.heatherville.co.uk
6 rooms, D £60-£80, No smoking, Closed Dec-Jan

DEVON

RECOMMENDED IN THE AREA

Exmoor National Park; Lynton & Lynmouth Cliff Railway; Lynton

Having a secluded and elevated south-facing position, Victorian Heatherville has splendid views over the River Lyn and surrounding woodland, yet is only a short walk from the heart of picturesque Lynmouth. Tea and coffee are served on arrival in the welcoming lounge, and the bedrooms are a pleasure, lovingly restored to a high standard. They combine luxury with the charm of a large country house, using fine coordinated fabrics - some have canopies over the bed and spectacular views, and most have a shower and bath en suite. An appetising English breakfast, featuring organic and free-range produce whenever possible, gets the day of to a good start and, by arrangement, evening meals are served by candlelight. There is also an intimate bar. Superb walks lead from the front door.

Sea View Villa ♦♦♦♦♦

Map ref 2 - SS74
6 Summer House Path, LYNMOUTH,
EX35 6ES
A39 from Porlock, 1st left after bridge, Sea View Villa on right 20yds along path opp church

T 01598 753460
F 01598 753496
E reservations@seaviewvilla.co.uk
W www.seaviewvilla.co.uk

5 rooms, S £30-£36, D £84-£110,
No smoking, Closed Jan

RECOMMENDED IN THE AREA

The Valley of the Rocks; Exmoor National Park; Watersmeet Valley

'Through Devonshire countryside we have roamed/ to Lynmouth, to find our palatial home/ Tastefully wrapped in all shades of vanilla/ We found our peace within Sea View Villa.' So wrote one satisfied guest, referring to Chris Bissex and Steve Williams' luxurious Lynmouth guesthouse. Steve and Chris bought the house in 2002, moving from London, where Steve was a design director for a department store chain and Chris was a drama teacher, and where they were both involved in the arts as performers and directors. Their dream was to open a bijou hotel offering incredible customer service and many thoughtful extras. The interiors are supremely elegant, with en suite rooms, plentiful hot water, powerful showers, and Egyptian cotton bed linen and bath towels. Walking and surfing are popular local pursuits, with wonderful walks directly from the door. Home-made bread is a feature of the English breakfast, and interesting alternatives include a vegetarian option, eggs Benedict or smoked salmon. Licensed evening meals are available.

Rock House ♦♦♦♦

Map ref 2 - SS74
Manor Grounds, LYNMOUTH, EX35 6EN
On A39, at the foot of Countisbury Hill. Turn right onto drive, follow down past the Manor green/play area to Rock House

T 01598 753508
F 01598 753796
E enquiries@rock-house.co.uk
W www.rock-house.co.uk

8 rooms, S £38, D £78-£84, No smoking in bedrooms or dining room, Closed 24-25 Dec

RECOMMENDED IN THE AREA
Beautiful waterfalls in the Lyn Valley; Valley of the Rocks; Scenic railway to Lynton

Set right at the harbour entrance, this Grade II listed building has stunning views whichever way you look. The charming early 19th-century property is partly thatched and has Gothic style windows. All of the cosy bedrooms have a breathtaking outlook, including those on the ground floor, and even when the weather is stormy - Lynmouth has the second highest tides in the world. Each room has a bathroom en suite, and alarm clock and hospitality tray. The restaurant looks out over the harbour, and freshly cooked meals are served either here or in the licensed bar. Regular boat trips leave the harbour to explore the cliffs with their colonies of razorbills, guillemots and kittiwakes.

Pine Lodge ♦♦♦♦

Map ref 2 - SS74
Lynway, LYNTON, EX35 6AX
500yds S of town centre off Lynbridge Rd opp Bridge Inn

T 01598 753230
E info@pinelodgelynton.co.uk
W www.pinelodgelynton.co.uk

6 rooms, S £24, D £54, No smoking, Closed Dec

Soak up the gorgeous views of the wooded West Lyn valley from the vantage point of this secluded old house. Set in an acre of peaceful landscaped gardens, Pine Lodge was built in the 19th century in the area nicknamed Little Switzerland by the Victorians. Hospitality trays make you feel at home in the bedrooms, which have a shower or bathroom en suite. This is a paradise for walkers, with Exmoor right on the doorstep and the coast nearby. Breakfast is memorable for the fresh flavours. Winter breaks are available.

RECOMMENDED IN THE AREA
Watersmeet House (NT); Valley of the Rocks, Lynton; Arlington Court (NT)

Highcliffe House ♦♦♦♦♦

Map ref 2 - SS74
Sinai Hill, LYNTON, EX35 6AR
Off A39 into Lynton, signs for Old Village. At pub turn right up steep hill, house 150yds on left

T 01598 752235
F 01598 753815
E info@highcliffehouse.co.uk
W www.highcliffehouse.co.uk

6 rooms, S £50-£60, D £72-£96, No smoking, Closed Dec-mid Feb

Once a private summer residence, this beautifully restored house is now more widely accessible, thanks to Karen and Michael Orchard. They aim to exceed all expectations of accommodation, facilities and service, and you are unlikely to be disappointed. Highcliffe House stands in grounds with stunning views over the Exmoor hills, and across the coastline and Bristol Channel towards south Wales. The elegant en suite bedrooms are very spacious, each one individual in design, and some have carved king-size beds. Fine furnishings, a welcoming decanter of sherry, and a hospitality tray are among the extras for your comfort. There are two inviting lounges, one with a splendid view. The candlelit conservatory restaurant serves imaginative home cooking in the evening and delicious breakfasts. Plenty of lovely walks begin from outside the house.

Recommended in the Area

Exmoor National Park; Cliff railway between Lynton & Lynmouth; South West Coast Path

Cottage B & B ♦♦♦♦

Map ref 2 - ST21
MARSH, EX14 9AJ
A303 Ilminster to Honiton, left off dual-carriageway, 1st right under bridge, 1st house on right

T 01460 234240
E buttonstephens@btopenworld.com
W www.cottagemarsh.co.uk

4 rooms, S £25-£29, D £35-£48, No smoking

Set in the beautiful Blackdown Hills on the border of Devon and Somerset, the Cottage B&B is well placed on the main route through the West Country. Chris and Michele maintain the property to a high standard, and the pair are ever friendly. All bedrooms are at ground level, come with hospitality trays, and have walk-in shower rooms en suite. Each room also has its own entrance, with no steps, from the small courtyard, and in warmer weather you can enjoy afternoon tea here from the on-site tea-shop (seasonal afternoon opening times). Breakfast features eggs from the host's own chickens and local produce.

RECOMMENDED IN THE AREA

Honiton; Forde Abbey & Gardens; Blackdown Hills

Hazelcott Bed & Breakfast ♦♦♦♦

Map ref 2 - SX78
Manaton, MORETONHAMPSTEAD, TQ13 9UY
A38 onto A382 through Bovey Tracey to Manaton. Pass Kestor Inn, right at x-rds, 0.5m past church

T 01647 221521
F 01647 221405
E hazelcott@dartmoordays.com
W www.dartmoordays.com

3 rooms, S £30-£40, D £50-£75, No smoking

Standing on the edge of Dartmoor, this secluded home from home accommodation is an ideal spot for ramblers. The best features of the house itself must be the delightful surroundings and the fantastic panoramic views. The bedrooms vary in size and style but all have bathrooms en suite. Breakfast is a real treat, all cooked in the Aga to perfection using local produce. Home-made preserves are a feature. Carole and Nigel, runners-up for AA Landlady of the Year 2005, are keen to ensure you are looked after and welcome everyone with tea and coffee and a slice of delicious home-made cake.

RECOMMENDED IN THE AREA

Becky Falls Woodland Park; Canon Teign Falls; Dartmoor National Park

Gate House ♦♦♦♦♦

Map ref 2 - SX78
North Bovey,
MORETONHAMPSTEAD,
TQ13 8RB
B3212 from Moretonhampstead to North Bovey

T / F 01647 440479
E gatehouseondartmoor@talk21.com
W www.gatehouseondartmoor.com

3 rooms, S £46, D £68-£70, No smoking

RECOMMENDED IN THE AREA

Buckland Abbey (NT); Castle Drogo (NT); Saltram (NT)

In a fast changing world it is good to know that some things stay the same, and John and Sheila Williams have succeeded in preserving a little bit of old Devon. Both gave up busy careers to retreat to this Grade II listed 15th-century thatched house and pursue their dream. The result is an idyllic hideaway filled with character, where you can savour the atmosphere and relax. Welcomed by a pot of tea and scrumptious home-made cake, guests are shown to bedrooms decorated in country style, with a view of the garden or the moors. Downstairs the wood-burning stove, set in a huge granite fireplace, is a magnet on cooler days. Hearty breakfasts feature local produce, and Sheila's imaginative candlelit dinners are available by arrangement. The outdoor swimming pool in the large garden is lovely in summer, and the beauty of Dartmoor is all around.

Castle Dyke House ♦♦♦♦♦

Map ref 2 - SX87
Highweek Village, NEWTON ABBOT, TQ12 1QG
A38 onto A382, 1.9m right at left-hand bend signed Highweek, right at T-junct, 0.2m left onto driveway before bus layby
Ⓣ 01626 367965
Ⓦ www.castledykehouse.co.uk
3 rooms, S £45, D £60-£65, No smoking, Closed 24 Dec-2 Jan

This charming Georgian house certainly lives up to its name: the 2 acres of beautiful grounds include the earthworks of a 12th-century motte and bailey castle, which still commands panoramic views of the nearby coast and moors. Guests can retreat indoors for a choice of smart en suite rooms, and there is a family/party suite with one twin room and one double room. Sue and Robin Ashworth's attention to detail is especially evident at breakfast. The bread and croissants are home made, while the garden produces the fruits in season, honey from the hives, and free-range eggs from the chickens. In summer you can enjoy this morning treat alfresco.

Recommended in the Area

Ashburton; Totnes; Exeter Cathedral

Berkeley's of St James ♦♦♦♦

Map ref 1 - SX45
4 St James Place East, The Hoe, PLYMOUTH, PL1 3AS
Off A38 towards city centre, left at sign The Hoe, over 7 sets of lights, left onto Athenaeum St, right to Crescent Av, 1st left
Ⓣ / Ⓕ 01752 221654
Ⓔ enquiry@onthehoe.co.uk
Ⓦ www.onthehoe.co.uk
5 rooms, S £35, D £55, No smoking, Closed 23 Dec-1 Jan

Recommended in the Area

National Maritime Museum; Historic Barbican; Dartmoor National Park

The Victorian residence lies in a quiet secluded square on Plymouth Hoe, just a short walk from the promenade and city centre and well placed for touring Devon and Cornwall. Its white façade conceals bedrooms decorated in pastel shades and pretty floral bedspreads, equipped with a number of thoughtful extras - family rooms are available too. The substantial traditional breakfast uses organic dry cure bacon and sausages and free-range eggs supplied by local farms, and is served in an attractive dining room. This welcoming guesthouse is a good choice for business and leisure, and there is secure private parking.

Lydgate House ♦♦♦♦♦

Map ref 2 - SX67
POSTBRIDGE, PL20 6TJ
B3212 SW into Postbridge, left down lane before bridge

T 01822 880209
F 01822 880202
E lydgatehouse@email.com
W www.lydgatehouse.co.uk

6 rooms, S £60, D £110-£130,
No smoking,
Closed mid Oct-mid Mar

Lydgate House is so tranquil the only sounds you can hear are the birds and the river tumbling downstream below. Nestled in the heart of Dartmoor National Park, this spot is a haven for wildlife. The lovely Victorian property lies down a private lane surrounded by acres of grounds with stunning views over the moorland. There is an enchanting lounge and sun terrace, and all the individual bedrooms have facilities en suite. Afternoon cream teas are available and you can end the day with a delicious home-cooked meal.

RECOMMENDED IN THE AREA
Castle Drogo (NT); Chagford; Buckland Abbey (NT)

Glendevon Hotel ♦♦♦♦

Map ref 2 - SY18
Cotmaton Rd, SIDMOUTH, EX10 8QX
A3052 onto B3176 to minirdbt, turn right, house 100yds on right

T 01395 514028
E enquiries@glendevon-hotel.co.uk
W www.glendevon-hotel.co.uk

8 rooms, S £29-£35, D £58-£70,
No smoking

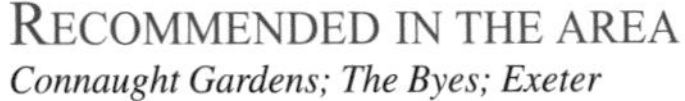

RECOMMENDED IN THE AREA
Connaught Gardens; The Byes; Exeter

This comfortable hotel is in a peaceful location on the western side of Sidmouth, just a short walk from the town's leisure facilities and the Esplanade. The bedrooms are all neatly presented with good beds and bathrooms en suite. The spacious lounge and sunny terrace are quiet places to relax, read or chat. Full English breakfasts are served at individual tables in the separate dining room. Evening meals, prepared from fresh local produce, are available by arrangement, while a good selection of wines and spirits can be enjoyed at any time. The friendly, attentive service extends to catering for special diets.

Thomas Luny House ◆◆◆◆◆

Map ref 2 - SX97
Teign St, TEIGNMOUTH, TQ14 8EG
A381 to Teignmouth, at 3rd lights turn right to quay, 50yds turn left onto Teign St, after 60yds turn right through white archway

T 01626 772976
E alisonandjohn@thomas-luny-house.co.uk
W www.thomas-luny-house.co.uk

4 rooms, S £55-£60, D £67-£85, No smoking

RECOMMENDED IN THE AREA
Tuckers Maltings; Powderham Castle; Cockington village

This delightful house was built in the late 18th century by the marine artist Thomas Luny and it has been run by John and Alison Allan since 1989. The large drawing room and dining room are beautifully furnished and have open fires to cosy up to in winter, while French doors open onto a lovely walled garden. John and Alison's laid back yet attentive approach is appreciated by guests whose comfort is well catered for. The individually designed en suite bedrooms vary in size, but all offer direct-dial telephones and hospitality trays, as well as fresh flowers, bottled water and toiletries. Home-made dishes and a full cooked breakfast are a speciality.

Hornhill Farmhouse ◆◆◆◆◆

Map ref 2 - SS91
Exeter Hill, TIVERTON, EX16 4PL
Signs to Grand Western Canal, right fork up Exeter Hill. Farmhouse on left at top of hill

T / F 01884 253352
E hornhill@tinyworld.co.uk
W www.hornhill-farmhouse.co.uk

3 rooms, S £30-£35, D £54-£60, No smoking

Panoramic views of Tiverton and the Exe valley grace this lovely farmhouse, which dates in part from the 18th century. Public rooms include an elegant sitting room with a log fire and an impressive dining room where guests are seated at one large table. The English and continental breakfasts are based on local produce, while proprietor Barbara Pugsley is happy to recommend local pubs for evening meals. The two bedrooms on the first floor have their own bathrooms along the landing, and one room has a Victorian four-poster bed. The ground-floor bedroom has a shower room en suite. All the rooms have facilities for making hot drinks.

RECOMMENDED IN THE AREA
Tiverton Museum of Mid Devon Life; Knightshayes Court (NT); Grand Western Canal

Colindale Hotel ♦♦♦♦♦

Map ref 2 - SX96
20 Rathmore Rd, Chelston, TORQUAY, TQ2 6NY
From Torquay station 200yds on left in Rathmore Rd
T 01803 293947
E bronte@eurobell.co.uk
W www.colindalehotel.co.uk
8 rooms, S £30-£35, D £60-£65, No smoking in bedrooms or dining room

RECOMMENDED IN THE AREA
Torre Abbey; Cockington village; Living Coasts Zoo

Barry Greenwood-Smith has worked as a butler for the rich and famous in Beverley Hills, Bermuda and Chelsea since the 1970s. Now he loves to share his antiques-filled home with visitors to Torquay. Well-kept grounds with tropical trees surround the elegant Victorian house set close to the sea. The bedrooms, some with views over Torbay, are mainly en suite and thoughtfully equipped to make you feel at home. Evening drinks are served in a snug bar, and there's a wonderful selection of books and videos in the pleasant sitting room. The freshly cooked breakfasts are sure to get the day off to a good start.

Cranborne House ♦♦♦♦♦

Map ref 2 - SX96
58 Belgrave Rd, TORQUAY, TQ2 5HY
Off A380 to Torquay, at Torre station signs for seafront & Belgrave Rd, premises on right by lights
T 01803 298046
W www.cranbornehotel.co.uk
10 rooms, S £35-£70, D £60-£85, No smoking, Closed Feb

The enthusiastic and hospitable owners ensure this Victorian terrace property is a premier place to stay. The superior accommodation is within easy walking distance of the town centre, seafront and harbour. Modern en suite bedrooms with pale pastel walls and crisp white bed linen are equipped with many useful facilities including hairdryers, complimentary toiletries, large luxury bath sheets and silent fridges. The bar-lounge is furnished with a Chesterfield suite, and there is a neat dining room where the breakfast is praised for its West Country sausages and home-made chutney. Dinner is available from April to October. No children under 12 years.

RECOMMENDED IN THE AREA
Riviera Centre; Torre Abbey; Living Coasts Zoo

Glenorleigh Hotel ♦♦♦♦

Map ref 2 - SX96
26 Cleveland Rd, TORQUAY,
TQ2 5BE
A3022 Newton Abbot/Torquay road to lights at Torre station, bear right onto Avenue Rd & Cleveland Rd 1st left
T 01803 292135
F 01803 213717
E glenorleighhotel@btinternet.com
W www.glenorleigh.co.uk
15 rooms, S £30-£40, D £60-£80, No smoking in bedrooms or dining room

Glenorleigh is an elegant Victorian villa set in a pleasant residential rea. This family-run establishment has a ange of smart bedrooms, a number of hich are on the ground floor. All rooms ave tea and coffee facilities and some verlook the garden. Other facilities cluding a solarium, a games room, a eated outdoor swimming pool and rrace, and a convivial bar. All amenities e within walking distance, from hopping to water sports. The day starts with a hearty full English breakfast in the elegant dining room, while dinner is four courses of good home cooking with choices for vegetarian and special diets. Light meals are available for lunch in summer.

RECOMMENDED IN THE AREA
Living Coasts; Paignton Zoo; Babbacombe Model Village

Headland View ♦♦♦♦

Map ref 2 - SX96
37 Babbacombe Seafront, Babbacombe, TORQUAY, TQ1 3LN
A379 for Babbacombe & seafront
T 01803 312612
E reception@headlandview.com
W www.headlandview.com
6 rooms, S £30-£35, D £48-£60, No smoking, Closed Dec-Feb

Headland View is a delightful seaside guesthouse with sea and downland views. s run by Colin and Sue Jezard, an thusiastic and professional team who will sure you have a memorable stay. Lovely aches are within easy walking distance and rquay town centre is just around the headland. The impressive, well-equipped bedrooms have private or en suite facilities, and all of the front-facing rooms have balconies, taking full advantage of the outlook - two of the other bedrooms feature four-poster beds. Breakfast is not to be missed, and for other meals there is a good choice of pubs and restaurants within the vicinity.

RECOMMENDED IN THE AREA
Oddicombe & Babbacombe beaches; South West Coast Path; Dartmoor National Park

Mulberry House ♦♦♦♦♦ 

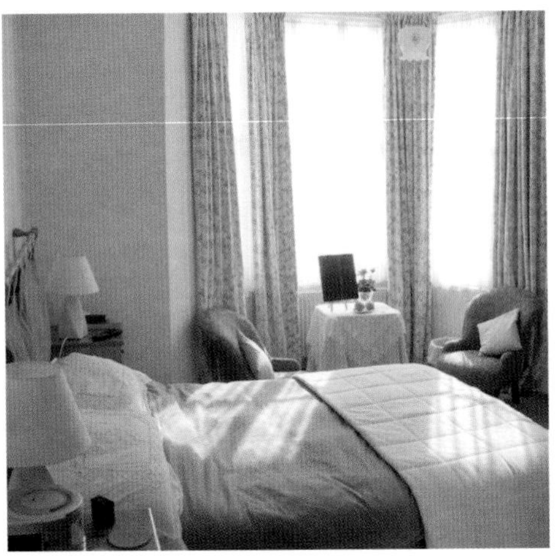

Map ref 2 - SX96
1 Scarborough Rd, TORQUAY, TQ2 5UJ
From Torquay seafront onto Belgrave Rd. Scarborough Rd 1st right, house on left on corner
T / F 01803 213639
E stay@mulberryhousetorquay.co.uk
W www.mulberryhousetorquay.co.uk
3 rooms, S £40-£45, D £60-£70, No smoking

RECOMMENDED IN THE AREA

Kent's Cavern; Cockington Forge; Coastal walks

This Victorian gem near the seafront is very much a family concern. The young hostess Laura Wood is a natural, and helped by a friend she runs Mulberry House with great confidence and flair. The spacious and immaculate bedrooms are light and airy, and retain an abundance of original charm. Each room has either a private bathroom or an en suite, and is equipped with a music system, bathrobes, fresh flowers, fresh fruit, spring water and tea and coffee facilities. Food is very important here and freshly prepared Creative English cuisine is available in the licensed restaurant served at round tables with crisp table cloths, fresh flowers and polished cutlery. A cosy log fire burns on cooler evenings in the soft lit lounge, where you can sup a pre-din drink relaxing to gentle music.

rquay Harbour

Marstan Hotel & Restaurant ♦♦♦♦♦

Map ref 2 - SX96

Meadfoot Sea Rd, TORQUAY, TQ1 2LQ

A3022 to seafront, left onto A379 Torbay Rd & Babbacombe Rd, right onto Meadfoot Rd, hotel on right

T 01803 292837
F 01803 299202
E enquiries@marstanhotel.co.uk
W www.marstanhotel.co.uk

10 rooms, S £55-£65, D £90-£160, No smoking

An elegant mid 19th-century villa on the English Riviera, this establishment has been stored with tremendous enthusiasm and mboyance to provide public areas that exude otic opulence. Plush en suite bedrooms are pointed with Victorian antiques and stylish tras such as crystal tumblers. Breakfast is a light in the stunning sun-lit dining room, iere Egyptian cotton covered tables are laid th sparkling cutlery and crystal, and you are t at ease by the sounds of Strauss and Vivaldi. The villa stands in secluded, flower-filled gardens, ideal for tea on the lawn or a glass of wine by the heated pool and spa.

Recommended in the Area

The Eden Project; South Devon Steam Railway; Living Coasts Zoo

The Southbourne Villa ♦♦♦♦

Map ref 2 - SX96
9 Cleveland Rd, TORQUAY, TQ2 5BD
A3022 towards town centre, at Halfords right fork over lights onto Avenue Rd, Cleveland Rd 1st left, hotel at end

T 01803 292960
F 01803 291299
E relax@thesouthbournevilla.co.uk
W www.thesouthbournevilla.co.uk

9 rooms, S £50, D £50-£90,
No smoking

RECOMMENDED IN THE AREA

Cockington village; Torre Abbey; Riviera Centre

The fine Victorian villa stands in a quiet tree-lined road in a conservation area, and is well placed for the town centre, theatres, conference centre, beaches and attractions. It is personally run by owner Gary Gilmore who has 28 years experience in the hospitality industry. The bright, sizeable rooms - one complete with four-poster bed - are all en suite, well furnished and have complimentary toiletries and tea and coffee facilities. A fully licensed bar leads onto the sun terrace and decking area, which has patio heaters for chilly evenings. A highlight is the hot spa tub with its relaxing massage features (open April to early October) - so bring a costume. A full traditional breakfast is served in the spacious dining room and freshly cooked evening bar meals are available. No children under 18 and no pets except guide dogs.

The Durant Arms ♦♦♦♦♦

Map ref 2 - SX86
Ashprington, TOTNES, TQ9 7UP
A381 from Totnes for Kingsbridge, 1m left for Ashprington
T 01803 732240
E info@thedurantarms.com
W www.thedurantarms.com
7 rooms, S £45, D £70, No smoking, Closed 25-26 Dec evenings

Immaculate whitewashed walls and masses of well-tended shrubs and plants make this country inn stand out the picturesque village of Ashprington in the South Hams. Owners Eileen and Graham Ellis proudly offer their own brand of hospitality, and provide attractive accommodation in either the main building or a refurbished annexe. Stylish furnishings, facilities en suite and a host of thoughtful touches ensure a memorable stay. The inn is renowned locally for its delicious food - a blackboard menu of home-cooked food is available in the character bar or smart dining room, and there is a choice of beers and wines (some from the local vineyard). Short walks lead from the village to the River Dart.

RECOMMENDED IN THE AREA

Historic Totnes; The Eden Project; Sharpham Vineyard

Eastacott Barton ♦♦♦♦♦

Map ref 2 - SS62
UMBERLEIGH, EX37 9AJ
1m E of Umberleigh. Off B3227 signed Eastacott, straight on at stone cross, Eastacott Barton 700yds on left

T 01769 540545
E stay@eastacott.com
W www.eastacott.com

5 rooms, S £50-£95, D £70-£115, No smoking, Closed occasionally

RECOMMENDED IN THE AREA
RHS Garden Rosemoor; Dartington Crystal; Arlington Court (NT)

The peaceful stone farmhouse stands in 27 acres with stunning views over the Taw Valley. Sue and James Murray ran a country house hotel before taking over here a few years ago, and they have stamped everything with quality. The spacious bedrooms are generously appointed with stylish modern bathrooms, stereo systems and quality linen. Three rooms are in a converted barn just across a courtyard, and all rooms share the same magnificent views. Superb breakfasts offer considerable choice, including porridge, kippers and home-made croissants. Dinner is available for large parties only. Relax in one of the elegant sitting rooms, or wander around the extensive grounds. A self-catering cottage is available.

Harrabeer Country House Hotel ♦♦♦♦

Map ref 2 - SX56
Harrowbeer Ln, YELVERTON, PL20 6EA
In village. Off A386 Tavistock Rd onto Grange Rd, right onto Harrowbeer Ln

T 01822 853302
E reception@harrabeer.co.uk
W www.harrabeer.co.uk

6 rooms, S £44.95-£80, D £59.95-£80, No smoking in bedrooms or dining room, Closed 3rd wk Dec, 2nd wk Jan

RECOMMENDED IN THE AREA
The Garden House; The Eden Project; Dartmoor National Park

Lovers of the outdoors will relish this traditional Devon longhouse on the edge of Dartmoor. The secluded garden is a delightful place to spend a lovely day, while indoors there is a relaxing lounge, and a bar for a convivial evening drink. Bedrooms vary from the splendid en suite Master Room overlooking the moor, with its video and DVD player and smart bathroom, to one room with a charming Victorian bed. Breakfast is a leisurely affair served in the dining room, and dinner can be cooked by arrangement (special diets can be catered for). Self-catering accommodation is available.

Dorset

selection of places to eat from the AA Restaurant & AA Pub guides

estaurants

Bistro on the Beach (British)
lent Promenade, Southbourne Coast
ad, Southbourne, Bournemouth BH6 4BE
l 01202 431473

Saint Michel (British, French)
urnemouth Highcliff Marriot, St
cheal's Road, Bournemouth BH2 5DU
l 01202 315716

Splinters (International)
Church Street, Christchurch BH23 1BW
l 01202 483454

Yalbury Cottage (British)
wer Brockhampton, Dorchester DT2 8PZ
l 01305 262382

Wayfarers Restaurant (European)
erborne Causeway, Shaftesbury SP7 9PX
l 01747 852821

Perry's Restaurant (British)
Trinity Road, The Old Harbour,
eymouth DT4 8TJ, Tel 01305 785799

Pubs

The Anchor Inn
High Street, Burton Bradstock DT6 4QF
Tel 01308 897228

The Anchor Inn
Seatown, Chideock DT6 6JU
Tel 01297 489215

The Acorn Inn
Evershot DT2 0JW
Tel 01935 83228

The Bottle Inn
Marshwood DT6 5QJ
Tel 01297 678254

The Brace of Pheasants
Plush DT2 7RQ
Tel 01300 348357

Three Horseshoes Inn
Powerstock DT6 3TF
Tel 01308 485328

Portman Lodge ♦♦♦♦♦

Map ref 2 - ST80
Whitecliff Mill St, BLANDFORD FORUM, DT11 7BP
On NW end of Blandford one-way system. To access follow signs from town centre to Shaftesbury & hospital
T / F 01258 453727
E enquiries@portmanlodge.co.uk
W www.portmanlodge.co.uk
3 rooms, S £45-£50, D £65,
No smoking

Hospitable owners Barbara and Robin Wrigley have filled their ctorian home with mementoes of their tensive travels, including interesting efacts, rugs and paintings. The ilding once housed a music school. lax and make yourself at home in the gant accommodation, which includes spacious lounge. The en suite double drooms are equipped with hairdryers and courtesy trays, and each has its own decorative theme. Breakfast is a special occasion, using fresh local produce, while delicious dinners are produced with great skill from quality ingredients.

Recommended in the Area

Georgian Blandford Forum; Monkey World; Jurassic Coast World Heritage Site

The Balincourt Hotel ♦♦♦♦♦

Map ref 3 - SZ09
58 Christchurch Rd,
BOURNEMOUTH, BH1 3PF
On A35 between Lansdowne & Boscombe Gardens, opp Lynton Court pub
T / F 01202 552962
E rooms@balincourt.co.uk
W www.balincourt.co.uk
12 rooms, S £45-£49, D £70-£78, No smoking, Closed Xmas

Owners Alison and Nigel Gandolfi are natural hosts, and you will very quickly feel at home in their delightful establishment. It's an ideal touring base, and the beach and town centre are easily reached on foot. The wide choice of individual bedrooms includes two on the ground floor. Each of the en suite rooms features a range of hand-painted ceramics, along with a hairdryer and a generous hospitality tray. The comfy armchairs in the bar-lounge are a magnet in the evenings, and traditional English cooki is served in the elegant dining room.

Recommended in the are

New Forest National Park; Bournemouth seafront; Poole Harbour & Brownsea Island

---

Cransley Hotel ♦♦♦♦

Map ref 3 - SZ09
11 Knyveton Rd, East Cliff,
BOURNEMOUTH, BH1 3QG
Off A338 at St Paul's rdbt by ASDA store, over next rdbt, Knyveton Rd 1st left
T 01202 290067
F 0709 2381721
E info@cransley.com
W www.cransley.com
11 rooms, S £30-£35, D £60-£70, No smoking

A quiet tree-lined road in the attractive East Cliff area of Bournemouth is the setting for this homely property. Owners Simon Goodwin and Jonathan Perry have decorated the house with respect for its Edwardian origins, mindful of the fact that King Edward VII and his mistress Lillie Langtry were once near neighbours. The sunny position means that bedrooms are bright and welcoming, and most have bath or shower en suite. Patio doors lead from the sitting room to the secluded south-facing garden, and the dining room, scene of traditional breakfasts (and evening meals by arrangement), is elegant and well furnished.

Recommended in the area

New Forest National Park; Thomas Hardy Country; Poole Harbour & Brownsea Island

Rosscourt Hotel ♦♦♦♦

Map ref 3 - SZ09
6 St Johns Rd, BOURNEMOUTH, BH5 1EL
A338 signed to Kings Park, then signs for Boscombe. Left off Christchurch Rd onto St Johns Rd

Ⓣ 01202 397537
Ⓔ enquiries@rosscourthotel.co.uk
Ⓦ www.rosscourthotel.co.uk

9 rooms, S £28-£35, D £56-£80, No smoking, Closed 20-30 Dec

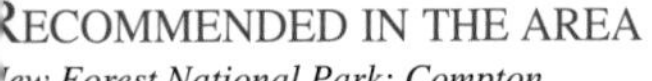

RECOMMENDED IN THE AREA
ew Forest National Park; Compton cres; Monkey World

A warm welcome is guaranteed by Debbie and Peter Payne at osscourt. Their family-run Victorian uesthouse is just a short walk from oscombe, Bournemouth's award-inning beach, and within easy reach of e shops and attractions. The ttractively decorated bedrooms, some of which are suitable for families, are finished with lots of added extras. The ground-floor en suite twin room is ideal for those who require easier access. Home-cooked evening meals are available by arrangement, and the substantial breakfast will set you up for a day sightseeing or walking along the spectacular coast. Free on-site parking is available.

Westcotes House Hotel ♦♦♦♦

Map ref 3 - SZ09
9 Southbourne Overcliff Rd, Southbourne, BOURNEMOUTH, BH6 3TE
1m E of pier on seafront road

Ⓣ 01202 428512
Ⓦ www.westcoteshousehotel.co.uk

6 rooms, S £40-£47, D £60-£74, No smoking

RECOMMENDED IN THE AREA
Poole Harbour; Thomas Hardy Country; Bournemouth

Overlooking Poole Bay from the cliff top at Southbourne, this small establishment is elegantly ecorated and has private car parking. The onservatory-lounge leads onto a sunny sea-facing errace, and a zigzag path and cliff lift give easy access the promenade and sandy beach. All the rooms e en suite and your friendly hosts Brenda and hristopher Burrell have added numerous extras cluding bathrobes, tissues and toiletries. One of the well-equipped bedrooms is on the ground floor. Excellent home cooking is served in the well-presented dining room, which has sea views. Dinner is available by arrangement.

Roundham House Hotel ♦♦♦♦♦

Map ref 2 - SY49
Roundham Gardens, West Bay Rd, BRIDPORT, DT6 4BD
A35 into Bridport, at the Crown Inn rdbt take exit signed West Bay. Hotel 400yds on left

T 01308 422753
F 01308 421500
E cyprencom@compuserve.com
W www.roundhamhouse.co.uk

8 rooms, S £44-£55, D £75-£94, No smoking, Closed Dec-Mar

Ever-present owners Steven and Deborah Hynes provide a warm welcome to their lovely home. There are stunning views from the acre of terraced gardens that surround this Edwardian country house overlooking the Brit valley and the sea. A country path leads to West Bay and the sea or to Bridport itself. Bedrooms come in all sizes with a variety of views and are filled with useful extras. Breakfast is a special occasion in the elegant dining room. Afternoon tea is served in the drawing room or on the terrace, and snacks and sandwiches are available every evening. Packed lunches and luxury hampers with champagne can be supplied for your day out.

Recommended in the Area

Abbotsbury Swannery & Gardens; Montacute House (NT); Forde Abbey & Gardens

---

The Casterbridge Hotel ♦♦♦♦♦

Map ref 2 - SY69
49 High East St, DORCHESTER, DT1 1HU
In town centre, 75yds from town clock

T 01305 264043
F 01305 260884
E reception@casterbridgehotel.co.uk
W www.casterbridgehotel.co.uk

14 rooms, S £58-£65, D £95-£125, Closed 24-26 Dec

This well-run establishment provides a traditional English welcome, with cheerful attentive staff, and a high standard of accommodation enhanced with antiques. Public rooms include an elegant dining room, drawing room, and a cosy bar-library. Breakfast in the conservatory is an extensive buffet or individually cooked breakfasts. All bedrooms are en suite with either bath or shower, tea and coffee facilities, direct-dial telephones, and one room is suitable for families. Children are welcome and high chairs are available. Special short breaks are available.

Recommended in the Area

Thomas Hardy Museum; Abbotsbury Swannery; Lulworth Cove

laiden Castle near Dorchester

Little Court ♦♦♦♦♦

Map ref 2 - SY69
5 Westleaze, Charminster, DORCHESTER, DT2 9PZ
A37 from Dorchester, 0.25m right at Loders Garage, Little Court 0.5m on right
T 01305 261576
F 01305 261359
E info@littlecourt.net
W www.littlecourt.net
8 rooms, S £49-£69, D £69-£99,
No smoking in bedrooms or dining room

RECOMMENDED IN THE AREA
rassic Coast World Heritage Coast; orchester; Weymouth

A picture-postcard Edwardian house in the style of Lutyens, Little Court estles in 4 acres of beautiful grounds ıd gardens. The property has been furbished to a very high standard and e proprietors are on hand to ensure ou have a excellent stay. Bedrooms ave a bath and shower en suite, and come with extras such as binoculars and even an umbrella. A delicious breakfast, including home-grown produce from the walled garden, is served in stylish dining room, which adjoins a restful lounge with log fires. There is a pub nearby that serves good food. A tennis court is available in the grounds.

Yalbury Cottage Hotel & Restaurant ♦♦♦♦♦

Map ref 2 - SY69
Lower Bockhampton,
DORCHESTER, DT2 8PZ
Off A35 past Thomas Hardy's cottage, over x-rds, 400yds on left, past telephone box, opp village pump
T 01305 262382
E yalburyemails@aol.com
W www.yalburycottage.com
8 rooms, S £59-£61, D £94-£98, No smoking in bedrooms or dining room

Situated in peaceful countryside, Yalbury Cottage was originally the home of the local shepherd and keeper of the water meadows. The thatched building dates from the 17th century, and teas and pre-dinner drinks are served in the attractive gardens in summer. The pretty restaurant served excellent food, in an atmosphere enhanced by oak beams and inglenook fireplaces. The cosy lounge, the only part of the building where smoking is permitted, is also in th[e] old part of the building. The spacious cottage-style bedrooms are in the modern annexe - all have bathrooms en suite, DVD players, hairdryers and tea and coffee facilities. Ample parking is provided in the grounds.

RECOMMENDED IN THE AREA

Thomas Hardy's birthplace; Athelhampton House; Walks in a conservation area

---

Farnham Farm House ♦♦♦♦♦

Map ref 2 - ST91
FARNHAM, DT11 8DG
Off A354 into Farnham, continue NW from village, 1m bear right at sign
T 01725 516254
F 01725 516306
E info@farnhamfarmhouse.co.uk
W www.farnhamfarmhouse.co.uk
3 rooms, S from £50, D from £70, No smoking

Farnham Farm House with its flagstone floors and open log fires dates back to the 1850s, and has been home to the same family for the last 80 years. You are welcome to walk around the 350 acres of the working farm, part of a private estate owned by the descendants of archaeologist General Pitt-Rivers. Facilities include a heated outdoor swimming pool, and the Sarpenela Treatment room in the converted stable for therapeutic massage and natural therapies. Delicious Aga-cooked breakfasts are served in the attractive dining room with its magnificent views. Local produce is used whenever possible with healthy and vegetarian options well catered for. All the en suite bedrooms have magnificent views.

RECOMMENDED IN THE AREA

Cranborne Chase; Kingston Lacey (NT); Larmer Tree Gardens

Frampton House ♦♦♦♦♦

Map ref 2 - SY69
FRAMPTON, DT2 9NH
A356 into village, from green over bridge & left onto driveway past houses
T 01300 320308
F 01300 321600
E maynardryder@btconnect.com
W www.framptonhouse.com
2 rooms, D £65-£85, No smoking in bedrooms or dining room

RECOMMENDED IN THE AREA

Weymouth; Cerne Abbas Giant; Dorchester

Georgina and Nicholas Maynard make you feel at home instantly when you enter their delightful property in a quiet village just outside Dorchester. Set back in landscaped grounds up a gravel drive, two Labradors run to greet you as you approach the grand grey-stone Grade II listed building, which provides exceptionally high standards of quality and comfort throughout. Georgina has retired from running an antiques shop and many of the goods have found their way into her home. There are two en suite bedrooms - one double with a four-poster bed and one twin room. Dinner by arrangement is highly recommended.

The Marquis of Lorne ♦♦♦♦

Map ref 2 - SY59
NETTLECOMBE, DT6 3SY
N from Bridport on A3066, 1.5m over minirdbt, turn right, through West Milton, over junct (signed Powerstock), pub 500yds on left
T 01308 485236
E enquiries@marquisoflorne.com
W www.marquisoflorne.com
7 rooms, S £45-£60, D £75-£95, No smoking in bedrooms or dining room

Lovely unspoiled countryside surrounds this cosy late Georgian inn, the focal point of the hamlet of Nettlecombe. The en suite bedrooms have stunning views, and come with modern facilities. The pretty beer garden is popular in summer, while log fires provide comfort in winter. The bar and restaurant areas are as unspoiled as the setting, offering real ales and cosy seating, and the interesting and delicious home-cooked food uses local produce. Julie and David Woodroffe are engaging hosts who look after their guests with a natural warmth.

RECOMMENDED IN THE AREA

West Dorset Heritage Coast, West Bay; Bridport market town; Fossil beach, Charmouth

The Poachers Inn ♦♦♦♦

Map ref 2 - SY79
PIDDLETRENTHIDE, DT2 7QX
8m N from Dorchester on B3143, inn on left

Ⓣ 01300 348358
Ⓕ 01300 348153
Ⓔ thepoachersinn@piddletrenthide.fsbusiness.co.uk
Ⓦ www.thepoachersinn.co.uk

21 rooms, S £45-£60, D £70-£100

The River Piddle gently runs through the garden of this delightful 17th-century inn. Original features survive in the character bar and dining areas, and open fires and traditional pub games add to the character. The inn is known for its good home-cooked food, which can be served in the garden or next to the swimming pool on fine days. The pool is heated during the summer, and is set in an enclosed sun trap with parasols and padded sun recliners. The bedrooms are in a modern extension surrounding the pool area, and are furnished with quality pieces. Some have baths in addition to showers, and each has a hairdryer, hospitality tray, radio and direct-dial telephone. A suite with a Jacuzzi and its own sitting room is a good choice for a luxurious stay.

RECOMMENDED IN THE ARE

Monkey World; Bovington Tank Museum; Thomas Hardy's Cottage (NT)

Town Farm Bungalow ♦♦♦♦

Map ref 2 - ST91
SIXPENNY HANDLEY, SP5 5NT
A354 onto B3081 to Sixpenny Handley, bungalow 250yds on right
T 01725 552319 &
F 01725 552319
E townfarmbungalow@tiscali.co.uk
W www.bandbtownfarmbungalow.co.uk
3 rooms, S £35-£50, D £50-£70, No smoking

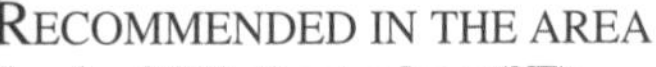

RECOMMENDED IN THE AREA
Stourhead (NT); Kingston Lacey (NT); New Forest National Park

It may seem like it's in the middle of nowhere, but Town Farm is certainly worth finding. There are wonderful views of the surrounding Cranborne Chase countryside from all rooms of this delightful bungalow, where Mrs Inglis gives very warm welcome and attentive service. Delicious dinners are available by arrangement and, like breakfast, are served around one large table. The breakfast menu includes a choice of fresh fruit, a continental option, a full English, or cooked salmon, kippers or haddock. A wood fire warms the cosy lounge in winter. The neat rooms are well maintained, and feather duvets and pillows are the norm (synthetic available on request).

Stourcastle Lodge ♦♦♦♦

Map ref 2 - ST71
Goughs Close, STURMINSTER NEWTON, DT10 1BU
Off town square opp cross
T 01258 472320
F 01258 473381
E enquiries@stourcastle-lodge.co.uk
W www.stourcastle-lodge.co.uk
5 rooms, S £48-£55, D £78-£92, No smoking

RECOMMENDED IN THE AREA
Stourhead (NT); Kingston Lacey (NT); Dorset country walks

This splendid 18th-century family home is traditionally decorated and set in delightful cottage-tyle gardens. Jill and Ken Hookham-Bassett have run ne Lodge for over 20 years, providing delicious Aga-ooked meals that accomplished chef Jill prepares from ocal produce every evening. These are served in the ttractive dining room, charmingly decorated with Ken's ollection of antique kitchenware and overlooking the icturesque gardens. For chillier evenings there is a cosy lounge complete with crackling log fire. The spacious bedrooms are furnished with antique brass bedsteads as well as modern conveniences such as bathrooms en suite with showers or whirlpool baths.

West Coombe Farmhouse ♦♦♦♦

Map ref 2 - SY88
WEST LULWORTH, BH20 5PS
Off A352 at Wool onto B3071, 1.5m left into Coombe Keynes (signed), 1st house left after phone box

Ⓣ 01929 462889
Ⓕ 01929 405863
Ⓔ westcoombefarmhouse@yahoo.co.uk
Ⓦ www.westcoombefarmhouse.co.uk

3 rooms, S £25-£31, D £50-£62, No smoking, Closed Xmas

Located in a peaceful hamlet, this delightful former farmhouse backs onto open fields and is a good base for exploring the unspoiled countryside of Hardy Country. The original part of the house is 17th century, but the front wing is 19th century built in a late Georgian style. Bedrooms are pleasantly furnished with beautiful coordinated fabrics - the double has an shower room en suite and the twin a private bathroom. The library of books and maps in the lounge will help you discover more about the area. No children under 12 years.

Recommended in the Area

Monkey World; Bovington Tank Museum; Lulworth Cove

Esplanade Hotel ♦♦♦♦

Map ref 2 - SY67
141 The Esplanade, WEYMOUTH, DT4 7NJ
E end of Esplanade, opp pier bandstand

Ⓣ / Ⓕ 01305 783129
Ⓔ esplanadehotel@weymouth10.fsnet.co.uk
Ⓦ www.theesplanadehotel.co.uk

11 rooms, S £30-£44, D £50-£74, No smoking, Closed Nov-Jan

Recommended in the Area

Abbotsbury Swannery; Dorset beaches; Sea Life Park

You can be assured of a warm welcome from owners Colin and Brenda Jolliffe at this Georgian seafront terrace built in 1835. The front-facing public rooms, including the first-floor lounge, all have fabulous views of beautiful Weymouth Bay. The good-size en suite rooms are particularly well furnished and attractively decorated, with many thoughtful extras - some have views over the sea. There are ground-floor bedrooms too and parking is available. It is just a short walk to the station, the town centre and the harbour.

Chandlers Hotel ♦♦♦♦♦

Map ref 2 - SY67
4 Westerhall Rd, WEYMOUTH, DT4 7SZ
500yds N of town centre, off A353 junct Esplanade & Greenhill
T 01305 771341
F 01305 830122
E debbiesare@chandlershotel.com
W www.chandlershotel.com
10 rooms, S £45-£75, D £75-£120,
No smoking in bedrooms or dining room

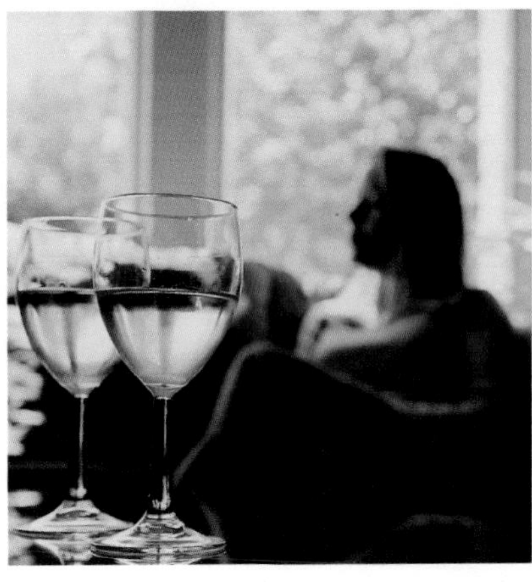

RECOMMENDED IN THE AREA

Weymouth beach & harbour; Abbotsbury Swannery & Gardens; Jurassic World Heritage

The simple philosophy of providing a peaceful retreat filled with comforts works very well at this beautiful Victorian house. Debbie and Colin Sare have created a unique port of call filled with contemporary style - Internet access in all bedrooms, stylish bathrooms with luxury towels and quality toiletries for pampering, and many attractive plants. After a long day sightseeing you can nestle into luxurious down duvets, and there are also generous hospitality trays. The attractive public rooms include a spacious sitting room and separate bar, and the dining room leads to the terrace and garden. Breakfast is a real treat, a wide choice beautifully presented in relaxed surroundings and including a daily-changing special. There are large front and rear car parks, and the beach is just 150 yards away.

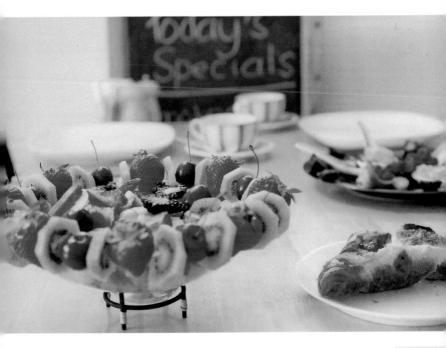

Co Durham

A selection of places to eat from the AA Restaurant & AA Pub guides

Restaurants

Beamish Park Hotel (European)
Beamish Burn Road, Beamish NE16 5EG
Tel 01207 230666

Bistro 21 (European)
Aykley Heads House, Aykley Heads, Durham DH1 5TS
Tel 0191 384 4354

Parkmore Hotel (International)
636 Yarm Road, Eaglescliffe, Stockton-on-Tees TS16 0DH, Tel 01642 786815

Headlam Hall Hotel (British, French)
Headlam, Gainford DL2 3HA
Tel 01325 730238

Rose and Crown (British)
Romaldkirk DL12 9EB
Tel 01833 650213

Seaham Hall Hotel
Lord Byron's Walk, Seaham SR7 7AG
Tel 0191 5161400

Pubs

The County
13 The Green, Aycliffe Village DL5 6LX
Tel 01325 312273

The Morritt Arms Hotel
Greta Bridge, Barnard Castle DL12 9SE
Tel 01833 627232

The Fox and Hounds
Cotherstone DL12 9PF
Tel 01833 650241

Ship Inn
Low Road, Middlestone DL14 8AB
Tel 01388 810904

Dun Cow Inn
43 Front Street, Sedgefield TS21 3AT
Tel 01740 620894

Seven Stars Inn
High Street North, Shincliffe Village, Durham DH1 2NU
Tel 0191 3848454

Greenhead Country House Hotel ♦♦♦♦

Map ref 7 - NZ13
FIR TREE, DL15 8BL
On A68, turn right at Fir Tree Inn
T / F 01388 763143
E info@thegreenheadhotel.co.uk
W www.thegreenheadhotel.co.uk
8 rooms, S £60, D £70-£75,
No smoking

Greenhead is an extended early 18th-century property, just 500 yards from the A68, set in well-tended gardens at the foot of the Weardale valley. The peaceful establishment is convenient for Durham and the Durham Dales. The spacious modern en suite bedrooms include one with a four-poster bed, and all rooms have tea and coffee facilities and clock radios. The central stone arched lounge is a relaxed centre for planning excursions. There are three restaurants in Fir Tree, all serving dinner, and two are within easy walking distance. Menus are available to view in the house, no advance booking is required.

RECOMMENDED IN THE AREA
Durham Cathedral; Beamish Open Air Museum; Weardale Area of Outstanding Natural Beauty

Clow Beck House ♦♦♦♦♦

Map ref 7 - NZ21
Monk End Farm, Croft on Tees, DARLINGTON, DL2 2SW
A167 from Darlington to Northallerton for 2m into Croft, over bridge & follow brown tourist signs to Clow Beck House

T 01325 721075
F 01325 720419
E heather@clowbeckhouse.co.uk
W www.clowbeckhouse.co.uk

13 rooms, S £65, D £95, Closed Xmas-New Year

Recommended in the Area
Raby Castle; Beamish Open Air Museum; Yorkshire Dales & Moors

Clow Beck House gets its name from the beck that winds its way through the grounds of the farm to meet the River Tees, providing a perfect opportunity for trout fishing. The bedrooms are in a cottage and in separate chalets in the gardens - each one has been decorated with great expertise to give a sense of period style. An imaginative carte and a good wine list are available in the beamed dining room. The inviting lounge with attractive blue upholstery is in the house itself. Heather and David Armstrong are dedicated to making you feel at home, and they are keen to help you plan your route for an outing through the rolling countryside of this lovely area.

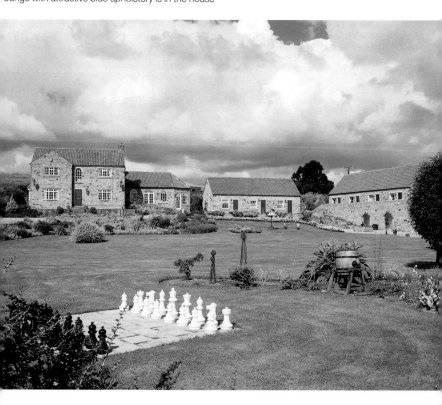

Hillrise Guest House ♦♦♦♦

Map ref 7 - NZ24
13 Durham Rd West, Bowburn, DURHAM, DH6 5AU
A1 junct 61, Hillrise 300yds on left
Ⓣ 0191 377 0302
Ⓕ 0191 377 0898
Ⓔ enquiries@hill-rise.com
Ⓦ www.hill-rise.com
5 rooms, S £35, D £60-£70, No smoking

Recommended in the Area

Beamish Open Air Museum; Durham Cathedral & Castle; The Bowes Museum, Barnard Castle

Small and friendly, this guest house exudes hospitality and comfort. Durham city centre is just a few miles away, and the A1(M) is nearby for visiting the many places of interest in the area. The bedrooms offer versatile accommodation that includes double, twin-bed and family rooms, all with private facilities. Furnishings and soft fabrics are smart and modern, and the rooms are equipped with hospitality trays. The homely lounge with inviting leather seating has a television and a huge video collection. Hearty breakfasts are served in the bright and airy dining room, from where there is access to an enclosed garden terrace. Your host is George Webster, who has had long experience in the hotel trade.

selection of places to eat from the AA Restaurant & AA Pub guides

estaurants

Marygreen Manor (International)
ondon Road, Brentwood CM14 4NR
1277 225252

The Rose & Crown Hotel (Indian, rench)
ast Street, Colchester CO1 2TZ
el 01206 866677

Milsoms (International)
tratford Road, Dedham CO7 6HN
el 01206 322795

The Carved Angel (British, Mediterranean)
pper Holt Street, Earls Colne CO6 2PG
el 01787 222330

deVere Arms
3 High Street, Earls Colne CO6 2PB
el 01787 223353

Five Lakes Resort (British)
olchester Road, Tolleshunt Knights CM9 8HX
el 01621 868888

Pubs

Axe & Compasses
High Street, Arkesden CB11 4EX
Tel 01799 550272

The Green Dragon at Young's End
Upper London Road, Braintree CM77 8QN
Tel 01245 361030

The Swan at Felsted
Station Road, Felsted CM6 3DG
Tel 01371 820245

Bell Inn & Hill House
High Road, Horndon on the Hill SS17 8LD
Tel 01375 642463

The Mistley Thorn
High Street, Manningtree CO11 1HE
Tel 01206 392821

The Ferry Boat Inn
Ferry Lane, North Fambridge CM3 6LR
Tel 01621 740208

Potash Farmhouse ♦♦♦♦

Map ref 4 - TL62
Cobblers Green, Causeway End Rd, FELSTED, CM6 3LX
B1417 S from Felsted, 0.5m left signed Cobler's Green, farm signed 400yds on left
T / F 01371 820510
E jill@potashfarm.co.uk
W www.potashfarm.co.uk
3 rooms, S £25-£35, D £48-£50, No smoking

Quietly situated in a large half-moated garden, this Grade II listed 15th-century farmhouse retains any original features, including exposed beams and pen fireplaces. The homely bedrooms are filled with oughtful extras, including tea and coffee facilities. The ound-floor rooms include an elegant breakfast room nd a choice of cosy or conservatory lounges. A full nglish or continental breakfast is offered and packed nches are made on request. You can play croquet on the lawn in the extensive mature gardens. A taxi service to and from Stansted Airport (10 miles) or station is available. No children under 12 and no dogs.

Recommended in the Area

Paycockes, Coggeshall (NT); Thaxted; Mountfitchet Castle & Norman Village, Stansted Mountfitchet

The White House ♦♦♦♦

Map ref 4 - TL52

Smiths Green, TAKELEY, CM22 6NR

400yds E of Takeley on corner of B1256 & Smiths Green

T 01279 870257
F 01279 870423
E enquiries@whitehousestansted.co.uk
W www.whitehousestansted.co.uk

3 rooms, S £60, D £65, No smoking, Closed 24-25, 31 Dec, 1 Jan

Recommended in the Area

Hatfield Forest (NT); Duxford Imperial War Museum; Newmarket Races

This carefully refurbished family home displays many original 16th-century features alongside modern comforts. The Grade II listed building is close to Stansted Airport and is enclosed by extensive gardens. Accommodation is stylish with large beds, and one room has a luxurious private Victorian bathroom. Served around one table in the farmhouse-style kitchen the full cooked breakfast is a wholesome start to the day. A range of interesting dishes, using quality local ingredients, is available in the Lion and Lamb pub a mile up the road, which is owned by the same proprietors who offer free transport to and fro.

Gloucestershire

A selection of places to eat from the AA Restaurant & AA Pub guides

Restaurants

(1 rosette) The Amberley Inn
Culver Hill, Amberley GL5 5AF,
Tel 01453 872565

(1 rosette) The Village Pub (European)
Barnsley GL7 5EF, Tel 01285 740421

(4 rosettes) Le Champignon Sauvage (French)
24 Suffolk Road, Cheltenham GL50 2AQ
Tel 01242 573449

(2 rosettes) The New Inn at Coln (British, French)
Coln St Aldwyns GL7 5AN, Tel 01285 750651

(1 rosette) Egypt Mill (British)
Nailsworth GL6 0AE, Tel 01453 833449

(3 rosettes) 5 North Street
5 North Street, Winchcombe GL54 5LH
Tel 01242 604566

Pubs

The Kilkeney Inn
Kilkeney, Andoversford GL54 4LN
Tel 01285 770310

Kings Head Inn & Restaurant
High Street, Bledington OX7 6XQ
Tel 01608 658365

Eight Bells Inn
Church Street, Chipping Campden
GL55 6JG, Tel 01386 840371

Fossebridge Inn
Fossebridge GL54 3JS, Tel 01285 720721

The Fox
Lower Oddington GL56 0UR
Tel 01451 870555

Churchill Arms
Paxford GL55 6XH, Tel 01386 594000

Badger Towers at Beechworth Lawn Hotel ♦♦♦♦

Map ref 2 - SO92
133 Hales Rd, CHELTENHAM, GL52 6ST
Off A40 London Rd onto Hales Rd, hotel 0.5m on right
T 01242 522583
F 01242 574800
E info@beechworthlawnhotel.co.uk
W www.beechworthlawnhotel.co.uk
7 rooms, S £45-£55, D £60-£95, No smoking, Closed Xmas-New Year

A comfortable, relaxed atmosphere is felt as soon as you enter this ıpressive Victorian property, set in ature gardens in a quiet residential ea. Owners Claire and Peter ıristensen have owned and run hotels Europe, the Middle East and Canada, ıd they bring a wealth of experience to eir latest venture. They offer elegantly ecorated and furnished bedrooms, cluding two on the ground floor. The eakfast room, where a full English breakfast is freshly cooked from local produce, is bright and cheerful, and there is also a spacious sitting room.

RECOMMENDED IN THE AREA
Sudeley Castle; Prestbury Park; Cheltenham Promenade & Montpellier

---

Holly House ♦♦♦♦

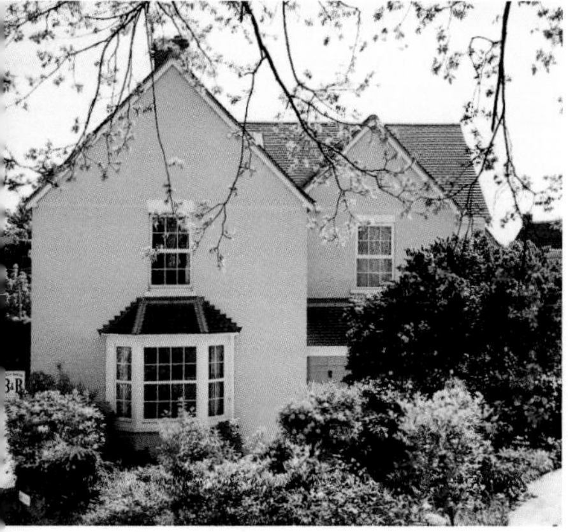

Map ref 3 - SP13
Ebrington, CHIPPING CAMPDEN, GL55 6NL
B4035 from Chipping Campden towards Shipston on Stour, 0.5m left to Ebrington & signed
T 01386 593213
F 01386 593181
E hutsbybandb@aol.com
W www.hollyhousebandb.co.uk
3 rooms, S £50-£65, D £60-£70, No smoking, Closed Xmas

RECOMMENDED IN THE AREA
Hidcote Manor Gardens (NT); Stratford-upon-Avon; Snowshill Manor (NT)

A picturesque Cotswold village is the appealing setting for this Victorian guest house. Surrounded quaint thatched cottages and close to the Norman age church, Holly House is well placed for visiting ratford, Hidcote Manor Gardens, and Chipping ampden. The en suite ground-floor bedrooms, cluding a twin, are in converted outbuildings around a urtyard - each room is thoughtfully equipped and has own private entrance. Make use of the tourist information in the attractive Garden Room, and delicious Cotswold breakfasts are served in the cosy dining room. Parking spaces are plentiful, and the village pub serving traditional food is just a short walk away.

The Moda Hotel ♦♦♦♦

Map ref 2 - ST78
1 High St, CHIPPING SODBURY, BS37 6BA
In town centre
T 01454 312135
F 01454 850090
E enquiries@modahotel.com
W www.modahotel.com
10 rooms, S £58.50, D £75-£85, No smoking

RECOMMENDED IN THE AREA

Bath; Westonbirt Arboretum; Dyrham Park (NT)

The Grade II listed Georgian house has an imposing position on the High Street. It's a popular venue with wonderful views of the town and country, and the interesting rooms offer quality, space and comfort. The hotel has been refurbished to provide modern bedrooms and restful public areas while retaining original features. Watch out for the enormous ancient wooden door in the breakfast room – quite a talking point. Jo and Duncan MacArthur treat tourists and business travellers to a first-class personalised service and provide an excellent English breakfast sourced from local suppliers. Chipping Sodbury is an ideal base for exploration as well as offering pubs and restaurants within a short walk.

Chapel Cottage ♦♦♦♦

Map ref 2 - SO51
3 Chapel Rd, Berry Hill, COLEFORD GL16 7QY
Off A4136 at Five Acres onto Park Rd. 1st left, B&B 200yds on left
T 01594 836547
E chapelcottagefod@aol.com
W www.chapelcottagebedandbreakfast.co.uk
3 rooms, D £50-£60, No smoking

The welcome at Chapel Cottage is very genuine and the friendly proprietor makes every effort to ensure you have a relaxing and comfortable stay. The lovely 19th-century cottage is well situated for exploring the The Forest of Dean, and it is within easy driving distance of Chepstow, Monmouth and Ross-On-Wye. The attractive bedrooms are furnished to a high standard and come with a host of thoughtful extras - the stylish modern bathrooms are also of a high quality. Breakfast is a tasty event, served in the light and airy dining room.

RECOMMENDED IN THE AREA

Tintern Abbey; Forest of Dean; Wye Valley

The Plough Inn ♦♦♦♦

Map ref 3 - SP02
FORD, GL54 5RU
On B4077 in village
T 01386 584215
F 01386 584042
E info@theploughinnatford.co.uk
W www.theploughinnatford.co.uk
3 rooms, S £35, D £60, No smoking in bedrooms or dining room

Here you can find everything that is traditionally associated with an English inn - exposed beams ind flagstone floors, log fires and solid wood furniture. 'his charming 16th-century pub is popular for a drink or meal, and is a comfortable base for visiting the area. It ffers accommodation in a converted stable block pening out onto a courtyard, next to the pretty beer arden. The inviting rooms are well equipped, and a ood breakfast starts the day. Home-cooked food is a feature of the bar and restaurant, and fresh asparagus in season is a speciality.

RECOMMENDED IN THE AREA
Sudeley Castle; Cotswold Farm Park; Birdland

Guiting Guest House ♦♦♦♦♦

Map ref 3 - SP02
Post Office Ln, GUITING POWER, GL54 5TZ
In village centre
T 01451 850470
E info@guitingguesthouse.com
W www.guitingguesthouse.com
8 rooms, S £37.50, D £70-£75, No smoking

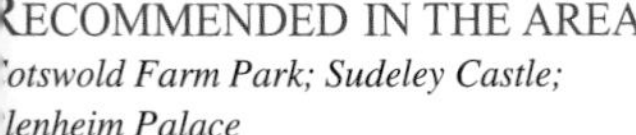

RECOMMENDED IN THE AREA
'otswold Farm Park; Sudeley Castle; lenheim Palace

Guiting Guest House is an engaging family home at one with its urroundings in a beautiful Cotswold llage. Bedrooms are individually ecorated and full of charm. Most have cilities en suite and four-poster beds, nd all of them are equipped with teddy ears, hairdryers, bathrobes, quality iletries, and hospitality trays with biscuits, fresh fruit and flowers. Exposed beams, inglenook fireplaces, solid elm floorboards and candlelight provide character in the inviting public rooms. Breakfast and evening meals, based on fresh local produce, are served in the dining room. Please give at least 24 hours notice for a dinner booking.

Cambrai Lodge ♦♦♦♦

Map ref 3 - SU29
Oak St, LECHLADE ON THAMES, GL7 3AY
In town centre, off High St onto A361 Oak St
T 01367 253173
E cambrailodge@btconnect.com
W www.cambrailodgeguesthouse.co.uk
7 rooms, S £30-£40, D £50-£60, No smoking

The pleasant house lies on the edge of the historic market town of Lechlade and is only a stroll from a number of pubs serving food - owner John Titchener will be happy to recommend places. The bedrooms are all carefully decorated and furnished. Some rooms are in a pretty cottage across the garden and include a four poster, and there are two ground-floor bedrooms. All the rooms have tea and coffee facilities and central heating, and some are en suite. Hearty, freshly cooked breakfasts are served in the conservatory overlooking the large gardens. Packed lunches are available and there is parking on site.

RECOMMENDED IN THE AREA
Cirencester; Oxford; The Cotswolds

Heavens Above at The Mad Hatters Restaurant ♦♦♦♦

Map ref 2 - ST89
3 Cossack Sq, NAILSWORTH, GL6 0DB
In town centre. Off A46 onto Spring Hill, left onto Old Market
T / F 01453 832615
E mafindlay@waitrose.com
3 rooms, S £35, D £60, No smoking

Set in the heart of the historic mill town of Nailsworth, with its individual shops and art galleries featuring local artists, this appropriately named guest house is located above a delightful organic restaurant. There's no television to spoil the peace and quiet in the spacious bedrooms, which have the feel of a comfortable country home, complete with pine furniture and bay windows looking out onto the village street below. The intimate dining rooms are furnished in the style of a traditional parlour. The restaurant lives up to its reputation, using fresh, organic ingredients, many grown on the premises, simply prepared with love and care.

RECOMMENDED IN THE AREA
Ruskin Mill; Rivers Gallery; Ropestore Studio Gallery.

Mill View Guest House ♦♦♦♦

Map ref 3 - SP12
2 Mill View, NAUNTON, GL54 3AF
Off B4068 to E end of village
T 01451 850 586
F 01451 850970
E ralph.boult@care4free.net
W www.millviewguesthouse cotswolds.com
3 rooms, S £40-£55, D £55-£70, No smoking

This guest house is in the Cotswolds Area of Outstanding Natural Beauty d stands opposite a former watermill the quiet village of Naunton. Great nsideration for comfort is evident from e numerous thoughtful extras oughout the house, and the urbished property includes a ound-floor bedroom. Well-cooked ndle-lit dinners are a delicious option, and like breakfasts are served in the conservatory. Patricia Boult descends from four generations of Nauntonians, and husband Ralph is a mine of local information. You can be collected from the local bus or train stations by arrangement.

RECOMMENDED IN THE AREA

Cotswold Farm Park rare breeds; Gloucestershire Warwickshire Railway; Snowshill Manor (NT)

Northfield Guest House ♦♦♦♦

Map ref 3 - SP11
Cirencester Rd, NORTHLEACH, GL54 3JL
Signed off A429 Northleach-Cirencester road, 1m from Northleach lights
T / F 01451 860427
E nrthfield0@aol.com
W www.northfieldbandb.co.uk
3 rooms, S £35-£45, D £65-£70, No smoking, Closed 23-31 Dec

nimals graze in the fields around this Cotswold stone house set in immaculate gardens. Indoors ere is a clear commitment to presentation and the drooms are a pleasure to stay in - two rooms have ect access to the gardens. The homely atmosphere ends to the lounge. The friendly dining room is the ene of delicious country breakfasts including eggs m the resident hens, and the imaginative evening als leave a lasting impression. Northfield is handy for visiting the historic towns of Cirencester, Gloucester, Cheltenham and Stow-on-the-Wold

RECOMMENDED IN THE AREA

Chedworth Roman Villa (NT); Keith Harding's Musical Museum

Kings Head Inn & Restaurant ♦♦♦♦ 

Map ref 3 - SP12
The Green, Bledington, STOW-ON-THE-WOLD, OX7 6XQ
4m SE off B4450

Ⓣ 01608 658365
Ⓕ 01608 658902
Ⓔ kingshead@orr-ewing.com
Ⓦ www.kingsheadinn.net

12 rooms, S £55-£125, D £70-£125, No smoking in bedrooms or dining room, Closed 25-26 Dec

RECOMMENDED IN THE AREA

Blenheim Palace; Cotswold Farm Park; Cheltenham Races

Located next to the picturesquevillage green with a brook running past, this classic English country pub is well worth seeking out. In the 16th century it was used as a cider house, and its timeless interior has low ceilings, beams, exposed stone walls and open fires. Nicola Orr-Ewing was once a milliner in London, and she has used her creative talents to transform the accommodation. Husband Archie, born in the next village, helps to maintain a relaxed but efficient atmosphere. The stylish bedrooms ar individually decorated and each has a modern bathroom. Some rooms are above the inn, wh others arein a quiet courtyard annexe set well back fromthe pub. Tasty meals are served in t smart restaurant, including Aberdeen Angus beef fromthe family's own farm. The interestin breakfast menu is a choice of delicious and sustaining dishes.

The Mews ♦♦♦♦

Map ref 3 - SP12
Fox Ln, Digbeth St, STOW-ON-THE-WOLD, GL54 1BN
Off Stow Sq onto Digbeth St, left after 2nd speed bump, The Mews on left

T 01451 831633
E enquiries@themewsfoxlane.co.uk
W www.themewsfoxlane.co.uk

1 room, S £40-£50, D £55-£65, No smoking, Closed Xmas, New Year, Feb

Expect to be greeted by a cat that thinks it's a dog, and welcomed by the owners with home-made ˌke and tea on arrival. There can be no doubting the ˌlight all three take in sharing their home, though Katie ˌe cat keeps well away from non pet-lovers. Barbara ˌd Peter King have travelled widely, and know what ˌople like when they are away from home. The en ˌite bedroom is filled with goodies like sherry and nuts, ˌme-made biscuits, fruit and herb teas, and of course tea and coffee. Enjoy a memorable breakfast in the smart dining room, with freshly squeezed juice and wide choice of quality preserves.

RECOMMENDED IN THE AREA

Pubs & restaurants nearby; Cotswold villages; Scotts of Stow

Rectory Farmhouse ♦♦♦♦♦

Map ref 3 - SP12
Lower Swell, STOW-ON-THE-WOLD, GL54 1LH
B4068 from Stow-on-the-Wold signed Lower Swell, left before Golden Ball Inn onto private road, farmhouse at end of gravel driveway

T 01451 832351
E rectory.farmhouse@cw-warwick.co.uk

2 rooms, D £80-£86, No smoking

RECOMMENDED IN THE AREA

ˌdcote Manor Garden (NT); Stunning ˌuntry walks; Stratford-upon-Avon theatre

Discerning guests will love this Grade II listed 17th-century former ˌmhouse, refurbished to provide luxury ˌcommodation. Built of Cotswold ˌone and set in the pretty hamlet of ˌwell, it has stunning country views. ˌobert and Sybil Gisby - only the ˌcond private owners in over 300 years ˌnjoy having guests and not surprisingly have many return visits. Bedrooms are full of thoughtful extras, and have superb bathrooms en suite with immaculate fittings. The spacious lounge with wood-burning stove is full of charm, while tasty country breakfasts are served in the elegant dining room. The attractive mature gardens and the excellent restaurants and inns nearby are further advantages.

Tavern House ♦♦♦♦

Map ref 2 - ST89
Willesley, TETBURY, GL8 8QU
4m SW of Tetbury. A433 to Willesley Tavern House set back from road
Ⓣ 01666 880444
Ⓔ robertson@tavernhouse.co.uk
4 rooms, S £45-£80, D £65-£85,No smoking in bedrooms or dining room

Within easy reach of Bath and Bristol, this lovely former inn and staging post dates from the 17th century. Oak beams, an open fireplace and a secluded walled garden survive from the building's former life and add to its charm. Now restored, the smart accommodation offers bedrooms with spacious bath and shower rooms en suite, all equipped with modern conveniences. A range of traditional and more exotic cuisine is on offer, and for those with a lighter appetite there is a selection of sandwiches and snacks available.

RECOMMENDED IN THE AREA
Westonbirt Arboretum; The Cotswolds; Gloucester

Isbourne Manor House ♦♦♦♦♦

Map ref 3 - SP02
Castle St, WINCHCOMBE, GL54 5JA
On B4632 in village centre, onto Castle St & house on left before bridge
Ⓣ / Ⓕ 01242 602281
Ⓔ felicity@isbourne-manor.co.uk
Ⓦ www.isbourne-manor.co.uk
3 rooms, S £60, D £70-£90,No smoking, Closed 25-26 Dec

Isbourne Manor is part-Elizabethan and part-Georgian, set in peaceful gardens alongside the River Isbourne. The house's elegant rooms are furnished with comfort to the fore. Owners Felicity and David King have shown considerable attention to detail in the bedrooms - each has an individual character and a host of luxury extras such as mineral water, fresh flowers and plenty of books and guide books. Choose from a huge four poster, a Victorian half tester, or twin beds. Breakfast is an enjoyable meal with home-made preserves and local produce, served in the dining room.

RECOMMENDED IN THE AREA
Sudeley Castle; GWR at Toddington; The Cotswold Way

Hampshire

selection of places to eat from the AA Restaurant & AA Pub guides

estaurants

Simply Poussin (British)
ne Courtyard, Brookley Road,
rockenhurst SO42 7RB
el 01590 623063

Star Inn (British)
ast Tytherley SO51 0LW
el 01794 340225

36 on the Quay (European)
7 South Street, Emsworth PO10 7EG
el 01234 375592

The Gurkha Square (Nepalese)
27 Fleet Road, Fleet GU51 3BU
el 01252 810286 & 811588

Nippon-Kan (Japanese)
ld Thorns Hotel, Griggs Green, Liphook
U30 7PE
el 01428 724555

Chesil Rectory (British, French)
Chesil Street, Winchester SO23 0HU
el 01962 851555

Pubs

The Globe on the Lake
The Soke, Broad Street, Alresford SO24 9DB
Tel 01962 732294

The Hampshire Arms
Pankridge Street, Crondall GU10 5QU
Tel 01252 850418

The Rose & Thistle
Rockbourne SP6 3NL
Tel 01725 518236

The Plough Inn
Main Road, Sparsholt SO21 2NW
Tel 01962 776353

The Red House Inn
21 London Street, Whitchurch RG28 7LH
Tel 01256 895558

Wykeham Arms
75 Kingsgate Street, Winchester SO23 9PE
Tel 01962 853834

The Cottage Hotel ♦♦♦♦♦

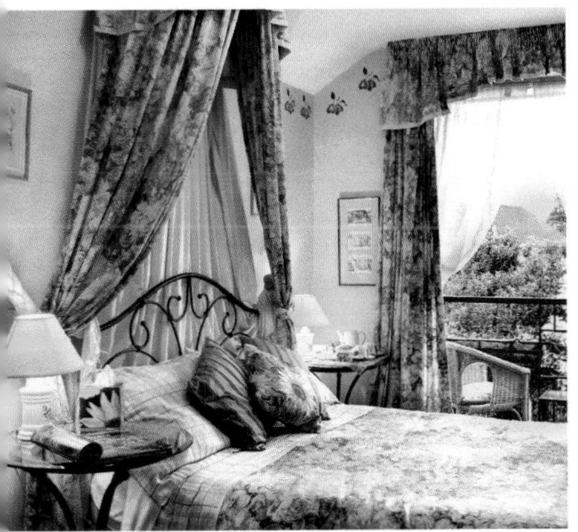

Map ref 3 - SU30
Sway Rd, BROCKENHURST,
SO42 7SH
Off A337 opp Careys Manor Hotel onto Grigg Ln, 0.25m over x-rds, cottage next to war memorial
T 01590 622296
F 01590 623014
E enquiries@cottagehotel.org
W www.cottagehotel.org
6 rooms, S £50-£95, D £50-£155 (depending on season), No smoking, Closed Xmas

Owners David and Christina welcome guests to the cosy 17th-century Cottage Hotel with omplimentary tea or coffee, served in front of the oaring fire in the Snug Bar (mind your head on the eams). The small market town of Brockenhurst is one f the few New Forest settlements where grazing onies and cattle still have right of way. The hotel is a hort walk from the railway station and only 200 yards om the high street, cycle hire, and the open forest. The individually furnished bedrooms are en-suite and a hearty English breakfast is served. Children over 10 years are welcome and dogs by arrangement.

Recommended in the Area

National Motor Museum, Beaulieu; Exbury Gardens; Walking, cycling & horse riding

Springfield Hotel ♦♦♦♦

Map ref 3 - SU50
67 The Avenue, FAREHAM,
PO14 1PE
On A27 W of Fareham station
🅣 01329 828325
6 rooms, S £45, D £55, No smoking in bedrooms or dining room, Closed 21 Dec-1 Jan

Spacious gardens surround this large and attractive property, which is in a pleasant residential area on the outskirts of Fareham. Dating from the 1930s, its comfortable atmosphere is due to the pleasant, hospitable hosts. There are plenty of useful extras in the coordinated bedrooms, which are of a good size and have facilities en suite. Tasty breakfasts provide a hearty start to the day in the elegant dining room, which looks over the delightful garden, and the cosy lounge shares the same views.

Recommended in the Area

Westbury Manor Museum; Naval Dockyard, Portsmouth; Netley Abbey

---

Alderholt Mill ♦♦♦♦

Map ref 3 - SU11
Sandleheath Rd, FORDINGBRIDGE,
SP6 1PU
1m W from Fordingbridge, left at x-rds in Sandleheath, 0.5m over bridge on right
🅣 01425 653130
🅕 01425 652868
🅔 alderholt-mill@zetnet.co.uk
🅦 www.alderholtmill.co.uk
5 rooms, S £27-£32, D £60-£68, No smoking

One of the many pleasures of staying at Alderholt Mill is the home-baked bread. It is made from wholemeal flour stone- ground in the water mill that forms part of this delightful property - all the machinery is intact and you can watch milling demonstrations. Bedrooms are individually decorated and furnished and all have facilities en suite. A comfortable lounge is also provided. The dining room is decorated in lovely bold colours, and a super breakfast is served around one large table. Dinner is available by arrangement. This is an ideal spot from which to tour the New Forest with its wonderful walks and cycle paths. The Wiltshire Downs and Dorset coast are also within easy reach.

Recommended in the Area

Salisbury Cathedral; Breamore House; Rockborne Roman Villa

Ravensdale ♦♦♦♦

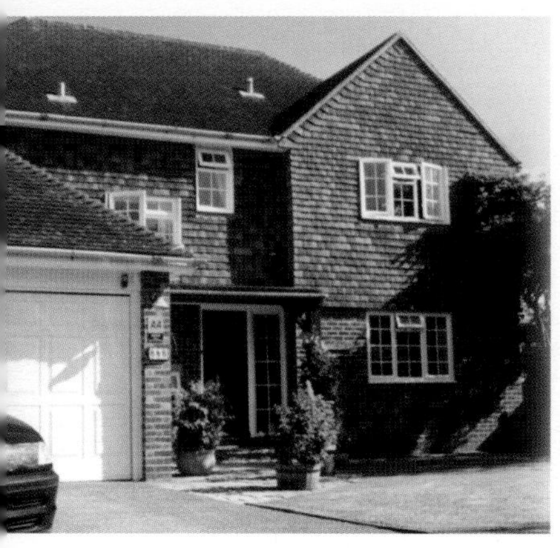

Map ref 3 - SU70
19 St Catherines Rd, HAYLING ISLAND, PO11 0HF
A3023 at Langstone, cross Hayling Bridge & continue 3m until minirdbt, right onto Manor Rd. After 1m, right by Barley Mow onto Station Rd & 3rd left onto St Catherines Rd
T / F 023 9246 3203
E phil.taylor@tayloredprint.co.uk
W www.ravensdale-hayling.co.uk
3 rooms, S £34-£38, D £58-£62, No smoking, Closed last 2 wks Dec

A relaxed and friendly environment is easily created by natural hosts Jane and Phil Taylor. Ravensdale is t far from the beach and golf course and has the nus of good parking. The attractive bedrooms are y comfortable with en suite or private facilities, and ve a host of thoughtful extras. There is an inviting inge-dining room. Food is a highlight at Ravensdale, ether you sample the excellent breakfast or book in a delicious evening meal. The combination of Jane's culinary skills and Phil's table presentaiton and service ensure an enjoyable occasion.

RECOMMENDED IN THE AREA
Chichester Cathedral ; HMS Victory *& the* Mary Rose *historic ships, Portsmouth; Walking on the South Downs*

The Penny Farthing Hotel ♦♦♦♦

Map ref 3 - SU30
Romsey Rd, LYNDHURST, SO43 7AA
M27 junct 1, A337, hotel on left entering village
T 023 8028 4422
F 023 8028 4488
E stay@pennyfarthinghotel.co.uk
W www.pennyfarthinghotel.co.uk
0 rooms, S £52.50-£78, D £68-£98, No smoking in bedrooms or dining oom, Closed Xmas

RECOMMENDED IN THE AREA
w Forest Visitor Centre; National Motor seum, Beaulieu; Exbury Gardens

The Penny Farthing is a friendly establishment ideally situated for siness guests or visitors wishing to plore the New Forest and local actions. Two adjacent buildings have en incorporated and furnished with e furniture. The attractive bedrooms all en suite and offer a range of well-pointed accommodation from single to family - they also have direct-dial telephones, tea and coffee trays and central heating. Some rooms are in an adjacent cottage. Other facilities include a spacious dining room where hearty breakfasts are served, a comfortable lounge bar, a bicycle store, and garaging for motorcycles and specialist cars.

Rufus House Hotel ♦♦♦♦♦

Map ref 3 - SU30
Southampton Rd, LYNDHURST, SO43 7BQ
From Lyndhurst centre onto A35 Southampton Rd, hotel 300yds on left

T 023 8028 2930
E rufushouse@aol.com
W www.rufushousehotel.co.uk

11 rooms, S £25-£45, D £50-£85, No smoking

Rufus House is a delightful Victorian property on the edge of Lyndhurst, an ideal base for exploring the beautiful New Forest. Traditional comforts and modern conveniences are promised here, and the en suite bedrooms are exceptionally well appointed - the turret suites have four-poster beds. There are lovely views, and thoughtful extras such as radios, and tea and coffee facilities make for an enjoyable stay. Relax in the turret lounge, while the dining room overlooks the garden terrace. There is an extensive menu at breakfast, but the highlight of any stay is the superb hospitality and service provided by Alma and Paul Carter, who welcome you with refreshments on arrival.

RECOMMENDED IN THE ARE
National Motor Museum, Beaulieu; Exb Gardens; New Forest National Park

---

Alma Mater ♦♦♦♦

Map ref 3 - SZ29
4 Knowland Rd, MILFORD ON SE SO41 0RH
A337 at Everton onto B3058 to Milford on Sea. Pass South Lawn Hotel, right onto Manor Rd, 1st left onto Knowland Dr

T / F 01590 642811
E bandbalmamater@aol.com
W www.newforestalmamater.co.u

3 rooms, S £40, D £60-£66, No smoking

Eileen and John Haywood enjoy welcoming guests to their beautifully kept home, a large detached bungalow overlooking landscaped gardens in a quiet residential area. It is a good base for exploring the New Forest and coast, and the yachting centre of Lymington is close by. Ample secure parking is provided, and the attractive village and the beach are just a walk away. A full four-course or continental breakfast is served in the dining room. The en suite bedrooms are centrally heated and equipped with eatras suc as radios, tea and coffee provisions, a toiletries and bath robes.

RECOMMENDED IN THE AR
Hurst Castle; Exbury Gardens; Nationa Motor Museum, Beaulieu

Quinhay Farmhouse ♦♦♦♦

Map ref 3 - SU72
Alton Rd, Froxfield, PETERSFIELD, GU32 1BZ
A3(M), Winchester exit, signed Petersfield. At rdbt, exit signed Froxfield/Steep, 3.5m on right
Ⓣ 01730 827183
Ⓕ 01730 827184
Ⓔ janerothery@hotmail.com
Ⓦ www.quinhaybandb.co.uk
2 rooms, D £50-£60, No smoking, Closed 15 Dec-15 Jan

Jane Rothery takes great delight in welcoming you to her delightful odern farmhouse set in rolling untryside outside Petersfield, one of e highest spots in Hampshire. The acious bedrooms are designed with mfort in mind and have a wealth of oughtful extras, including daily fresh wers, and tea and coffee facilities. A ge lounge comes with comfy sofas d access to a sun-filled terrace in mmer or a wood-burning stove for oler months. Quinhay is popular with walkers and cyclists exploring this Area of Outstanding Natural Beauty. There are two good pubs just a short drive away. No dogs (except guide dogs) or children under ten.

Recommended in the Area

Winchester; Portsmouth Historic Dockyard; Jane Austen's House, Chawton

---

Amberwood ♦♦♦♦

Map ref 3 - SU10
3-5 Top Ln, RINGWOOD, BH24 1LF
A31 onto B3347, over rdbt, left onto School Ln, left onto Top Ln
Ⓣ / Ⓕ 01425 476615
Ⓔ maynsing@aol.com
Ⓦ www.amberwoodbandb.co.uk
2 rooms, S £30, D £48-£62
No smoking in bedrooms or dining room, Closed Xmas, New Year

With the New Forest and the sea right on the doorstep, this elightful Victorian property is well cated for a holiday. Amberwood ands in pretty gardens in a quiet sidential area, and is within walking stance of the attractive town of ngwood. The two bedrooms - an en ite double and a twin with large private bathroom - are equipped with hospitality trays and are carefully maintained. A generous breakfast is served around one large table in the conservatory, and there is also a lounge. The nearby River Avon is a haven for anglers, and various lakes are also close by.

Recommended in the Area

New Forest; Exbury Gardens; Moors Valley Country Park

The Old Cottage ♦♦♦♦

Map ref 3 - SU10
Cowpitts Ln, North Poulner,
RINGWOOD, BH24 3JX
A31 E, 0.75m E of Ringwood left to Hangersley, 1st right, 0.5m to x-rds & over, cottage 100yds on right

T / F 01425 477956
E forestgatewines@btinternet.com

3 rooms, D £56-£70, No smoking, Closed Nov-Dec

RECOMMENDED IN THE AREA

New Forest National Park; Bournemouth & south coast beaches; Salisbury

This 300-year-old thatched cottage stands in a beautiful garden within the peaceful New Forest. The market town of Ringwood is just 1.5 miles away, where you can find a good choice of pubs and restaurants for an evening meal. The cottage is full of character, where original beams and an inglenook fireplace blend with contemporary comforts. Mr and Mrs Theobald are very hospitable, greeting their guests with offers of refreshment. The bedrooms are well equipped - one has a four-poster bed and all have facilities en suite. A freshly cooked breakfast is served in the elegant lounge-dining room.

Greenvale Farm ♦♦♦♦

Map ref 3 - SU32
Melchet Park, Sherfield English,
ROMSEY, SO51 6FS
5m W of Romsey. On S side of A27 through red-brick archway for Melchet Court, Greenvale Farm 150yds on left. Drive to slatted barn & right fork to bungalow

T 01794 884858
W www.greenvalefarm.com

1 room, D £60, No smoking

The well-planned property is on a working farm close to the northern edge of the New Forest. The accommodation is modern and self-contained, and offers spacious twin or double rooms with showers en suite, and plenty of homely extras. Dawn is often heralded by the cock crowing, and eggs from the farm hens feature in the delicious breakfasts, along with bacon from a local farm shop, and honey from New Forest. (The free-range guinea fowl provide an effective guard on the property.) Winchester and Salisbury are within easy reach, as are the amenities of the New Forest, and Mottisfont Abbey is nearby.

RECOMMENDED IN THE AREA

Eling Tide Mill; Florence Nightingale's grave, East Wellow; Hillier Arboretum

Landguard Lodge ♦♦♦♦

Map ref 3 - SU41
21 Landguard Rd, SOUTHAMPTON, SO15 5DL
500yds NW of Southampton Central station. Off A3057 Shirley Rd onto Languard Rd
T 023 8063 6904
F 023 8063 2258
E landguard.lodge@mail.com
W www.landguardlodge.co.uk
10 rooms, S £35, D £55, No smoking in bedrooms or dining room

A friendly welcome awaits you at this comfortable Victorian house set in a quiet sidential area. The family-run Landguard odge offers a variety of smart en suite edrooms, all with shower rooms and plenty of oughtful extras to help you feel at home. A full English breakfast is served in the sunny dining room, and there is also a cosy lounge. This is an ideal base for the city's theatres, shopping centre, university, museums and leisure facilities. The docks, ferry terminals, airport, central railway and coach stations are within easy reach.

Recommended in the Area

The Titanic Trail, Southampton; Sports stadiums; New Forest National Park

---

Dormy House Hotel ♦♦♦♦

Map ref 3 - SU40
21 Barnes Ln, Sarisbury, WARSASH, SO31 7DA
M27 junct 9, A27 W towards Southampton. At Sarisbury Green left onto Barnes Ln, Dormy House 1mile on right
T 01489 572626
F 01489 573370
E dormyhousehotel@warsash.globalnet.co.uk
W www.dormyhousehotel.net
12 rooms, S £52-£58, D £62-£78

Recommended in the Area

ew Forest National Park; Isle of Wight; uthampton Boat Show

Situated not far from the River Hamble and the Solent, this tranquil Victorian house has een tastefully modernised. The pretty garden id patio are enjoyable places on warm days, hile indoors are all the expected comforts. The suite bedrooms come with direct-dial lephones and hospitality trays, and some have pacious seating areas. The rooms on the ground floor have access to the garden, and there is a welcoming lounge and a licensed bar for relaxing. Home-cooked breakfasts in the charming dining room are an appealing start to the day, and Angela Holloway and her hospitable staff offer a friendly service.

Herefordshire

A selection of places to eat from the AA Restaurant & AA Pub guides

Restaurants

Castle House (Creative)
Castle Street, Hereford HR1 2NW
Tel 01432 356321

Royal Oak Hotel (British)
South Street, Leominster HR6 8JA
Tel 01568 612610

The Feathers Hotel (British)
High Street, Ledbury HR8 1DS
Tel 01531 635266

The Lough Pool Inn (European)
Sellack HR9 6LX
Tel 01989 730236

The Stagg Inn & Restaurant (British)
Titley, Kington HR5 3RL
Tel 01544 230221

Three Crowns Inn (British, French)
Ullingswick HR1 3JQ
Tel 01432 820279

Pubs

The Penny Farthing Inn
Aston Crews HR9 7LW
Tel 01989 750366

Riverside Inn & Restaurant
Aymestrey HR6 9ST
Tel 01568 708440

Stockton Cross Inn
Kimbolton HR6 0HD
Tel 01568 612509

Ye Olde Salutation Inn
Market Pitch, Weobley HR4 8SJ
Tel 01544 318443

Saracens Head Inn
Symonds Yat HR9 6JL
Tel 01600 890435

The Moody Cow
Upton Bishop, Ross-on-Wye HR9 7TT
Tel 01989 780470

Tan House Farm ♦♦♦♦

Map ref 2 - SO33
ABBEY DORE, HR2 0AA
A465 onto B4347 to Dore Abbey
T / F 01981 240204
E jppowell@ereal.net
W www.golden-valley.co.uk/tanhouse
3 rooms, S £26, D £52,
No smoking in bedrooms or dining room

A traditional working farm is the setting for this traditional stone building in the heart of the Golden Valley. Expect a warm welcome from owners Glenys and Gerald Powell and their eager collie, who all strive to make you feel at home. The 12th-century Dore Abbey, now the parish church, is next door. Despite its age, Tan House has all modern comforts, and the bedrooms are each equipped with a hairdryer, iron, radio and a hospitality tray. A hearty breakfast is served around a large table i the dining room, where the antique furniture is in keeping with the age of the house.

Recommended in the Area

Hereford; Ross-on-Wye; Abergavenny

Linton Brook Farm ♦♦♦♦

Map ref 2 - SO65

Malvern Rd, Bringsty, BROMYARD, WR6 5TR

Off A44 1.5m E of Bromyard onto B4220 signed Malvern. Farm 0.5m on left

T / F 01885 488875

3 rooms, S £25-£35, D £55-£70, No smoking, Closed Xmas, New Year

Sheila and Roger Steeds not only know the names of their current sitors, they also know who lived here in 285 - their 400-year old farmhouse ands on an ancient site. With such a story behind it, this charming house is ed with atmosphere, fostered by the glenook fireplace and enormous beam the dining room, and wood-burning stove in the sitting room. Bedrooms are spacious and homely. At breakfast, enjoy Sheila's tasty home-smoked food, and afterwards wander through the 68-acre arable farm with access to wonderful scenic walks.

Recommended in the Area

Brockhampton Estate (NT); Elgar Birthplace Museum; Berrington Hall (NT)

Little Hegdon Farm House ♦♦♦♦

Map ref 2 - SO65

Hegdon Hill, Pencombe, BROMYARD, HR7 4SL

Between Pencombe & Risbury, at top of Hegdon Hill down farm lane for 500yds

T 01885 400263

E info@bedandbreakfastherefordshire.co.uk

W www.bedandbreakfastherefordshire.co.uk

2 rooms, S £30, D £50, No smoking in bedrooms or dining room

A 17th-century former farmhouse, Little Hegdon lies in the heart of Herefordshire with clear views over rmland, cider orchards and hop yards to the Malvern nd Cotswold hills. Restored to provide high standards f comfort, the period character of the house survives in e open fires and plenty of exposed oak beams. acilities include a drawing room and attractive garden. here is one double and one twin room, en suite or with private bathroom, and they have hairdryers and tea and coffee facilities. Children and pets are welcome.

Recommended in the Area

Brockhampton Estate (NT); Historic towns of Hereford & Ledbury

The Bowens Country House ♦♦♦♦

Map ref 2 - SO53
FOWNHOPE, HR1 4PS
6m SE of Hereford on B4224. In Fownhope, opp church
T / F 01432 860430
E thebowenshotel@aol.com
W www.thebowenshotel.co.uk
10 rooms, S £38, D £76

This 300-year-old stone house has been altered and extended, but it is still small enough to provide a cosy atmosphere. The owners have preserved the original character, discovering a magnificent inglenook fireplace in the oak-beamed lounge, and reclaiming the old lawn tennis court, which had been lost to a field for 40 years. The house is convenient for the Wye Valley, the Brecons and Malverns, and there is ample car parking. The gardens are beautiful, with mature trees and shrubs. Besides the tennis court, there is a putting green. The en suite bedrooms overlook the gardens and countryside, and come with telephones - four are ground-floor courtyard rooms. Delicious home-made meals are served in the beamed dining room, much of the produce coming from the vegetable garden and greenhouse.

Recommended in the Area

Black and White Village Trail; Mappa Mundi, Hereford Cathedral; Eastnor Castle

The Vauld House Farm ♦♦♦♦

Map ref 2 - SO53
The Vauld, Marden, HEREFORD, HR1 3HA
6m N of Hereford. Off A49 onto A417, right at Englands Gate Inn, Bodenham. 2m turn right for The Vauld and Litmarsh, at junct farm opp
T 01568 797347
F 01568 797366
E wellsthevauld@talk21.com
2 rooms, S £38, D £58, No smoking
Closed Dec-Feb

Vauld House is set in beautifully landscaped grounds with ponds, a moat and wooded gardens, beyond which is the family-run stock farm and the hamlet of The Vauld. Guests have their own comfortable lounge with open log fire and television. The spacious en suite bedrooms retain many original features and are thoughtfully equipped. Start the day with a full traditional breakfast served family style in the beamed dining room overlooking the gardens. Light suppers are available or book an imaginatively cooked four-course dinner using local seasonal produce - it may even include some home-reared Herefordshire beef.

Recommended in the Area

Hampton Court Gardens; Hereford Cathedral; Broadfield Vineyard, Bodenha

Ford Abbey ♦♦♦♦♦

Map ref 2 - SO45
Pudleston, LEOMINSTER, HR6 0RZ
A44 Leominster towards Worcester, turn left to Pudleston

T 01568 760700
F 01568 760264
E info@fordabbey.co.uk
W www.fordabbey.co.uk

6 rooms, No smoking in bedrooms or dining room

‹ECOMMENDED IN THE AREA

roft Castle (NT); Hergest Croft Gardens; errington Hall (NT)

A n absolutely stunning guesthouse where quality, character and comfort are present spades. It nestles in a sheltered valley ırrounded by 320 acres, and was once the roperty of Benedictine monks. Drafty corridors ıd spartan sleeping arrangements have given ay to pure luxury, with blazing log fires and elicious food for the lucky traveller. Weathered one, timber ceilings and inglenook fireplaces e found in the comfortable drawing room and osy study, and the farmhouse kitchen is the scene of wonderful breakfasts and dinners. Across the courtyard, the converted farm buildings house four self-catering units and an indoor swimming pool complex. In the main house, six luxury suites have stylish bathrooms and every conceivable comfort. One suite is on the ground floor for ease of access, and the landscaped gardens beyond are delightful for strolling in at any time. For a romantic weekend or a complete break, this place is hard to beat.

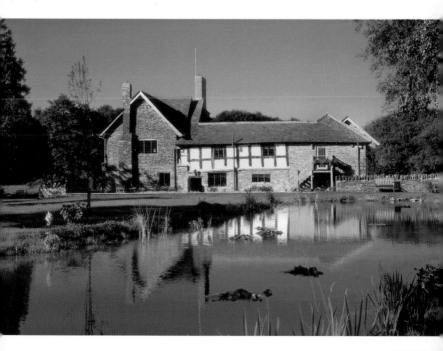

Moccas Court ♦♦♦♦♦

Map ref 2 - SO34
MOCCAS, HR2 9LH
T 01981 500019 &
F 01981 500095
E bencmaster@aol.com
W www.moccas-court.co.uk
5 rooms, S £116-£156, D £145-£195, No smoking

RECOMMENDED IN THE AREA

Hay on Wye; Black Mountains; Brecon Beacons National Park

Dwell in the lap of luxury looked after by charming and genial hosts. If you are seeking a unique and memorable bed and breakfast need look no further than this grand Georgian house perched above the River Wye. The country house has such historic interest that it is open to the public. If a little imposing outside, the atmosphere inside is warm and welcoming, and family portraits and restrained furnishings echo the period style of the house. The generous size en suite bedrooms each have their own appeal and extraordinary vistas over the grounds. The largest room, often chosen by honeymooners, includes a dramatic oak armoire and contemporary works of art. You are welcome to use the sitting room that overlooks the gardens and pre-dinner drinks ar offered in the elegant library. Not be missed is the delicious dinner round a large circular table in the splendid candlelit dining room.

Cwm Craig Farm ♦♦♦♦

Map ref 2 - SO53
LITTLE DEWCHURCH, HR2 6PS
Off A49 into Little Dewchurch, turn right in village, Cwm Craig 1st farm on left
T / F 01432 840250
3 rooms, S £22-£23, D £44-£45, No smoking

Cwm Craig Farm is midway between Hereford and Ross-on-Wye and stands on the edge of a village ırrounded by superb countryside. The Georgian ·operty retains many original features and offers ›acious accommodation furnished with fine period eces. The bedrooms are all en suite and include two ›ubles and a family room. Guests have access to their oms all day, and hospitality trays are provided. Home-›oked breakfasts are served in the dining room and morning room around large tables, and you can relax in the sitting room or the games room with its three-quarter-size snooker/pool table and dartboard. Pets cannot be accommodated.

Recommended in the Area

Hereford Cathedral & city; Forest of Dean; Wye Valley

The Bridge House ♦♦♦♦

Map ref 2 - SO52
Wilton, ROSS-ON-WYE, HR9 6AA
Off junct A40 & A49 into Ross, 300yds on left
T 01989 562655
F 01989 567652
E info@bridge-house-hotel.com
W www.bridge-house-hotel.com
9 rooms, S £65-£110, D £96-£120, No smoking in bedrooms or dining room

Recommended in the Area

›ss-on-Wye; Symonds Yat; Forest of Dean

Built in about 1740, this elegant house Georgian house stands ›side the River Wye and just a stroll ›ross the bridge from delightful Ross-ı-Wye. Since acquiring Bridge House 2003, Mike and Jane Pritchard have eated an establishment with real ıaracter and contemporary design. ·andards are impressive and the bedrooms offer ample space, comfort and genuine quality. Period features in the public areas add to the stylish ambience. The partially walled gardens run down to the river and the vegetables and herbs grown here are used by the top class chef. The highly acclaimed restaurant serves accomplished cuisine with tempting dishes such as Welsh salt-marsh lamb with aubergine and tomato timbale and fondant potato.

Brookfield House ♦♦♦♦

Map ref 2 - SO52
Over Ross St, ROSS-ON-WYE, HR9 7AT
Junct A40 & A449 onto B4234 Ledbury Rd, 0.5m left onto Brookmead & up driveway
T 01989 562188
W www.brookfield-house.co.uk
3 rooms, D £54-£64, No smoking

Dating from the 18th century, detached Brookfield House stands in a perfect position just north of Ross town but close to splendid countryside. Owners Maggie and Ken decided to take a slower pace of life after many years of working in the antique costume business. Refurbished to a high standard throughout with impressive housekeeping, the spacious en suite bedrooms have king-size beds and courtesy trays. Breakfast is served in a light and airy dining room. A relaxing lounge is available as are the attractive gardens.

RECOMMENDED IN THE AREA
Symonds Yat; Royal Forest of Dean; Hereford Cathedral

Lumleys ♦♦♦♦

Map ref 2 - SO52
Kern Bridge, Bishopswood, ROSS-ON-WYE, HR9 5QT
Off A40 onto B4229 at Goodrich, over Kern Bridge, right at Inn On The Wye, 400yds opp picnic ground
T 01600 890040
F 0870 7062378
E helen@lumleys.force9.co.uk
W www.lumleys.force9.co.uk/
3 rooms, D £60-£70, No smoking

RECOMMENDED IN THE AREA
Symonds Yat; Forest of Dean; Goodrich Castle

A former Victorian roadside hostelry, Lumleys has been transformed into a quality modern guesthouse while retaining much of its original character. The house is situated south of the historic town, on the banks of the River Wye, in an Area of Outstanding Natural Beauty. From Lumleys you can see Goodrich Castle, with Symonds Yat and the Royal Forest of Dean not far away. The en suite bedrooms have plenty of thoughtful extras, and there are some fine period pieces and ornaments in the public areas, all in keeping with the style of the propert[y]. Helen Mattis and Judith Hayworth are caring hosts, who will welcome you to their home with justifiable pride.

Thatch Close ♦♦♦♦

Map ref 2 - SO52
Llangrove, ROSS-ON-WYE,
HR9 6EL
Off A40 at Symonds Yat West/Whitchurch junction into Llangrove (1.9m), right at x-rds after Post Office, Thatch Close 0.6m on left

Ⓣ 01989 770300
Ⓔ info@thatchclose.co.uk
Ⓦ www.thatchclose.com

3 rooms, S £32-£37.50, D £50-£60, No smoking

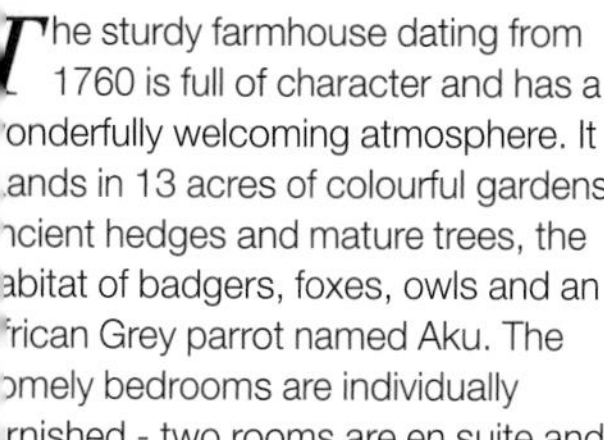

The sturdy farmhouse dating from 1760 is full of character and has a 'onderfully welcoming atmosphere. It .ands in 13 acres of colourful gardens, ıcient hedges and mature trees, the abitat of badgers, foxes, owls and an rican Grey parrot named Aku. The omely bedrooms are individually rnished - two rooms are en suite and one has a private bathroom. A wholesome breakfast and dinner are served in the regal dining room, and the leather sofas in the lounge are a pleasant place to retire after dinner. The extensive patios and gardens are popular in summer, providing plenty of space to find a quiet corner with a good book.

RECOMMENDED IN THE AREA
Symonds Yat; Forest of Dean; Monmouth

Trecilla Farm ♦♦♦♦♦

Map ref 2 - SO52
Llangarron, ROSS-ON-WYE,
HR9 6NQ
A40 onto A4137 to Hereford. 2m x-rds, left signed Llangarron. 1m Llangarron sign, Trecilla Farm 2nd drive on right

Ⓣ 01989 770647
Ⓔ info@trecillafarm.co.uk
Ⓦ www.trecillafarm.co.uk

3 rooms, S £40-£45, D £57-£80, No smoking, Closed 23 Dec-2 Jan

Dating from the 16th century, this lovely farmhouse lies in a rural location close to Ross on Wye. It ızes character with exposed beams and an inglenook eplace, and stands in picturesque gardens with a ring-fed stream. Excellent breakfasts feature home-own and local produce including home-made eserves, and are served in the elegant dining room. e spacious en suite bedrooms are furnished with fine riod pieces including a four-poster bed. Fishing is available on nearby Garron Brook. Other facilities include a garden hideaway complete with snooker table. No children under 13.

RECOMMENDED IN THE AREA
Symonds Yat; Wye Valley; Forest of Dean

Norton House ♦♦♦♦

Map ref 2 - SO51
Whitchurch, Symonds Yat,
SYMONDS YAT (WEST), HR9 6DJ
0.5m N of Symonds Yat. Off A40 into Whitchurch village

T 01600 890046
F 01600 890045
E su@norton.wyenet.co.uk
W www.norton-house.com

3 rooms, S £40-£45, D £56-£72, No smoking, Closed 25-Dec

Originally a farmhouse dating back 300 years, the wealth of character here is evident in the locally quarried stone walls, flagstone floors and oak beams. Hospitality is a notable feature, and traditional English, vegetarian and continental, along with a choice of speciality breakfasts are offered. Guests sit at a mahogany table in the dining room full of curios, with a fine old dresser and inglenook fireplace. Evening meals are available, served by candlelight and oil lamp.

Bedrooms, including one four-poster room, are all en suite, with hot drinks and mineral water, patchwork quilts, crisp cotton sheets, fluffy white towels and fresh flowers. No children under 12. Dogs welcome by arrangement.

RECOMMENDED IN THE AREA

Symonds Yat; Forest of Dean; Hereford & Hay-on-Wye

Isle of Wight

A selection of places to eat from the AA Restaurant & AA Pub guides

Restaurants

Windmill Inn Hotel (British)
1 Steyne Road, Bembridge PO35 5UH
Tel 01983 875806

Farringford (International)
Bedbury Lane, Freshwater PO40 9TQ
Tel 01983 752500

Priory Bay Hotel (French)
Priory Drive, Seaview PO34 5BU
Tel 01983 613146

The Royal Hotel (British, French)
Belgrave Road, Ventnor PO38 1JJ
Tel 01983 852186

George Hotel (European)
Quay Street, Yarmouth PO41 0PE
Tel 01983 760331

Pubs

The Crab & Lobster Inn
32 Foreland Fields Road,
Bembridge PO35 5TR, Tel 01983 872244

The Folly
Folly Lane, Cowes PO32 6NB
Tel 01983 297171

The Red Lion
Church Place, Freshwater PO40 9BP
Tel 01983 754925

Seaview Hotel & Restaurant
High Street, Seaview PO34 5EX
Tel 01983 612711

The New Inn
Mill Lane, Shalfleet PO30 4NS
Tel 01983 531314

The Spyglass Inn
The Esplanade, Ventnor PO38 1JX
Tel 01983 855338

Chale Bay Farm ♦♦♦♦♦

Map ref 3 - SZ47
Military Rd, CHALE, PO38 2JF
By A3055 Military Rd in Chale, near St Andrew's Church

Ⓣ 01983 730950
Ⓕ 01983 730395
Ⓔ info@chalebayfarm.co.uk
Ⓦ www.chalebayfarm.co.uk

8 rooms

Situated on National Trust coastline with uninterrupted views of the Needles and Tennyson Downs, Chale Bay Farm is a tranquil place to unwind. The spacious bedrooms are all on the ground floor, around a courtyard with a floodlit Japanese-style water garden. The rooms are all en suite with king-size beds, and are equipped to a high standard including tea and coffee facilities, hairdryers, and several have their own private patio. Before setting off to explore the island, enjoy a hearty home-cooked breakfast, served at individual tables dressed with fresh flowers in the pleasant dining room.

Recommended in the Area

Blackgang Chine; Freshwater Bay; Dinosaur Farm

The Old House ♦♦♦♦

Map ref 3 - SZ47
Gotten Manor, Gotten Ln, CHALE, PO38 2HQ
1m N of Chale. Off B3399 onto Gotten Ln (opp chapel), house at end

Ⓣ 01983 551368
Ⓔ aa@gottenmanor.co.uk
Ⓦ www.gottenmanor.co.uk

2 rooms, S £50-£60, D £60-£80, No smoking

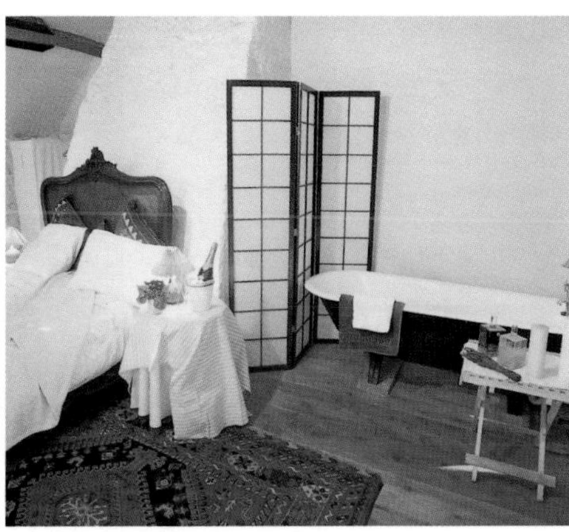

Part of Gotten Manor, this self-contained annexe was first mentioned in 1305 as 'a Hall, a Grange, an Oxstall with half an acre of garden, a Dovecote with 30 acres of arable and 10 acres of pasture'. Both of the double bedrooms are traditionally decorated with lime-washed walls and wooden floors and each has a huge cast-iron bath within the room - a television is optional. Downstairs there is a spacious lounge with an open fire, and a cosy dining room where comprehensive breakfasts using the finest ingredients are served. There is also a peaceful walled garden.

Recommended in the Area

Dimbola Lodge; Osborne House; Freshwater Bay

Braunstone House Hotel ♦♦♦♦

Map ref 3 - SZ58
33 Lugley St, NEWPORT, PO30 5ET
T 01983 822994
F 01983 522071
E lugleys@aol.com
W www.isleofwight.com
5 rooms, S £65-£80, D £70-£95, No smoking in bedrooms or dining room

The renovation of this Grade II listed building, just a stone's throw from Newport centre, has carefully retained its original Georgian charm. The dedicated staff do an excellent job, and the elegant, good-size bedrooms have individual character and many extras. The building houses a popular brasserie, Lugley's, where Flagstone floors and a modern aspect set the scene for tasty, well-prepared meals - there's a bar lounge where you can sit while you make your choice. In summer meals can be served in the sheltered gardens.

RECOMMENDED IN THE AREA
Carisbrooke Castle; Robin Hill; Osborne House

Bedford Lodge Hotel ♦♦♦♦

Map ref 3 - SZ58
4 Chine Av, SHANKLIN, PO37 6AQ
A3055 from Sandown. At lights take Queens Rd to end. Right onto Chine Av, hotel opp Tower Cottage Gardens
T 01983 862416
F 01983 868704
E aa@bedfordlodge.co.uk
W www.bedfordlodge.co.uk
12 rooms, D £50-£70, Closed Jan

The Lodge Hotel stands proud over sloping lawns, mature trees and flowering shrubs, a secluded haven on a sunny elevated spot. A licensed bar and breakfast room on the first floor lead to the lounge, gardens and sun terrace where you can enjoy a drink and the fine views. All bedrooms are en suite, and are equipped with modern amenities and comfy duvets on the beds. The lodge is in the enchanting village of old Shanklin, an ideal place to relax in a pretty tea room or a traditional coaching inn. Ferry crossings can be arranged by the hotel.

RECOMMENDED IN THE AREA
Ventnor; Sandown; Godshill

*B*elmont Hotel ♦♦♦♦

Map ref 3 - SZ58
8 Queens Rd, SHANKLIN,
PO37 6AN
From Sandown half left at Five Ways lights signed Ventnor, 0.25m on right opp St Saviour's Church

Ⓣ 01983 867875
Ⓔ enquiries@belmont-iow.co.uk
Ⓦ www.belmont-iow.co.uk

13 rooms, S £27-£61, D £50-£82, No smoking in bedrooms or dining room, Closed Nov-Feb

The Belmont is an imposing Victorian residence offering friendly personal ervice and a relaxing atmosphere close the pretty thatched old village, nanklin Chine and the beach. The ecluded garden is an attractive suntrap th a heated swimming pool available om late May to early September, and e colonial style-veranda is another elightful spot to catch the sun. Indoors u can unwind in the cosy lounge and well-stocked bar. The bedrooms mostly face the sea or the garden and are well equipped, some having king-size or four-poster beds. Full English or continental breakfasts are served in the elegant dining room.

RECOMMENDED IN THE AREA

Shanklin old village; Osborne House; The Needles

Clifton Hotel ♦♦♦♦

Map ref 3 - SZ58
1 Queens Rd, SHANKLIN,
PO37 6AN
Off A3055 at lights, signed to the beach. Bear left signed Ventnor onto Queens Rd

Ⓣ 01983 863015
Ⓕ 01983 865911
Ⓦ www.hotelclifton.co.uk

17 rooms, S £31.50-£40, D £63-£80, No smoking, Closed Jan

RECOMMENDED IN THE AREA

Shanklin old village; Shanklin Chine; Botanic Gardens, Ventnor

A family-run hotel with stunning views over Sandown Bay, the Clifton stands in grounds in the peaceful ation of Keats Green, one of the Isle of Wight's most autiful cliff-top areas. The smart bedrooms, many h a sea view and some with access to a balcony, me equipped with tea, coffee and chocolate drink ilities. Good home cooking is a highlight and local nd ingredients are used whenever possible. Meals served in the pretty blue and white dining room. Special diets are catered for, and organic and Fairtrade produce are used. For a relaxing drink try the panelled bar with local beer, soft drinks and good wines. Children over five welcome.

*F*oxhills ♦♦♦♦♦

Map ref 3 - SZ58
30 Victoria Av, SHANKLIN, PO37 6LS
A3020 from Shanklin centre towards Newport, Foxhills 450yds on left

T 01983 862329
F 01983 866666
E info@foxhillshotel.co.uk
W www.foxhillshotel.co.uk

8 rooms, S £45-£90, D £90-£100,
No smoking, Closed 3-31 Jan

Recommended in the area

Shanklin Chine; Rhylstone Gardens; Osborne House

Every effort is made to pamper guests at this superbly refurbished establishment. It is set in beautiful gardens just a short walk from Shanklin Chine and the town centre. Hospitality is exemplary, and you are welcomed with tea and chocolates on arrival. There are high levels of comfort in the en suite bedrooms, where DVD and CD players, direct-dial telephones and modem, hairdryers and refreshment trays are all provided. A four-poster suite has a touch of modernised Victorian luxury. Bathrooms are beautifully fitted with quality units, and furnished with luxury towels, dressing gowns and toiletries. A whirlpool bath and beauty treatments are relaxing options, or else take a drink or afternoon tea in front of the log fire. Guests can use a neighbouring swimming poc sauna and a gym for a small additional cost. There is also as much tourist and other information as you need.

St Brelades Hotel ♦♦♦♦

Map ref 3 - SZ58
15 Hope Rd, SHANKLIN, PO37 6EA
A3055 into Shanklin, left onto Hope Rd signed Esplanade, 1st hotel on right

T 01983 862967
E info@st-brelades-hotel.co.uk
W www.st-brelades-hotel.co.uk

15 rooms, S £27-£28, D £50-£54, No smoking in rooms

A warm welcome is assured at this delightful family-run hotel located thin easy walking distance of safe ›lden beaches, cliff top walks and ›anklin town centre. Paul and Julie ındborg offer a high standard of ›eanliness and comfort combined with ›od food and excellent service. The ›sy bedrooms are brightly decorated ›d equipped with tea and coffee ›cilities, complimentary toiletries and ›her attentive touches. There is a lounge and bar with a range of beers, spirits, wines, liqueurs and soft drinks, and tasty evening meals are available by arrangement. Children are especially welcomed here and there is a good selection of child-friendly meals.

Recommended in the Area

Shanklin old village; Shanklin Chine; Osborne House

The Hoo ♦♦♦♦

Map ref 3 - SZ38
Colwell Rd, TOTLAND BAY, PO39 0AB
From Yarmouth ferry right onto A3054, 2.25m enter Colwell Common, The Hoo on corner Colwell & Warden Rd

T 01983 753592
F 01983 753973
E jerjohnston@btinternet.com
W www.thehoo.co.uk

3 rooms, S £26.50-£52.50, D £40-£70, No smoking in bedrooms or dining room, Closed 18 Dec-23 Mar

This elegant Victorian property is just a short walk from the beach at Colwell Bay. Much of the original ›aracter has been retained to complement the ›dern accommodation. The very comfortable ›drooms are equipped with minibars, hospitality trays ›d hairdryers, and are bright and attractive. Two ›drooms share a private bathroom, and are ideal for a ›ily or friends. Freshly cooked quality local produce, ›uding farm eggs, sausages and smoked salmon, with freshly squeezed orange juice, makes breakfast a pleasure. The colourful well-kept gardens give a charming first impression.

Recommended in the Area

The Needles; Yarmouth Castle; Freshwater Bay

The Old Rectory ♦♦♦♦

Map ref 3 - SZ57
Ashknowle Ln, Whitwell, VENTNOR
PO38 2PP
Next to church at S end of Whitwell
T 01983 731242
E rectory@ukonline.co.uk
W www.wightonline.co.uk/oldrectory
3 rooms, S £35-£40, D £65-£72, No smoking

Formerly a rectory and a popular youth hostel, but this stone country house is now firmly established as a guesthouse. Beautifully restored with its Victorian character carefully preserved by the present owners, it offers spacious en suite bedrooms with traditional and antique furniture. Modern comforts include a fridge, toaster and hairdryer, and laundry facilities are available.Tasty, well-presented breakfasts are served in the elegant dining room, and there is also a bright, lofty sitting room and a large garden with su beds and garden furniture.

RECOMMENDED IN THE AREA
Ventnor Botanic Gardens; Isle of Wight Glass Studio; Osborne House

Kent

A selection of places to eat from the AA Restaurant & AA Pub guide

Restaurants

The Dove Inn (European)
Plum Pudding Lane, Dargate, Canterbury ME13 9HB, Tel 01227 751360

Sandgate Hotel (International)
The Esplanade, Sandgate, Folkestone CT20 3DY, Tel 01303 220444

Read's Restaurant (British)
Macknade Manor, Canterbury Road, Faversham ME13 8XE, Tel 01795 535344

Crab & Winkle Seafood Restaurant
South Quay, The Harbour, Whitstable CT15 1AB, Tel 01227 779377

Soufflé Restaurant (European)
The Green, Bearsted ME14 4DN
Tel 01622 737065

Thackeray's (Modern French)
Tunbridge Wells (Royal) TN1 1EA
Tel 01892 511921

Pubs

The Bottle House Inn
Coldharbour Road, Penshurst, Tonbridge TN11 8ET, Tel 01892 870306

Castle Inn
Chiddingstone TN8 7AH, Tel 01892 87024

Red Lion
The Green, Hernhill ME13 9JR
Tel 01227 751207

The Ringlestone Inn
Ringlestone Hamlet, near Harrietsham, Maidstone ME17 1NX, Tel 01622 859900

The Star & Eagle Hotel
High Street, Goudhurst TN17 1AL
Tel 01580 211512

Chislet Court Farm ♦♦♦♦

Map ref 4 - TR15
Chislet, CANTERBURY, CT3 4DU
Off A28 in Upstreet, farm on right 200yds past church
T 01227 860309
F 01227 860444
E chisletcourtfarm@dial.pipex.com
W www.chisletcourtfarm.com
2 rooms, S £40-£42.50, D £65-£70, No smoking, Closed Xmas

Chislet Court is an 800-acre arable farm with a substantial farmhouse built in the 18th century on medieval foundations. It is set in mature gardens overlooking the village church, a three-kiln oast house and surrounding countryside, just 6 miles east of Canterbury. Accommodation is provided in two spacious en suite double bedrooms, both with modern bath and shower rooms, and tea and coffee facilities. You are welcome to wander in the garden and relax in the conservatory dining room, where breakfast is served. There is a good choice of pubs and restaurants in the area for lunch and dinner. Guests are asked not to smoke in the house.

RECOMMENDED IN THE AREA
Canterbury Cathedral; Sandwich; Howletts Zoo Park

Magnolia House ♦♦♦♦♦

Map ref 4 - TR15
36 St Dunstan's Ter, CANTERBURY, CT2 8AX
A2 E onto A2050 for city centre, 1st rdbt left signed University of Kent, St Dunstan's Ter 3rd right
T / F 01227 765121
E info@magnoliahousecanterbury.co.uk
W www.magnoliahousecanterbury.co.uk
7 rooms, S £60-£65, D £95-£135, No smoking

This attractive Georgian house stands in a quiet residential street just a short walk from the city centre. The property is beautifully maintained and exudes hospitality, making it highly desirable for a holiday or short break. The bedrooms are equipped with plenty of useful features, including a fridge, and guests are provided with their own key. A cosy lounge looks across the front garden, while the dining room looks onto the stunning walled garden at the rear. Delicious evening meals are served by arrangement, and in the morning breakfast is a special treat, with plenty of choice on offer.

RECOMMENDED IN THE AREA
Canterbury Cathedral; St Augustine's Abbey; Canterbury Tales Museum

Waterside Guest House ♦♦♦♦

Map ref 4 - TR12
15 Hythe Rd, DYMCHURCH,
TN29 0LN
On A259 4m SW of Hythe near Dymchurch
T / F 01303 872253
E info@watersideguesthouse.co.u
W www.watersideguesthouse.co.u
5 rooms, S £32-£37, D £45-£55,
No smoking

As the name suggests, this charming house stands on the banks on a quiet stretch of water, beyond which are marshes as far as the eye can see. Proprietor Sharon Tinklin and family are keen gardeners, growing most of their own vegetables and fruit, while supporting local suppliers for the remainder of their needs. Meals are served in the cottage-style dining room or on the waterside terrace, and include English breakfast (or lighter alternative), afternoon tea, and dinner from a varied menu of Kentish fare. A choice single, twin, double or family rooms is available, all en suite with clock radios, and you can relax in the lounge or oak beamed bar.

RECOMMENDED IN THE ARE

Romney, Hythe & Dymchurch Railway; Port Lympne Animal Park; Dover Castle White Cliffs

---

Beesfield Farm ♦♦♦♦♦

Map ref 4 - TQ56
Beesfield Ln, FARNINGHAM,
DA4 0LA
From village centre S onto Beesfield Ln, farm 0.5m on left
T / F 01322 863900
E kim.vingoe@btinternet.com
W www.beesfieldfarm.co.uk
3 rooms, S £70-£80, D £90,
No smoking, Closed 8 Dec-Jan

Bee-keeping has been revived at this working farm, and honey can be purchased in season. You are invited to join in the fun and count the number of bee motifs found throughout this lovely house. Doug and Kim Vingoe's farm is part arable and part dairy, but Doug's extensive record collection is more likely to engage the attention of guests. The attractive house is set in mature gardens and surrounded by open farmland yet close to major roads. Bedrooms are beautifully presented and fitted with many thoughtful touches for a homely stay. Bathrooms too are luxurious and well appointed, with quality towels. The rich furnishing in the stylish lounge make for an irresistible retreat, an really satisfying breakfasts are served from a wide choice at one large polished table in the dining room.

RECOMMENDED IN THE AREA

Bluewater Shopping Mall; Brands Hatch; Eagle Heights Birds of Prey

Yaldings ♦♦♦♦

lap ref 4 - TR06
taplestreet Rd, Goodnestone,
AVERSHAM, ME13 9HT
*'2 junct 7, A299, 0.25m left, on
orner on right*
01795 538680
yaldings@btinternet.com
www.yaldingsguesthouse.com
rooms, S £45-£55, D £65-£75,
o smoking

aldings is an elegant and spacious house located in peaceful ntryside and is well placed for loring Kent. It is also convenient as a o over to and from the continent or Kent International Airport. The house been refurbished to a very high ndard. Bedrooms vary in size, but all attractively furnished and have tea coffee facilities. An Aga-cooked breakfast or continental breakfast is served around a communal dining table and newspapers are provided. A self-catering cottage is also available in the grounds. There is ample secure parking for cars, boats and bicycles.

RECOMMENDED IN THE AREA
Faversham; Whitstable Bay; Leeds Castle

Hotel Relish ♦♦♦♦♦

lap ref 4 - TR23
Augusta Gardens, FOLKESTONE,
T20 2RR
ff A2033 Sandgate Rd
01303 850952
01303 850958
reservations@hotelrelish.co.uk
www.hotelrelish.co.uk
rooms, S £55-£120, D £79-£130,
o smoking, Closed 24 Dec-2 Jan

ou will get a warm welcome from Andrew and Michael at this stylish orian terrace property, which rlooks Augusta Gardens in the ionable West End of town. The erior has been restored to the original od style and the interior beautifully sented and stylishly decorated. On val you will be greeted with a nplimentary glass of wine or beer, unlimited fresh coffee and tea and ne-made cakes are available during stay. The bedrooms feature geous contemporary wood furniture, ly coordinated fabrics and added touches like DVD players, free Broadband access, crisp white linen and sumptuous towels. Public rooms include a modern lounge-dining room, and a sun terrace where breakfast is served in the summer.

RECOMMENDED IN THE AREA
Dover Castle; Romney, Hythe and Dymchurch Railway; Canterbury Cathedral

Seabrook House ♦♦♦♦

Map ref 4 - TR13
81 Seabrook Rd, HYTHE,
CT21 5QW
0.9m E of Hythe on A259

T 01303 269282
F 01303 237822
E info@seabrook-house.co.uk
W www.seabrook-house.co.uk

13 rooms, S £35-£45, D £60-£75, No smoking in bedrooms or dining room

The striking Victorian property is recognised by the heavily timber-framed frontage and pretty gardens. Handy for the M20 and Eurotunnel, it is also close to beach, and many of the art-deco style bedrooms have lovely sea views. These spacious en suite rooms, with their attractive decor and furnishings, also have hospitality trays and hairdryers. A memorable full English breakfast s you up for the ferry or sightseeing, and there are ple of comfortable places for relaxation, including a sun conservatory and an elegant lounge.

RECOMMENDED IN THE AREA

Romney, Hythe & Dymchurch Railway; Dover Castle; Port Lympne Animal Park

---

The Black Horse Inn ♦♦♦♦

Map ref 4 - TQ75
Pilgrims Way, Thurnham,
MAIDSTONE, ME14 3LD
M20 junct 7, N onto A249. Right i Detling, opp pub onto Pilgrims Wa for 1m

T 01622 737185
F 01622 739170
E wellie.boot@virgin.net
W www.wellieboot.net/home_blackhorse.htm

6 rooms, S £50-£60, D £70-£80, No smoking in bedrooms

Tucked beneath the steep face of the North Downs on the Pilgrims Way, this 17th-century inn has public areas adorned with hops, oak beams, exposed brickwork and open fireplaces. The thoughtfully equipped bedrooms are in a timber-clad annex in a courtyard behind the premises, and each room is stylishly furnished with wood-laminate floors and well-chosen furnishings. The inn's popular restaurant is open all day, and is candlelit in the evening - it serves very good food using local produce. On th doorstep is a network of footpaths popular with walkers and cyclists, an bikes can be hired.

RECOMMENDED IN THE AR

Leeds Castle; Huckling Woodland Trus Estate; Museum of Kent Life

Joldings ♦♦♦♦♦

lap ref 4 - TQ75
:lphicks Farm, Hunton,
/AIDSTONE, ME15 0SG
m SW of Maidstone. A229 W onto 32163 through Coxheath, 1st left to Hunton, pass church & school, left onto driveway
01622 820758
01622 820754
goldingsoast@btconnect.com
www.goldingsoast.co.uk
3 rooms, D £65-£80, No smoking, Closed 21 Dec-12 Jan

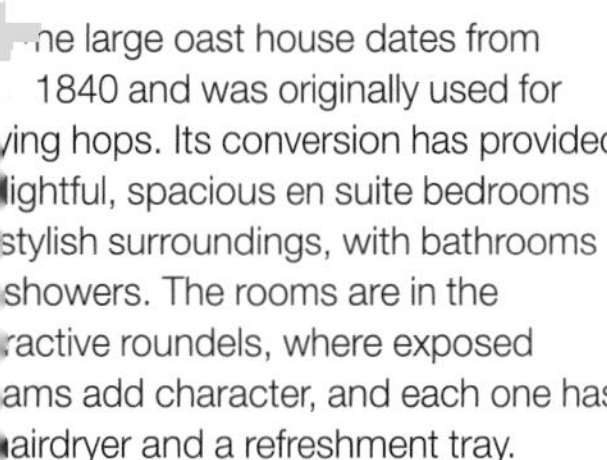

ne large oast house dates from 1840 and was originally used for ying hops. Its conversion has provided lightful, spacious en suite bedrooms stylish surroundings, with bathrooms showers. The rooms are in the ractive roundels, where exposed ams add character, and each one has airdryer and a refreshment tray.

Simon Day was born here and still farms the 180 acres of fruit, arable and pasture. He and his wife Liz are welcoming owners who can direct guests to local walks, places of interest, and good local pubs and restaurants. Breakfast is a tasty treat.

RECOMMENDED IN THE AREA
Sissinghurst Castle Garden (NT); Yalding Organic Gardens; Penshurst Place

---

Langley Oast ♦♦♦♦

Map ref 4 - TQ75
Langley Park, Langley,
MAIDSTONE, ME17 3NQ
2.5m SE of Maidstone off A274. After Parkwood Business Estate lane signed Maidstone Golf Centre
T / F 01622 863523
E margaret@langleyoast.freeserve.co.uk
3 rooms, S £35-£50, D £50-£85, No smoking, Closed Xmas

short drive from Maidstone, this traditional Kentish oast house has lovely views over surrounding fields d a swan lake. Margaret and Peter Clifford have erseen an elegant conversion of the traditional rking buildings. Two spacious bedrooms are in the indels, each 24 feet in diameter, one with a Jacuzzi d the other with a shower room. Two twin rooms are o available with half-tester canopies. All rooms have and coffee facilities. A full English breakfast is served in the roundel dining room around one large table.

RECOMMENDED IN THE AREA
Leeds Castle; The Hop Farm Country Park; Sissinghurst Castle Garden (NT)

Ringlestone House ♦♦♦♦♦

Map ref 4 - TQ75
Ringlestone Hamlet, Harrietsham, MAIDSTONE, ME17 1NX
M20 junct 8, A20, at rdbt opp Ramada Hotel left to Hollingbourne, through village, right at x-rds at top of hill

T 01622 859911
F 01622 859740
E bookings@ringlestone.com
W www.ringlestone.com

3 rooms, S £89-£120, D £99-£120, No smoking in bedrooms, Closed 25-Dec

Oozing charm and history, the Ringlestone was once a hospice for monks before becoming an alehouse in 1615. Hospitality comes naturally to the present owners, the extended Millington-Buck family, who bring a wide range of skills to the business. Candlelit suppers, hot and cold lunch menus, and Sunday roasts can all be enjoyed here, surrounded by old brick and flint walls, inglenooks and antiques. Across the road, the converted farmhouse provides three bedrooms, one with a four-poste bed, and all with spacious bathrooms suite. Lots of thoughtful extras help to make a stay here memorable.

RECOMMENDED IN THE ARE
Leeds Castle; Cobtree Museum of Kent Life; Canterbury Cathedral

---

Merzie Meadows ♦♦♦♦♦

Map ref 4 - TQ74
Hunton Rd, MARDEN, TN12 9SL
A229 onto B2079 for Marden, 1st right onto Underlyn Ln, 2.5m Large Chainhurst sign, right onto drive

T / F 01622 820500
E pamela.mumford@onetel.net
W www.smoothhound.co.uk/hotels/merzie.html

2 rooms, S £60, D £65-£75, No smoking, Closed mid Dec-mid Feb

Merzie Meadows is set in 20 acres of lovely mature gardens in the Kent countryside. The grounds are made up of conservation areas for wildlife, woodland, and an environment for waterfowl. This peaceful setting is ideal relaxing after visiting nearby attractions, including several famous historic houses. The generously proportioned bedrooms are housed in two wings, which overlook a terrace with a swimming pool. The ground-floor location makes for easy access, and one room is a suite wit its own terrace. The rooms are carefully decorated and furnished, and are well equipped. The attractive breakfast room has an Italian tiled floor and superb views of the garde

RECOMMENDED IN THE AREA
Sissinghurst Castle Garden (NT); Leeds Castle; The Hop Farm Country Park

Danehurst House ♦♦♦♦♦

Map ref 4 - TQ53
1 Lower Green Rd, Rusthall,
TUNBRIDGE WELLS (ROYAL),
TN4 8TW
1.5m W of Tunbridge Wells in Rusthall. Off A264 onto Coach Rd & Lower Green Rd
T 01892 527739
F 01892 514804
E info@danehurst.net
W www.danehurst.net
4 rooms, S £45-£65, D £75-£89.50, No smoking, Closed Xmas, last week Aug

Angela and Michael Godbold's spacious Victorian home stands just west of the historic spa town of Tunbridge Wells. The lovely garden has a waterfall and koi swim happily in the pond, while flair in both decor and furnishings enhance the house's intrinsic charm. There is a baby grand piano in the drawing room, and the Victorian-style conservatory is a delightful setting for breakfast, whether full English, fish, cold meats or continental. The four cosy bedrooms are en suite, and have a wealth of thoughtful extras and notably comfortable beds. Private parking is available. No children under eight, and no pets.

Recommended in the Area

Groombridge Place; Hever Castle; Chartwell (NT)

The Chequers Inn ♦♦♦♦

Map ref 4 - TQ84
The Street, SMARDEN, TN27 8QA
On main street next to church
T 01233 770217
F 01233 770623
E jan-mich@supernet.co.uk
4 rooms, No smoking in bedrooms or dining room

The Chequers, only 40 minutes from the Eurotunnel terminal, stands next to the historic parish church in Smarden, a pretty village in the heart of Kent. The charming 16th-century or older inn offers comfortable accommodation with modern facilities en suite, while retaining the original character. Meals are a highlight, with a daily changing and varied menu using the best of local produce. If the weather is good breakfast is served in the south facing courtyard surrounded by attractive flowers and shrubs. There are several notable golf courses in the vicinity.

Recommended in the Area

South of England Rare Breeds Centre; Leeds Castle; Sissingshurst Castle Garden (NT)

Lancashire

A selection of places to eat from the AA Restaurant & AA Pub guides

Restaurants

Kwizeen (European)
47-49 Kings Street, Blackpool FY1 3EJ
Tel 01253 290045

The Longridge Restaurant (British)
104-106 Higher Road, Longridge PR3 3SY
Tel 01772 784969

Greens Bistro (International)
3-9 St Andrews Road, St Annes On Sea, Lytham St Annes FY8 1SX
Tel 01253 789990

Pines Hotel (International)
570 Preston Road, Clayton-le-Woods, Preston PR6 7ED, Tel 01772 338551

The Mulberry Tree (British, French)
Wrightington Bar, Wrightington WN6 9SE
Tel 01257 451400

Pubs

Millstone Hotel
Church Lane, Mellor, Blackburn BB2 7JR
Tel 01254 813333

Assheton Arms
Downham, Clitheroe BB7 4BJ
Tel 01200 441227

The Bay Horse Inn
Forton LA2 0HR, Tel 01524 791204

The Eagle & Child
Maltkin Lane, Parbold L40 3SG
Tel 01257 462297

Cartford Country Inn & Hotel
Little Eccleston, Preston PR3 0YP
Tel 01995 670166

The Inn At Whitewell
Forest of Bowland, Whitewell BB7 3AT
Tel 01200 448222

The Park Restaurant Hotel ♦♦♦♦♦

Map ref 6 - SD52
209 Tulketh Rd, Ashton-on-Ribble,
PRESTON, PR2 1ES
1m NW of town centre off A5085 Blackpool Rd
T 01772 726250
F 01772 723743
E parkrestauranthotel@hotmail.com
W www.theparkpreston.com
14 rooms, S £48-£59, D £75-£90, No smoking

Fronted by mature gardens and a large landscaped car park, this impressive detached building built in 1903 benefits from a modern extension. Original features include a magnificent stained-glass window in the tiled reception hall. Breakfast and à la carte dinners are served in the spacious Edwardian Park Restaurant with its grand black marble fireplace. Snacks are available in the bar lounge, and room service is offered for all menus. The en suite bedrooms are attractively furnished to a high standard, each with a television with teletext, direct-dial telephone, radio alarm clock, hairdryer and tea and coffee facilities. Ground-floor rooms are available.

Recommended in the area

Riversway Business village & marina; National Football Museum; Harris Museum

he Bower ♦♦♦♦♦

ap ref 6 - SD57
:ALAND CONYERS, LA5 9SF
6 junct 35, A6 towards Milnthorpe r 0.75m, under narrow bridge, take ›xt left onto Snape Ln & bear left at ıd

/ 🅕 01524 734585
info@thebower.co.uk
www.thebower.co.uk

rooms, S £43-£53, D £66-£76,
o smoking

:COMMENDED IN THE AREA

·hton Hall; RSPB Reserve, Leighton :s; Sizergh Castle (NT)

'he Bower is in a beautiful village setting with views of Ingleborough surrounding hills. Affable hosts hael, an accomplished pianist, and y-Ann, an excellent cook, are both n bridge players who are happy to guests at cards. Just 10 minutes n the M6, the house is well placed for loring the Lake District and the Yorkshire Dales. The modernised property retains many original features and provides stylish accommodation in spacious bedrooms and opulent public rooms. There are two double rooms, one en suite and with an additional single bed, and the other with a private bathroom. Clock radios, hairdryers, and tea and coffee facilities are useful extras. Both candlelit kitchen suppers and formal dinners are available.

Leicestershire

selection of places to eat from the AA Restaurant & AA Pub guides

›staurants

The Priest House on the River
ıgs Mills, Castle Donington DE74 2RR
. 01332 810649

Best Western Yew Lodge Hotel
ckington Hill, Kegworth DE74 2DF
. 01509 672518

The Horse & Trumpet
d Green, Medbourne LE16 8DX
. 01858 565000

Stapleford Park
ıpleford, Melton Mowbray LE14 2EF
. 01572 787522

Red Lion Inn
d Lion Street, Stathern LE14 4HS
. 01949 860868

Pubs

The Nags Head
Hilltop, Castle Donington DE74 2PR
Tel 01332 850652

Peacock Inn
1 School Lane, Croxton Kerrial NG32 1QR
Tel 01476 870324

The Bell Inn
Main Street, East Langton LE16 7TW
Tel 01858 545278

Cow & Plough
Gartree Road, Stoughton Farm,
Oadby LE2 2FB
Tel 0116 2720852

The Stilton Cheese Inn
High Street, Somerby LE14 2QB
Tel 01664 454394

Kegworth House ♦♦♦♦♦

Map ref 3 - SK42 (airport symbol)
42 High St, NOTTINGHAM EAST MIDLANDS AIRPORT, Kegworth DE74 2DA
M1 junct 24, A6 to Loughborough. 0.5m 1st right onto Packington Hill. Left at junct, Kegworth House 50yds on left

T 01509 672575
F 01509 670645
E tony@kegworthhouse.co.uk
W www.kegworthhouse.co.uk

11 rooms, No smoking, Closed 20 Dec-1 Jan

Kegworth House is an impressive 17th-century and Georgian property set in the village of Kegworth, 11 miles south-west of Nottingham. It is convenient for major routes and East Midlands Airport. The individually styled en suite bedrooms are spread over three floors. They are are luxuriously appointed with interesting furniture and equipped with a wealth of thoughtful extras - some have queen-size beds. The ground-floor Garden Room looks out to the lovingl restored walled garden. All rooms come with DVDs, CD players, fluffy dressing gowns, trouser presses, hairdryers, broadband connection - and more. Dinner i served by arrangement in the elegant dining room, whi comfy sofas and an open fire draw tired guests into the relaxing drawing room. Memorable and wholesome English or continental breakasts are served around a large refectory table in the kitchen, and feature local produce.

RECOMMENDED IN THE AREA

Donington Park; Calke Abbey (NT); Great Central Railwa

A selection of places to eat from the AA Restaurant & AA Pub guides

Restaurants

Branston Hall Hotel (International)
Branston Park, Branston LN4 1PD
Tel 01522 793305

Harry's Place (British, French)
17 High Street, Great Gonerby NG31 8JS
Tel 01476 561780

Beeches Hotel (European)
42 Waltham Road, Scartho,
Grimsby DN33 2LX
Tel 01472 278830

Restaurant in the Jew's House
(British, French)
15 The Strait, Lincoln LN2 1JD
Tel 01522 524851

Winteringham Fields
(French, British)
Winteringham DN15 9PF
Tel 01724 733096

Pubs

The Welby Arms
The Green, Allington NG32 2EA
Tel 01400 281361

The Old Lea Gate Inn
Leagate Road, Coningsby LN4 4RS
Tel 01526 342370

Wig & Mitre
30/32 Steep Hill, Lincoln LN2 1TL
Tel 01522 535190

Masons Arms
Cornmarket, Louth LN11 9PY
Tel 01507 609525

Pyewipe Inn
Fossebank, Saxilby Road LN1 2BG
Tel 01522 528708

The George of Stamford
71 St Martins, Stamford PE9 2LB
Tel 01780 750750

Church Farm B & B ♦♦♦♦

Map ref 8 - SK98
High St, FILLINGHAM, DN21 5BS
On outskirts of village
T 01427 668279
E enquiries@churchfarm-fillingham.co.uk
W www.churchfarm-fillingham.co.uk
3 rooms, S £35, D £49-£54, No smoking, Closed 24 Dec-1 Jan

Relax and unwind in this 19th-century stone farmhouse set in secluded mature gardens overlooking farmland. The traditional bedrooms offer one en suite twin, and a double and a single that share a bathroom. Plush sofas and chairs and an open fire in the lounge make for a relaxed atmosphere. The traditional English breakfast includes cereals, porridge, local bacon and sausages, and free-range eggs cooked to your liking. Host Kathleen Needham is very proud (and rightly so) of her housekeeping and warm hospitality - on arrival you are greeted with complimentary tea and home-made cake.

Recommended in the Area

Lincoln; RAF Scampton (Red Arrows); Antiques at Newark, Swinderby & Hemswell

Wesley Guest House ♦♦♦♦

Map ref 8 - SE70
16 Queen St, EPWORTH, DN9 1HG
In town centre, 200yds off Market Place

T 01427 874512
F 01427 875361
E bookings@wesleyguesthouse.co.uk
W www.wesleyguesthouse.co.uk

4 rooms, S £40-£50, D £60-£80, No smoking

Recommended in the Area

Wesley Museum; Lincoln; York

A pleasurable stay is a certainty at this friendly and well-maintained detached house in the market town of Epworth. Epworth is the birthplace of John Wesley, founder of Methodism, and the Wesley family home, the Rectory Museum and the Wesley Methodist Memorial Church are all within walking distance. For those interested in the roots of Methodism and John Wesley, there are volumes of the published Wesley diaries on display in the house. The good-size en suite bedrooms, decorated in soft pastels, are well equipped and include minifridges, fresh flowers and complimentary toiletries. Cheerful tablecloths and lovely views over the large garden enhance the pristine breakfast room. Unwind with a game on the full-size snooker table or try one of the leisure options nearby, such as golf and fishing. Secure off-road parking is a bonus.

St Clements Lodge ♦♦♦♦

Map ref 8 - SK97
21 Langworth Gate, LINCOLN, LN2 4AD
350yds E of cathedral, down Eastgate onto Langworth Gate
T / F 01522 521532
3 rooms, S £40, D £56, No smoking

Janet and Bill Turner used to keep pigs and grow 'pick your own' fruit nd Christmas trees before setting up is guesthouse in Lincoln and earning n enviable reputation for hospitality. The iendly couple's house is handily close the cathedral, the castle and the nops, with a good choice of restaurants earby. The luxurious bedrooms are beautifully appointed and individually decorated. Twin and double rooms are available, two are en suite and one has a private bathroom. Each room comes with a hospitality tray and a hairdryer. Breakfasts are freshly cooked and served at separate tables in the dining room. Private parking is provided.

RECOMMENDED IN THE AREA
Lincoln Cathedral; Lincoln Castle; Boat trips

Bailhouse & Mews ♦♦♦♦♦

Map ref 8 - SK97
34 Bailgate, LINCOLN, LN1 3AP
100yds N of catherdral
T 01522 520883
F 01522 521829
E info@bailhouse.co.uk
W www.bailhouse.co.uk
10 rooms, D £79-£165, No smoking in bedrooms or dining room

Bailhouse commands a prime position on the Bailgate in the cathedral quarter of the city, just 230 rds from the cathedral and castle. The outwardly eorgian house encapsulates remains of a 14th ntury hall, including part of the beamed roof and posed stone walls. The building has evolved over the ars into a carefully restored guesthouse with teresting bedrooms furnished with antique and production pieces and the most up to date facilities. There is an outdoor swimming pool, and to the rear is a secure car park.

RECOMMENDED IN THE AREA
Lincoln Castle; Lincoln Cathedral; Lincolnshire Wolds

Black Swan Guest House ♦♦♦♦

Map ref 8 - SK88
21 High St, MARTON (VILLAGE), DN21 5AH
On A156 in village centre
T / F 01427 718878
E reservations@blackswanguesthouse.co.uk
W www.blackswanguesthouse.co.uk
10 rooms, S £35-£45, D £58-£68, No smoking

Located in the village centre, the 18th-century Black Swan offers good hospitality and homely bedrooms with modern facilities. A four-poster bedroom is also available. The guesthouse caters to business travellers, tourists and local families, who return frequently for the home from home comforts. Tasty generous breakfasts are served in the cosy dining room and a comfortable lounge is available. An added bonus is transport to and from nearby pubs and restaurants. Golf packages can be arranged to take advantage of several top-class courses in the vicinity. Children and guests attending local weddings or special celebrations are welcome.

Recommended in the area

Lincoln Cathedral; Humber Bridge & Humber Estuary nature reserves; Sherwood Forest

London

A selection of places to eat from the AA Restaurant & AA Pub guides

Restaurants

Blue Print Cafe (European)
The Design Museum, 28 Shad Thames SE1 2YD
Tel: 020 7378 7031

The Oxo Tower Restaurant
8th Floor, Oxo Tower Wharf SE1 9PH
Tel: 020 7803 3888

Le Caprice Restaurant (European)
Arlington House, Arlington Street SW1A 1RT, Tel: 020 7629 2239

Bibendum Restaurant (European)
Michelin House, 81 Fulham Road SW3 6RD
Tel: 020 7581 5817

Rasa W1 (Indian)
6 Dering Street, W1S 1AD
Tel: 020 7629 1346

Archipelago (International)
110 Whitfield Street W1T 5ED
Tel: 020 7283 3346

Pubs

The Crown
223 Grove Road E3 5SW
Tel: 020 8981 9998

The Bleeding Heart Tavern
19 Greville Street EC1N 8SQ
Tel: 020 242 8238

The Eagle
159 Farringdon Road EC1R 3AL
Tel: 020 7837 1353

The Abbey Road Pub
63 Abbey Road NW8 OAE
Tel: 020 7328 6626

The Fire Station
150 Waterloo Road SE1 8SB
Tel: 020 7620 2226

The Cow
89 Westbourne Park Road W2 5QH
Tel: 020 7221 5400

The Cottage ♦♦♦♦

Map ref 3 - TQ17
150-152 High St, Cranford, HOUNSLOW, TW5 9WB
M4 junct 3, A312 towards Feltham, left at lights, left after 1st pub on left Jolly Gardner

T 020 8897 1815
F 020 8897 3117
E bermuthecottage@tinyworld.co.uk
W www.cottageguesthouse-heathrow.co.uk

17 rooms, S £49.50-£67, D £59-£75, No smoking

It is hard to believe that Heathrow Airport is just 3 miles away, so peaceful is this attractive guesthouse Tucked away in a cul-de-sac behind the high street, with a large garden and pleasant outlook. Hospitality is particularly strong, and the willing family owners go to great lengths to ensure an enjoyable visit. The en suite bedrooms are attracively presented in keeping with the style of the house, and equipped with beverage trays, hairdryers and radio alarm clocks. The homely atmosphere exends to the public areas, which include a stylish dining room, the scene of delicious breakfasts served at separate tables. Secure parking is a welcome feature here, and as well as being close to the airport, there is easy access to central London via the nearby M4 or the underground.

Recommended in the Area

Syon House, Isleworth; Kew Gardens; Windsor Castle & Legoland

MIC Hotel & Conference Centre ♦♦♦♦

Map ref 3 - TQ38
81-103 Euston St, NW1 2EZ
Euston Rd left at lights onto Melton St, 1st left onto Euston St, MIC 100yds on left

T 020 7380 0001
F 020 7387 5300
E sales@micentre.com
W www.micentre.com

28 rooms, S £85-£130, D £85-£130, No smoking

The top floor of the MIC building was completely overhauled in 2004 and has been designed to offer the highest standards and value for money. The hotel is staffed around the clock, thus ensuring a safe environment - it also has a concierge service until 10.30pm. The stylish, air-conditioned bedrooms are en suite and come with LCD radios and televisions, room safes, Internet access, complimentary hospitality trays and mineral water. The spacious and airy Atrium Bar and Restaurant is perfect for an informal meeting, drink or meal. For breakfast, a traditional English buffet features eight hot items with eggs cooked to order, fruit juices, a good selection of cereals, a fruit and yoghurt bar, plus tea and coffee. The centre also offers a range of meeting rooms and private dining rooms for special events, which can be catered for. Special weekend discount rates. The hotel is located in a quiet street close to Euston station

Recommended in the Area

West End theatres; The BA London Eye; Madame Tussauds

Claverley Hotel ♦♦♦♦

Map ref 3 - TQ38
13-14 Beaufort Gardens, Knightsbridge,
SW3 1PS
Off A4 Brompton Rd, 350yds SW of Knightsbridge tube station
T 020 7589 8541
F 020 7584 3410
E reservations@claverleyhotel.co.uk
W www.claverleyhotel.co.uk
30 rooms, S £60-£120, D £120-£195

ECOMMENDED IN THE AREA
arrods; South Kensington museums; Hyde Park

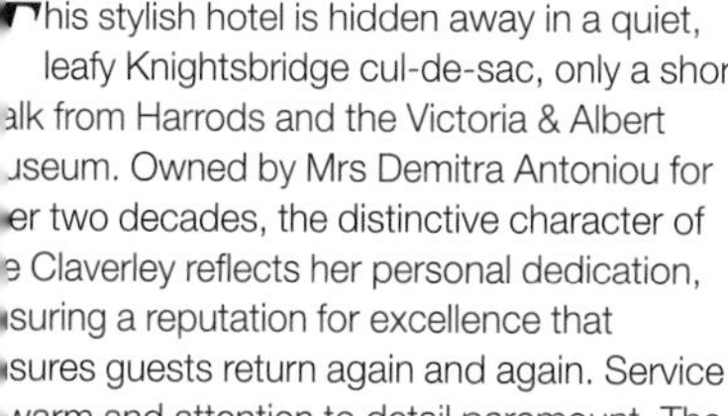

This stylish hotel is hidden away in a quiet, leafy Knightsbridge cul-de-sac, only a short alk from Harrods and the Victoria & Albert useum. Owned by Mrs Demitra Antoniou for er two decades, the distinctive character of e Claverley reflects her personal dedication, suring a reputation for excellence that sures guests return again and again. Service warm and attention to detail paramount. The bedrooms, most with a marble bathroom and power shower, are individually designed and some have four-poster beds. The public areas include a panelled reading room where you can enjoy tea, coffee, hot chocolate and biscuits throughout the day. Impressive breakfasts include mouth-watering croissants and brioche, which are delivered daily from a local bakery.

L'Hotel ♦♦♦♦♦

Map ref 3 - TQ38
28 Basil St, Knightsbridge, SW3 1AS
W along A4, turn left after Harrods onto Hans Rd, at end turn left onto Basil St

Ⓣ 020 7589 6286
Ⓕ 020 7823 7826
Ⓔ isabel@lhotel.co.uk
Ⓦ www.lhotel.co.uk
12 rooms, D £146.88-£211.50, No smoking in bedrooms

Recommended in the Area

Harrods; Victoria & Albert Museum; Hyde Park

This friendly hotel, under the same ownership as The Capital Hotel, has an enviable location just a stone's throw from Harrods and Harvey Nichols and is close to Hyde Park. The quiet residential street is in the heart of Belgravia, with its flower-filled mews, tranquil garden squares and attractive buildings. Individually styled bedrooms, many with Nina Campbell fabrics and original artwork on the walls, are crammed with indulgent extras including minibars, tea and coffee facilities, Egyptian cotton sheets and cookies at bedtime - all are en suite. The basement Le Metro bar-restaurant, popular with locals, serve memorable breakfasts and brasserie-style lunc and dinners. In the morning savour excellent croissants and pain au chocolate baked on the premises and served with home-made preserves, or go for the full substantial breakfast. Afternoon teas or sandwiches are also served, as are wines by the glass, deliciou coffee and indulgent cocktails.

Five Sumner Place Hotel ♦♦♦♦

Map ref 3 - TQ38
5 Sumner Place, South Kensington,
SW7 3EE
350yds SW of South Kensington tube station, off Old Brompton Rd
T 020 7584 7586
F 020 7823 9962
E reservations@sumnerplace.com
W www.sumnerplace.com

13 rooms, S £85-£100, D £130-£152

RECOMMENDED IN THE AREA

South Kensington museums; Royal Albert Hall; Hyde Park

Five Sumner Place is a smart terrace property in fashionable South Kensington, built around 1848. The family-run establishment is in a residential area between Old Brompton Road and Fulham Road, close to the famous museums. It is approached by a small pretty forecourt and is surrounded by equally impressive Victorian buildings. Period charm sits comfortably with modern facilities in the refurbished building, which is filled with flowers and plants, a welcome touch of greenery in the centre of town. A lift reaches to all floors. The individually styled bedrooms have an emphasis on traditional furnishings and furniture. Breakfast is served in a magnificent Victorian-style conservatory overlooking a small rear garden. Daily newspapers and magazines are provided while you linger over breakfast. The garden has a paved patio with tables and seating for relaxing on summer days. This is the perfect city retreat after a hectic day sightseeing or to unwind after that stressful business meeting.

*T*he Gallery ♦♦♦♦

Map ref 3 - TQ38

8-10 Queensberry Place, South Kensington, SW7 2EA

Off A4 Cromwell Rd opp Natural History Museum, near South Kensington tube station

T 020 7915 0000
F 020 7915 4400
E reservations@eeh.co.uk
W www.eeh.co.uk

36 rooms, S £129-£153, D £164-£188

RECOMMENDED IN THE AREA

Victoria & Albert Museum; Harrods; Kensington Palace

The concept behind The Gallery is 'the Victorian artist at home', and the hotel features original Victorian paintings and antiques throughout. The decor of the two master suites, Rosetti and Leighton, is stunning. They each have a private roof terrace, Jacuzzi, fax and CD and DVD players. The en suite bedrooms are well appointed and have bathrooms with marble tiling, brass fittings and soft white towels. Sumptuous public rooms include the mahogany-panelled reception, lobby and lounge, and the arts and crafts style Morris Room complete with an original Manxman pian and antique bar-billiards table. The highest leve of service is available 24hours a day, and business guests benefit from wired and wireles broadband in each room and the public areas, and there is a boardroom-style meeting room. All rooms have interactive televisions with pay movies. The Science, Natural History and Victoria & Albert museums are virtually on the doorstep.

The Victoria ♦♦♦♦

Map ref 3 - TQ38
10 West Temple Sheen, SW14 7RT
Off Upper Richmond Rd onto Temple Sheen Rd, left onto West Temple Sheen

T 020 8876 4238
F 020 8878 3464
E bookings@thevictoria.net
W www.thevictoria.net

7 rooms, S £98.50, D £98.50, No smoking in bedrooms or dining room, Closed 24-26 Dec, 1 Jan

Recommended in the Area

Richmond Park; Kew Gardens; Hampton Court Palace

The attentive staff provide an exceptional standard of service at this truly inviting small hotel and restaurant in leafy west London. More a gastro-pub with rooms, it has stylish double bedrooms, all with really good showers en suite. Two of the rooms can be used for twin occupancy, and another two can accommodate a travel cot or a camp bed. Egyptian cotton sheets and down pillows add to the comfort. Each room has a telephone, and a flat-screen computer with free broadband Internet access. Food is a major part of the enterprise, with highly regarded, imaginative food served in the modern bar. European-inspired menus are available for lunch and dinner. Coffee and home-baked cakes and pastries are served throughout the morning and afternoon, and breakfast is a delight.

*H*art House Hotel ♦♦♦♦

Map ref 3 - TQ38

51 Gloucester Place, Portman Sq, W1U 8JF

Off Oxford St behind Selfridges, near Baker St or Marble Arch tube stations

T 020 7935 2288
F 020 7935 8516
E reservations@harthouse.co.uk
W www.harthouse.co.uk

16 rooms, S £68-£75, D £95-£110, No smoking

RECOMMENDED IN THE AREA

Madame Tussauds; Oxford Street; Piccadilly theatres

This delightful, well-cared for property occupies a Georgian terrace just off Oxford Street. Much of its original elegance and grand ambience survive from the late 18th century, when during the French Revolution it was home for members of the French aristocracy. The hotel has been carefully restored so that modern comforts abound, and the en suite bedrooms have been refurbished to a high standard with quality furnishings and smart bathrooms. The rooms are each equipped with a desk or writing table, relaxing seating, direct-dial telephone with modem point, and a multi-channel television. A tasty English breakfast is served in the cottage-style dining room. Andrew Bowden, whose family has owned and run the hotel for many years, is a charming and helpful host. His hotel is well placed for visiting London.

The Mayflower Hotel ♦♦♦♦

Map ref 3 - TQ38
26-28 Trebovir Rd, SW5 9NJ
From Earls Court tube station left onto Trebovir Rd, hotel on left

T 020 7370 0991
F 020 7370 0994
E info@mayflower-group.co.uk
W www.mayflowerhotel.co.uk

46 rooms, S £62-£72, D £69-£99, No smoking

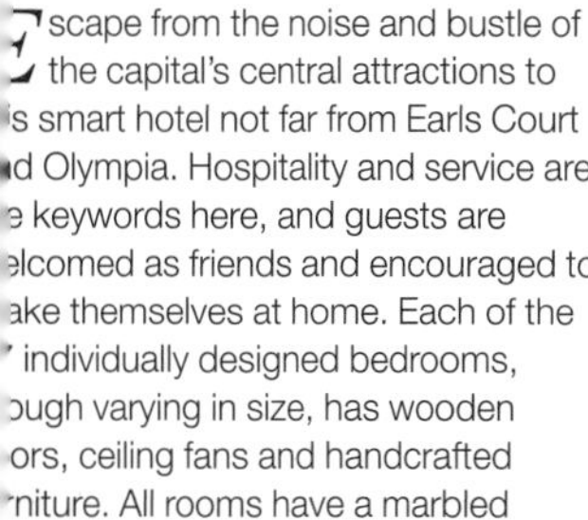

Escape from the noise and bustle of the capital's central attractions to is smart hotel not far from Earls Court d Olympia. Hospitality and service are e keywords here, and guests are elcomed as friends and encouraged to ake themselves at home. Each of the individually designed bedrooms, ough varying in size, has wooden ors, ceiling fans and handcrafted niture. All rooms have a marbled walk-in bath or shower room, as well as satellite televisions, direct-dial telephones and refreshment trays. A stylish lounge and a bright dining room where breakfast is served are in keeping with the elegant accommodation. Fax, photocopying and secretarial services are available.

RECOMMENDED IN THE AREA
Kensington Palace; Harrods; Madame Tussauds

The New Linden Hotel ♦♦♦♦

Map ref 3 - TQ38
59 Leinster Sq, Notting Hill, W2 4PS
Off A402 Bayswater Rd

T 020 7221 4321
F 020 7727 3156
E newlindenhotel@mayflower-group.co.uk
W www.newlinden.co.uk

52 rooms

At the end of a busy day, this smart hotel is a welcome treat from the hectic pace of the capital. ly a five-minute walk from underground stations and hin easy reach of the city's major sights and ractions, the New Linden offers bright and fresh drooms, individually furnished and equipped with dern features. Breakfast is served in a cheerful ing room. There are lifts available, and other services lude dry cleaning and laundry, and business facilities. The hotel staff is always on hand to ensure you feel at home.

RECOMMENDED IN THE AREA
Portabello Market; Hyde Park; Kensington Palace

Merseyside

A selection of places to eat from the AA Restaurant & AA Pub guide

Restaurants

Fraiche (French)
11 Rose Mount, Birkenhead CH43 5SG
Tel 0151 652 2914

Simply Heathcotes (British)
Beetham Plaza, 25 The Strand, Liverpool L2 0XL
Tel 0151 236 3536

60 Hope Street Restaurant (British)
60 Hope Street, Liverpool L1 9BZ
Tel 0151 707 6060

Warehouse Brasserie (International)
30 West Street, Liverpool PR8 1QN
Tel 01704 544662

Thornton Hall Hotel (International)
Neston Road, Thornton Hough CH63 1JF
Tel 0151 336 3938

Pubs

Fox and Hounds
Barnston Road, Barnston CH61 1BW
Tel 0151 6487685

Everyman Bistro
9-11 Hope Street, Liverpool L1 9BH
Tel 0151 708 9545

Ship & Mitre
133 Dale Street, Liverpool L2 2JH
Tel 0151 236 0859

The Red Cat
8 Red Cat Lane, St Helens WA11 8RU
Tel 01744 882422

The Berkeley Arms
19 Queens Road, Southport PR9 9HN

Cambridge Town House Hotel ♦♦♦♦♦

Map ref 5 - SD31
4 Cambridge Rd, SOUTHPORT, PR9 9NG
A565 N from town centre, over 2 rdbts
T 01704 538372
F 01704 547183
E info@cambridgehousehotel.co.uk
W www.cambridgehousehotel.co.uk
16 rooms, S £55-£60, D £69-£99.50, No smoking in bedrooms or dining room

This delightful hotel is close to Hesketh Park, and a short drive from Lord Street and the shops of Southport town centre. The sizeable en suite bedrooms, including a luxurious honeymoon suite, are furnished to a very high standard and offer many facilities including hospitality trays and direct-dial phones. The stylish public areas with their elegant Victorian furniture, include a relaxing lounge, a cosy bar and an attractive dining room. Sta the day with a traditional full English or continental breakfast. The varied menu changes regularly, offerin excellent cuisine and fine wines. Attentive service completes the picture.

Recommended in the Area

Royal Birkdale golf course; Manchester; Lake District

Bay Tree House B & B ♦♦♦♦

Map ref 5 - SD31
No 1 Irving St, Marine Gate, SOUTHPORT,
PR9 0HD
Off Leicester St
T 01704 510555
F 01704 510551
E baytreehouseuk@aol.com
W www.baytreehousesouthport.co.uk
6 rooms, S £25-£55, D £48-£79,
No smoking, Closed 14 Dec-1 Feb

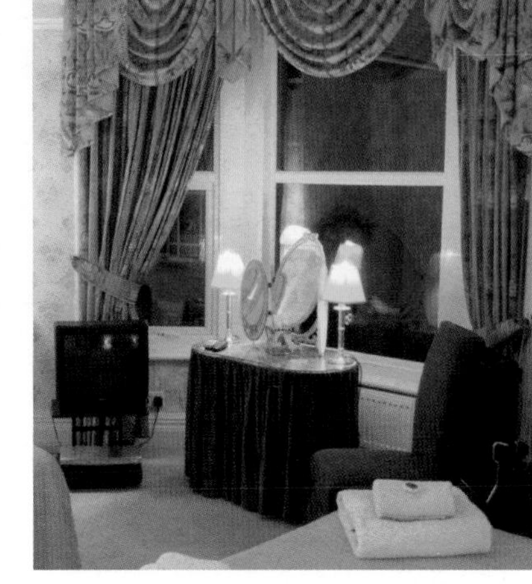

ECOMMENDED IN THE AREA
›yal Birkdale Golf Course; Knowsley Safari ›rk; Tate Liverpool

Baytree House is an immaculate and very welcoming retreat, located a short walk ›m the promenade and central attractions. ›ere are 15 golf courses within half an hour's ›ive, six of which are of championship ›andard. The individually decorated bedrooms › equipped with a wealth of extras. - towelling ›throbes, complimentary slippers, and a ›lection of high quality toiletries are offered as a ›atter of course. Minifridges, beverage facilities, ›luding fruit teas and chocolate, and iron and ironing board are available in every room. One room has a particularly large shower room. Delicious, imaginative breakfasts using local produce are a highlight. Don't miss the porridge with whisky, honey and cream, or the local free-range eggs, all served in an attractive dining room overlooking the pretty front patio garden. Evening meals are available by arrangement. Reiki and other complimentary therapy treatments and training courses are available.

Norfolk

A selection of places to eat from the AA Restaurant & AA Pub guide

Restaurants

🏵🏵🏵 Morston Hall (British, French)
Morston, Holt, Blakeney NR25 7AA
Tel 01263 741041

🏵🏵 The Hoste Arms (European)
The Green, Burnham Market PE31 8HD
Tel 01328 738777

🏵 Yetman's (British)
37 Norwich Road, Holt NR25 6SA
Tel 01263 713320

🏵🏵 Adlard's Restaurant (French)
79 Upper St Giles Street, Norwich NR2 1AB
Tel 01603 633522

🏵 The Crown Restaurant (Pacific Rim)
The Buttlands, Wells-next-the-Sea
NR23 1EX, Tel 01328 710209

Pubs

The White Horse
Main Road, Brancaster Staithe PE31 8BY
Tel 01485 210262

The Lord Nelson
Walsingham Road, Burnham Thorpe
PE31 8HL
Tel 01328 738241

The Saracen's Head
Wolterton, Erpingham NR11 7LZ
Tel 01263 768909

The Rose & Crown
Old Church Road, Snettisham PE31 7LX
Tel 01485 541382

Lifeboat Inn
Ship Lane, Thornham PE36 6LT
Tel 01485 512236

The Old Brick Kilns ♦♦♦♦

Map ref 4 - TF93
Little Barney Ln, BARNEY, nr
Fakenham NR21 0NL
Off B1354 to Barney, 0.3m left, B&B 0.75m at end of lane
T 01328 878305
F 01328 878948
E enquiries@old-brick-kilns.co.uk
W www.old-brick-kilns.co.uk
3 rooms, S £30, D £58, No smoking

Originally three separate cottages, this small country house has been converted to provide clean and well-maintained accommodation in peaceful grounds. The pretty en suite bedrooms, with plain walls and contrasting gingham or flowery bedding, are equipped with radio alarms and tea and coffee facilities. Breakfast, and dinner by arrangement, is served at a cottage-style communal table in the lounge-dining room. The guesthouse is ideal for visiting the long sandy beaches and nature reserves of the north and west Norfolk coasts, and exploring the peaceful undulating countryside.

Recommended in the Area

Village of Walsingham; The Thursford Collection; Georgian town of Holt

taffordshire House ♦♦♦♦

ap ref 4 - TF84
ation Rd, Docking, BURNHAM
ARKET, PE31 8LS
m SW of Burnham Market. On 153 in Docking, 300yds N of urch
01485 518709
enquiries@
staffordshirehouse.com
www.staffordshirehouse.com
ooms, S £36, D £56-£58,
smoking in bedrooms or dining
om

affordshire House, dating from 760, has been variously an inn, llery, haberdasher's and a radio r shop, and during the war itions were stored in its barns. se days the house provides informal ntry style bed and breakfast in a e 4.5 miles from the coast, and is ub of an Internet Art Gallery. There is a drawing room and an elegant dining room leading out onto a terrace and pretty garden. Bedrooms are individually furnished come with tea and coffee facilities.

RECOMMENDED IN THE AREA
Sandringham; Holkham Hall; North Norfolk coast, birdwatching

---

hrublands Farm ♦♦♦♦

Map ref 4 - TG24
Church St, Northrepps, CROMER, NR27 0AA
Off A149 to Northrepps, through village, past Foundry Arms, cream house 50yds on left
T / F 01263 579297
E youngman@farming.co.uk
W www.broadland.com/shrublands
3 rooms, S £37-£39, D £54-£58,
No smoking

rublands is a working family farm set in mature ardens amid 300 acres of arable farmland, an ideal for exploring the coastline and countryside of rural Norfolk. Traditional hospitality is a distinguishing re at the 18th-century farmhouse, with good Aga ing using home-grown and fresh local produce. kfast is served at one large table in the dining , and there is also a cosy lounge, with a log fire, s and a television. The bedrooms have radio alarms and tea and coffee facilities - one room is en suite and two have private bathrooms. No children under 12 or pets.

RECOMMENDED IN THE AREA
Blickling Hall & Felbrigg Hall (NT); Sandy beaches at Cromer & Overstrand; Blakeney Point

The White Cottage ♦♦♦♦

Map ref 4 - TG24
9 Cliff Rd, CROMER, NR27 0AW
Off A149 Norwich Rd onto Overstrand Rd, 2nd right
T 01263 512728
E jboocockwhitecottagecromer.freeserve.co.uk
W www.whitecottagecromer.co.u
3 rooms, D £66-£70, No smoking
Closed Xmas

This immaculate detached house, situated on the cliff path at Cromer, offers a high standard of comfort and attentive service. The spacious en suite bedrooms are individually decorated and equipped with every home comfort including tea and coffee trays, electric blankets and micro fridges. The delicious breakfast, using local produce, and home-made bread and preserves, is served in an elegant dining room, on the terrace in summer, or in the cosy breakfast room in winter. Packed lunches to order and special diets catered for. No childrer pets. panoramic views of the sea Off-road parking is a bonus.

RECOMMENDED IN THE AI

Felbrigg Hall (NT); Norfolk Shire Hor Centre; Cley bird reserves

---

Field House ♦♦♦♦♦

Map ref 4 - TF93
Moorgate Rd, HINDRINGHAM, NR21 0PT
Off A148 to Hindringham, through village, right onto Moorgate Rd at Lower Green, Field House 1st on left
T 01328 878726
E stay@fieldhousehindringham.co.uk
W www.fieldhousehindringham.co.uk
3 rooms, S £60-£80, D £80-£100, No smoking, Closed 25-26 Dec

Traditional materials are used to good effect in this handsome property, which is set in lovely gardens with a rural outlook. The house is a good base for exploring the Norfolk coast and countryside, and will appeal to cyclists and birdwatchers. Sumptuous accommodation is provided in two double bedrooms with bathrooms en suite and plenty of thoughtful extras, and an en suite twin-bed room on the ground floor. Both the lounge and dining room are beautifully furnished, and an excellent dinner, by arrangement, is prepared from local produce (gues can bring their own wine). No dogs and no smokin

RECOMMENDED IN THE AREA

Blickling Hall & Felbrigg Hall (NT); North Norfolk cc Shopping in Georgian Holt & Burnham Market

Wallington Hall ♦♦♦♦♦

Map ref 4 - TF62
KING'S LYNN, PE33 0EP
Off A10 left heading North 3.5m from Downham Market
T 01553 811567
F 01553 810661
E luddington@wallingtonhall.co.uk
W www.wallingtonhall.co.uk
3 rooms, D £80, No smoking in bedrooms or dining room

ECOMMENDED IN THE AREA
ndringham; African Violet Centre; ng's Lynn Arts Centre

The most impressive setting you can imagine for bed and breakfast :commodation is found at this agnificent Tudor manor house, rrounded by grounds with mature ees and attractive landscaped rdens. Public rooms are elegantly nished with antiques and wonderful intings. A choice of smoking and n-smoking lounges is provided, but noking is not permitted in the drooms and dining room. The panelled dining room is the scene for a hearty English breakfast served at one splendid antique table. The spacious, individually decorated bedrooms are all en suite and families can be accommodated in two of the rooms. Bedrooms are equipped with central heating, tea and coffee facilities, and many other thoughtful extras. In the grounds there is a heated outdoor swimming pool, a hard tennis court, badminton court and a croquet lawn. Parking for 10 cars on site. Dogs are not permitted, except for guide dogs.

The Gables Guest House ♦♦♦♦

Map ref 4 - TG20
527 Earlham Rd, NORWICH, NR4 7HN
Off S bypass onto B1108, signs to University of East Anglia, 300yds on left pass Fiveways rdbt, towards city centre
Ⓣ 01603 456666
Ⓕ 01603 250320
11 rooms, S £46-£51, D £68-£73, No smoking, Closed 20 Dec-1 Jan

The friendly, family-run Gables is close to the city of Norwich and within walking distance of the University of East Anglia. The sumptuous bedrooms, including single, double and twin rooms, a superior double and a family room on request, are individually decorated and have either bath or shower rooms en suite, and tea and coffee facilities. Public rooms include an elegant lounge with a conservatory dining room. There is secure, well-lit parking behind the house.

RECOMMENDED IN THE AREA

City of Norwich; University of East Anglia; Norfolk Broads

Old Thorn Barn ♦♦♦♦

Map ref 4 - TG20
Corporation Farm, Wymondham Rd, Hethel, NORWICH, NR14 8EU
6m SW of Norwich. Follow signs for Lotus Cars from A11 or B1113, on Wymondham Rd
Ⓣ 01953 607785
Ⓕ 01953 601909
Ⓔ enquires@oldthornbarn.co.uk
Ⓦ www.oldthornbarn.co.uk
7 rooms, S £31-£35, D £48-£52, No smoking

Reconstruction of a group of derelict buildings has resulted in this delightful conversion. The substantial 17th-century barns and stables feature a stylish open-plan dining room, where you can linger over breakfast around individual oak tables on a polished wood floor. At the other end of the room there is a cosy lounge area with a wood-burning stove. Antique pine furniture, polished floors and smart en suites are a feature of the spacious bedrooms - tea and coffee trays, trouser presses and hairdryers also contribute to an exceedingly comfortable stay.

RECOMMENDED IN THE AREA

Fairhaven Woodland & Water Garden; Pettitts Animal Adventure Park; Wolterton Park

Pheasant Cottage ♦♦♦♦♦

Map ref 4 - TG22
Long Common Ln, SWANTON ABBOTT, NR10 5BH
Off B1150 at x-rds signed Swanton Abbott, village x-rds right onto Long Common Ln, 1.5m on left
T / F 01692 538169
E melanie@pheasantcottage.freeserve.co.uk
3 rooms, S £35-£45, D £60-£80, No smoking

Tea and home-made scones are offered on arrival at 17th-century Pheasant Cottage, a home of exceptional quality. The cosy lounge has a log-burning stove, and former stables have been converted to a dining room with original oak beams. The spacious bedrooms have lovely coordinated fabrics and many thoughtful touches. The gardens are delightful and there are stunning views across fields to the church. Delicious English and continental breakfasts, prepared using local fresh produce, are a highlight. Afternoon teas, with tasty home-made preserves, are served in the Swedish log cabin in the orchard.

RECOMMENDED IN THE AREA
Blickling Hall (NT); Felbrigg Hall (NT); Norfolk Broads

Bramble House ♦♦♦♦

Map ref 4 - TG31
Cats Common, Norwich Rd, Smallburgh, WROXHAM, NR12 9NS
4m NE of Wroxham on A1151 Norwich Rd, off lay-by on left
T / F 01692 535069
E bramblehouse@tesco.net
W www.bramblehouse.com
3 rooms, S £37-£40, D £54, No smoking, Closed Xmas, New Year

This modern detached house is set in the heart of the Norfolk Broads, a short drive from the centre of Wroxham and not far from the coast. The luxury bedrooms are individually furnished, and supplied with equipment such as hairdryers, towelling robes and hospitality trays. All bedrooms are en suite, with bath or shower facilities; one room has a sauna. Breakfast is a farmhouse feast, served at individual tables in the smart dining room. Sausages come from a local pork specialist and eggs straight from the establishment's own free-range hens. Sue and James Ross are happy to cater for vegetarians and any other dietary requirements.

RECOMMENDED IN THE AREA
Cruises on the Broads; Blickling Hall (NT); East Ruston Old Vicarage Garden

Northamptonshire

A selection of places to eat from the AA Restaurant & AA Pub guide

Restaurants

@@@ Fawsley Hall Hotel (British)
Fawsley, Daventry NN11 3BA
Tel 01327 892000

@ The Sun Inn (British)
Main Street, Marston Trussell LE16 9TY
Tel 01858 465531

@@ Vine House Restaurant (British)
100 High Street, Paulerspury,
Towcester NN12 7NA
Tel 01327 811267

@ Roade House Restaurant (British)
16 High Street, Roade NN7 2NW
Tel 01604 863372

@@ Whittlebury Hall Hotel & Spa (European)
Whittlebury NN12 8QH
Tel 01327 857857

Pubs

The Queen's Head
Main Street, Bulwick NN17 3DY
Tel 01780 450272

Falcon Hotel
Castle Ashby NN7 1LF
Tel 01604 696200

George and Dragon
Silver Street, Chacombe OX17 2JR
Tel 01295 711500

The Sun Inn
Main Street, Marston Trussell LE16 9TY
Tel 01858 465531

The King's Head
Church Street, Wadenhoe PE8 5ST
Tel 01832 720024

The Courtyard ♦♦♦♦♦

Map ref 3 - SP97 (Rushden)
Rutland Lodge, West St,
STANWICK, NN9 6QY
A45 rdbt to Stanwick, 0.3m right onto drive

T 01933 622233
F 01933 622276
E bookings@thecourtyard.me.uk
W www.thecourtyard.me.uk

6 rooms, S £45-£50, D £60-£75, No smoking

Comfort and luxury abound at this attractive house, where the hospitality is unforgettable. The house stands in delightful large gardens on the edge of Stanwick village. The en suite bedrooms have garden or country views, and are well equipped and stamped with quality. The en suites are stylish and modern, and all rooms come with Internet access, satellite televisions, and tea and coffee facilities. A business meeting room is available. Breakfasts are in keeping with the high standards. Secure parkin is available.

RECOMMENDED IN THE ARE
Rockingham Castle; Oundle; Santa Pod

Thatches on the Green ♦♦♦♦

Лap ref 3 - SP88
;chool Ln, Weldon, CORBY, NN17 3JN
)ff A43, opp The Woolpack by village green
01536 266681
01536 266659
tom@thatches-on-the-green.fsnet.co.uk
www.thatches-on-the-green.fsnet.co.uk
0 rooms, No smoking in bedrooms or
ining room

ECOMMENDED IN THE AREA
:kingham Castle; Rockingham Speedway; Kirby 'l

ttractive gardens and grounds create a good first impression of this family home on ldon village green. Well presented inside and , the former public house was built in 1642 of al Weldon Stone. The main building is tched and retains some original features. The buildings house a new kitchen equipped with ooking range where the hearty breakfasts are ›ked. Choices include a selection of cereals, cooked or continental breakfast, and oked haddock or kippers. Evening meals are also served in the cosy dining room, which has a small honesty bar and overlooks the gardens. The bright individual rooms are furnished in a period style and are well equipped to include tea and coffee facilities. Single, double, twin and family options are available, and each bedroom has an endearing name such as Forget-me-not or Apple Tree. The helpful proprietors can make-up sandwiches to take away or put together a picnic basket for you.

A selection of places to eat from the AA Restaurant & AA Pub guid

Restaurants

Tillmouth Park Hotel (British)
Cornhill-on-Tweed TD12 4UU
Tel 01890 882255

De Vere Slaley Hall (British)
Slaley, Hexham NE47 0BX
Tel 01434 673350

Linden Hall Hotel (British)
Longhorsley NE65 8XF
Tel 01670 500000

Matfen Hall (British)
Matfen NE20 0RH
Tel 01661 886500

Café 21 (British)
35 The Broadway, Darras Hall,
Ponteland NE20 9PW
Tel 01661 820357

Pubs

The Manor House Inn
Carterway Heads DH8 9LX
Tel 01207 255268

Dipton Mill Inn
Dipton Mill Road NE46 1YA
Tel 01434 606577

The Pheasant Inn
Stannersburn, Falstone NE48 1DD
Tel 01434 240382

Queens Head Inn & Restaurant
Great Whittington NE19 2HP
Tel 01434 672267

The Feathers Inn
Hedley on the Hill NE43 7SW
Tel 01661 843607

Warenford Lodge
Warenford NE70 7HY
Tel 01668 213453

Market Cross Guest House ♦♦♦♦

Map ref 10 - NU13
1 Church St, BELFORD, NE70 7LS
In village next to Post Office
T 01668 213013
E details@marketcross.net
W www.marketcross.net
3 rooms, S £40-£60, D £55-£70, No smoking

Jill and John Hodge offer charming hospitality and friendship that encourage guests to return again and again to their attractive establishment. Added to the warmth of their welcome is the comfort and quality of the accommodation. Bedrooms are large and stylish, with sofas and armchairs, smart en suites, and a wealth of pleasing extras like chocolates, flowers, and milk and fruit in the fridge. The delightful breakfasts are a real feature, with an excellent choice of dishes that can include kedgeree, pancakes and grid scones. The lounge is a really inviting place to relax in after a busy day sightseeing or playing golf.

Recommended in the ar

Lindesfarne (Holy Island); Alnwick Cas ('Hogwarts' location in recent Harry Po films); Farne Islands birdwatching trips

Ivy Cottage ♦♦♦♦♦

Map ref 10 - NT83
1 Croft Gardens, Crookham,
CORNHILL-ON-TWEED, TD12 4ST
4m E of Cornhill. Off A697 onto B6353 into Crookham village
T / F 01890 820667
E ajoh540455@aol.com
2 rooms, S £38-£40, D £59-£67,
No smoking

Top quality accommodation is offered at this stone property in the village of Crookham, surrounded by fabulous walking country and much historic interest. There is a choice of twin or double bedrooms with private bathrooms, generous towels, bathrobes and Crabtree & Evelyn toiletries. Embroidered bed linen and fresh flowers are welcoming touches in the rooms, which are equipped with hairdryers and tea facilities. Breakfast includes fresh local produce, home-made bread and preserves, and is served in the farmhouse-style kitchen or more formal dining room. Restaurant and bar meals are available at a pub in the village. Dogs can be accommodated by arrangement.

Recommended in the Area

Holy Island; Walking in Cheviot Hills & St Cuthbert's Way; horse riding, fishing, gliding & golf nearby

---

Vallum Lodge ♦♦♦♦

Map ref 6 - NY76
Military Rd, Twice Brewed,
HALTWHISTLE, NE47 7AN
On B6318, 400yds W of Once Brewed National Park visitors centre
T 01434 344248
F 01434 344488
E stay@vallum-lodge.co.uk
W www.vallum-lodge.co.uk
6 rooms, S £40-£54, D £60,
No smoking, Closed Nov-Feb

This licensed roadside guesthouse provides a home from home in the heart of the Northumberland National Park, with easy access to Hadrian's Wall, the Pennine Way and local Roman sites. It is perfectly placed for walking and cycling in this truly unspoiled part of England. The en suite bedrooms are all on the ground floor. They have all been refurbished and feature hospitality trays, complimentary toiletries and crisp white linen. Laundry and drying facilities are also available. Breakfast is served in the smart dining room and there is a cosy lounge with a television and a selection of books and games.

Recommended in the Area

Vindolanda; Housesteads; Roman Army Museum

Pheasant Inn ♦♦♦♦

Map ref 6 - NY78
Stannersburn, FALSTONE, NE48 1DD
A68 onto B6320, signs for Kielder Water
T / F 01434 240382
E enquiries@thepheasantinn.com
W www.thepheasantinn.com
8 rooms, S from £45, D from £75,
No smoking in bedrooms or dining room,
Closed Xmas

RECOMMENDED IN THE AREA

Hadrian's Wall; Keilder Water Reservoir (sports facilities); Cragside House (NT)

Set close by the magnificent Kielder Water, this is a classic country inn. Built in 1624, it oozes character, with exposed stone walls, original beams, low ceilings, open fires and a display of old farm implements in the bar. Run by the welcoming Kershaw family since 1985, the inn has been refurbished to a very high standard. Bright modern bedrooms, some with their own entrances, are all contained in stone buildings adjoining the inn. All the rooms are spotless, well equipped, and have tea and coffee facilities and lovely country views. Delicious home-cooked breakfasts and evenin meals are served in the bar or in the attractive dining room. Irene and her son Robin are responsible for the traditional home cooking using the freshest of local produce, with Irene's husband Walter attending to the administrative side of the business. The Pheasant is perfect f visiting the superb Northumberland countrysid

Peth Head Cottage ♦♦♦♦

Map ref 7 - NY96

Juniper, HEXHAM, NE47 0LA

B6306 S from Hexham, 200yds fork right, next left. Continue 3.5m, house 400yds on right after Juniper sign

T 01434 673286
F 01434 673038
E info@peth-head-cottage.co.uk
W www.peth-head-cottage.co.uk

2 rooms, D £50, No smoking

ECOMMENDED IN THE AREA

eamish Open Air Museum; Hadrian's Wall; urham Cathedral

The lovingly maintained cottage dates back to 1825 and is popular for its warm elcome, idyllic setting, and home comforts. a and hand-made biscuits are offered on rival, and the delicious home baking is enjoyed breakfast too, along with freshly made bread d tasty preserves. This inviting sandstone ttage is set in peaceful, well-kept gardens. e two bright, south-facing bedrooms have owers rooms en suite, and are provided with hospitality trays. The cosy lounge is heavily beamed and furnished with comfy chairs; there is plenty of tourist information and maps are on hand for visitors to browse through. Peth Head Cottage is ideallly situated for visiting Durham and Newcastle, as well as nearby Roman sites. Owner Joan Liddle is an excellent host.

The Orchard House ♦♦♦♦♦

Map ref 10 - NU00
High St, ROTHBURY, NE65 7TL
In village centre
T 01669 620684
E graham@orchardhouserothbury.com
W www.orchardhouserothbury.com
5 rooms, S £60-£70, D £80-£135,
No smoking, Closed Xmas, New Year

Recommended in the Area

North Northumberland Heritage Coast; Bambur Castle; Alnwick Castle & Gardens

The Orchard House stands on an elevated location within easy walking distance of Rothbury village. This peaceful Georgian stone house has lots of character and offers excellent comfort. Bedrooms are sumptuous with crisp white linen and duck-down duvets, and well equipped with complimentary bathrobes, daily newspapers and fresh flowers, while the super bathrooms have luxury toiletries. Unwind in the antique-furnished drawing room, which has a bar service in the evenings. Breakfast has an emphasis on organic and Fairtrade produce. The free-range eggs come from a local farm, the orange juice is freshly squeezed, and the croissants are freshly baked. Traditional or lighter main dishes are available, including a generous selection of local cheeses, fresh frui and home-baked pastries. Vegetarian, wheat-free and special diets are available on request.

The Old Manse ♦♦♦♦♦

Map ref 10 - NT92
New Rd, Chatton, WOOLER, NE66 5PU
4m E of Wooler. On B6348 in Chatton
T / F 01668 215343
E chattonbb@aol.com
W www.oldmansechatton.co.uk
2 rooms, S £35-£50, D £60-£70, No smoking

Built in 1875 and commanding excellent views over the open countryside, this imposing former manse stands on the edge of the pretty village of Chatton between the Cheviot Hills and the scenic North Northumberland Heritage Coast. You approach the house by a sweeping gravel drive bordered with lawns and conifers. You can explore the extensive gardens, which include a wildlife pond. The Rosedale Suite is an elegant four-poster room with a Victorian-style bathroom en suite; Buccleuch has a sitting room and private patio. Both rooms are well appointed, spacious and luxurious. Enjoy home-made cakes and biscuits and hearty breakfasts in the elegant conservatory-dining room.

RECOMMENDED IN THE AREA

Alnwick Garden; Chillingham Castle & wild cattle; Bamburgh Castle

Nottinghamshire

A selection of places to eat from the AA Restaurant & AA Pub guides

Restaurants

Restaurant 1650 at Ye Olde Bell Hotel (European)
Barnby Moor DN22 8QS, Tel 01777 705121

Sonny's (British, French)
3 Carlton Street, Hockley NG1 1NL
Tel 0115 947 3041

Langar Hall (British)
Langar NG13 9HG, Tel 01949 860559

Merchants Restaurant & Bar (European)
29-31 High Pavement,
Nottingham NG1 1HE
Tel 0115 958 9898

Restaurant Sat Bains with Rooms (European)
Old Lenton Lane, Nottingham NG7 2SA
Tel 0115 986 6566

Pubs

The Martins Arms Inns
School Lane, Colston Bassett NG12 3FD
Tel 01949 81361

Robin Hood Inn
High Street, Elkesley DN22 8AJ
Tel 01777 838259

The Square & Compass
Eastgate, Normanton on Trent NG23 6RN
Tel 01636 821439

Star Inn
Melton Lane, Sutton Bonington LE12 5RQ
Tel 01509 852233

The Three Horse Shoes
High Street, Walkeringham DN10 4HR
Tel 01427 890959

The Grange ♦♦♦♦

Map ref 8 - SK73
Sutton Ln, ELTON, NG13 9LA
From Grantham A1 onto A52 to Elton x-rds, left 200yds, B&B on right
T / F 01949 851561
3 rooms, S £35-£40, D £50-£60, No smoking

RECOMMENDED IN THE AREA
Belvoir Castle; Newark; Trent Bridge Cricket Club

Parts of this traditional farmhouse date from the 17th century and the rooms have fine views across the gardens and rolling open countryside of the Vale of Belvoir, between Nottingham and Grantham. In the evening it is only a short walk to an excellent pub. The bedrooms consist of singles, doubles and twins - all have bathrooms en suite, and come with tea and coffee facilities and many thoughtful extras.

Mr and Mrs Masson provide fine hospitality and tasty, carefully presented food. Don himself is a retired Scottish International footballer, but don't expect any penalties here.

Browns ♦♦♦♦♦

Map ref 8 - SK57
The Old Orchard Cottage, Holbeck, HOLBECK, S80 3NF
0.5m off A616 Sheffield-Newark road, turn for Holbeck at x-rds
T / F 01909 720659
E browns@holbeck.fsnet.co.uk
W www.brownsholbeck.co.uk
3 rooms, S £50-£55, D £65-£75, No smoking in bedrooms or dining room, Closed Xmas week

The Old Orchard Cottage is tucked away at the end of a winding lane in a hamlet of a dozen houses, most of them, like the cottage, built around 1730. The entrance drive crosses a shallow ford that joins two ponds in the glorious cottage garden. The accommodation is in three garden lodges, stylishly converted from farm buildings, and thoughtfully equipped; all have four-poster beds. Each lodge has a garden terrace, lit by candles on summer evenings. Breakfast is served by the hospitable Brown family in an elegant dining room furnished in the Regency style, at mahogany tables set with white bone china and fresh flowers.

RECOMMENDED IN THE AREA
Sherwood Forest; Hardwick Hall (NT); Newark antiques shops & fairs

selection of places to eat from the AA Restaurant & AA Pub guides

estaurants

The Abingdon Arms (International)
igh Street, Beckley OX3 9UU
el 01865 351311

The Leatherne Bottel (British)
oring RG8 0HS
el 01491 872667

Le Manoir Aux Quat' Saisons
rench)
reat Milton OX44 7PD
el 01844 278881

Mill House Hotel (British, French)
ngham OX7 6UH
el 01608 658188

Gee's Restaurant (British)
Banbury Road, Oxford OX2 6PE
el 01865 553540

Thai Thai at the Crazy Bear (Thai)
azy Bear Hotel, Bear Lane,
adhampton OX44 7UR
el 01865 890714

Pubs

The Boars Head
Church Street, Ardington OX12 8QA
Tel 01235 833254

The Inn for All Seasons
The Barringtons, Burford OX18 4TN
Tel 01451 844324

The Lamb Inn
Sheep Street, Burford OX18 4LR
Tel 01993 823155

The Bull Inn
Sheep Street, Charlbury OX7 3RR
Tel 01608 810689

The Highwayman
Exlade Street, Checkendon RG8 0UA
Tel 01491 682020

Sir Charles Napier
Spriggs Alley, Chinnor OX39 4BX
Tel 01494 483011

The Boar's Head ♦♦♦♦

Map ref 3 - SU48
Church St, ARDINGTON, OX12 8QA
n village next to church
T / F 01235 833254
E info@boarsheadardington.co.uk
W www.boarsheadardington.co.uk
3 rooms, S £75-£120, D £85-£130,
No smoking in bedrooms or dining
room

ocated in the beautiful downland
village of Ardington, this characterful
has served the local community for
er 150 years, and now combines
age pub, first-class restaurant and
lish accommodation. The unspoiled
age, part of the Lockinge Estate, is a
eat base for walking, cycling, golf and
ning, and yet just a half-hour drive
m Oxford. Great care has gone into
eating a stylish and welcoming
nbience in the bedrooms, while retaining many original features. One room has a luxurious bathroom, another has an adjoining sitting room. Food is a passion, with ingredients fresh, local and seasonal whenever possible. Fish, sourced in Cornwall, is a particular speciality. Excellent wines and good local ales.

Recommended in the area

Oxford colleges; Vale of the White Horse; Blenheim Palace

Burford House ♦♦♦♦♦

Map ref 3 - SP21
99 High St, BURFORD, OX18 4QA
Off A40 into village centre

Ⓣ 01993 823151
Ⓕ 01993 823240
Ⓔ stay@burfordhouse.co.uk
Ⓦ www.burfordhouse.co.uk

8 rooms, S £85-£130, D £125-£155
No smoking in bedrooms or dining room

RECOMMENDED IN THE ARE
Historic Burford; Cotswold Wildlife Park River Windrush

In the heart of this famous Cotswold town, Burford House, with its leaded windows and half-timbered and stone exterior, is an individual hotel with many welcoming touches. The charming bedrooms, all individually furnished, have fresh flowers and are equipped with hairdryers, magazines, toiletries and complimentary mineral water. Many of the attractive bathrooms have free-standing Victorian tubs and separate shower stalls. Antique furniture, pictures and porcelain adorn the rooms. Downstairs, two lounges, one with a log fire and an honesty bar, are the perfect venues for relaxation, and you can sit and look out over the pretty courtyard garden with a relaxing drink. Superb breakfasts are served in the dining room and later, morning coffee, light lunches and the most delicious afternoon teas, featurin homemade scones, pastries and cake Your hosts, the Hentys, make a point c supporting local suppliers and much o what you'll enjoy - granary bread, hone smoked salmon, clotted cream - is top local produce.

The Mill House Country Guest House ♦♦♦♦

Map ref 3 - SP44
North Newington Rd, BANBURY, OX15 6AA
M40 junct 11, signs to Banbury Cross, onto B4035 (Shipston-on-Stour), 2m right for Newington
T 01295 730212
F 01295 730363
E lamadonett@aol.com
W www.themillhousebanbury.com
7 rooms, S £50-£75, D £75-£109, No smoking, Closed 2 wks Xmas

The former miller's house, now set in gorgeous gardens, is believed to iginate from the 17th century. ıakespeare referred to an adjacent mill his play Henry VI. Surrounded by ling countryside and only 1 mile from ınbury, The Mill House offers ımfortable accommodation and four furbished self-contained cottages in e courtyard. The en suite rooms come th telephones and tea and coffee equipment as standard. The cottages are available on a self-catering or bed and breakfast basis, and come with a separate lounge-kitchen. There is also a charming lounge bar and meeting facilities within the main house.

RECOMMENDED IN THE AREA
Blenheim Palace; Straftord-upon-Avon; The Cotswolds

The Forge ♦♦♦♦

Map ref 3 - SP32
Churchill, CHIPPING NORTON, OX7 6NJ
B4450 from Chipping Norton to Churchill 2.5m
T 01608 658173
E enquiries@cotswolds-bedandbreakfast.com
W www.cotswolds-bedandbreakfast.com
5 rooms, S £50-£60, D £60-£80, No smoking

The 200-year-old former smithy now offers a warm welcome and stylish accommodation.This lightful honey-stone house in the village of Churchill is st a short drive from Chipping Norton. Owners Debby d Martin Rushbrooke opted for dry land after erating a traditional pair of hotel narrow boats for years. The stylish bedrooms - one with a Jacuzzi th - are individually designed. Three rooms have ır-poster beds, and all are filled with a host of home from home comforts and pampering extras. The cottage-style breakfast room leads into a pleasant lounge. Breakfast is a feast of sausages and bacon from the local butcher. There are numerous eateries locally, including the village pub almost opposite. No young children or pets.

RECOMMENDED IN THE AREA
Blenheim Palace; Warwick Castle; Stratford-upon-Avon

The Baskerville ♦♦♦♦

Map ref 3 - SU78
Station Rd, Lower Shiplake,
HENLEY-ON-THAMES, RG9 3NY
2m S of Henley in Lower Shiplake. Off A4155 onto Station Rd, B&B signed
T 0118 940 3332
F 0118 940 4735
E enquiries@thebaskerville.com
W www.thebaskerville.com
5 rooms, S £35-£45, D £65-£75,
No smoking in bedrooms or dining room

Recommended in the Area

River & Rowing Museum, Henley; Maharajah's Well, Stoke Row; Basildon Park (NT)

The Baskerville is located in Lower Shiplake close the Thames Path, and only a few minutes from the lovely riverside town of Henley. There are regular rail links to Henley and connections to London. Graham Cromack has been in the pub and restaurant trade for many years and has combined good food, fine wine and great accommodation in attractive and relaxed surroundings. The en suite bedrooms are well appointed and have a full hospitality tray. You are in for a first-class feast here - the slogan at The Baskerville is 'where food really matters'. Whether it is a full English breakfast, fine dining in the main restaurant or a snack at the bar, the quality is excellent. Choose from starters such as prawn and crab crumbles or Stilton soup, main courses featuring char-grille loin tuna or seared spiced duck breast, all washed down with a choice from the carefully chosen wine list or a glass of real ale. In summ regular barbecues in the attractive garden are popular.

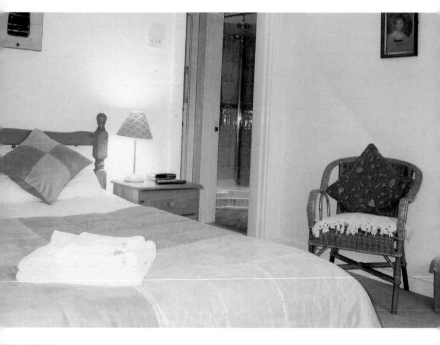

The Cherry Tree Inn ♦♦♦♦

Map ref 3 - SU78
Stoke Row, HENLEY-ON-THAMES,
RG9 5QA
6m W of Henley. Off B841 into Stoke Row
T 01491 680430
F 01491 682168
W www.thecherrytreeinn.com
4 rooms, D £65-£85, No smoking

RECOMMENDED IN THE AREA
Rowing & River Museum, Henley; Oxford; Mahajarah's Well, Stoke Row

The Cherry Tree is in an Area of Outstanding Natural Beauty within the Chilterns, yet only 20 minutes from Reading and motorway connections. New owners Paul Gilchrist and Richard Coates have over 25 years' experience in the hospitality industry, which includes working in several prestigious restaurants. The contemporary furnishings and strong colours complement the original flagstone floors, beamed ceilings and fireplaces. Bedrooms have a modern design, and spacious bathrooms with luxurious toiletries. Added touches include mineral water, fresh fruit, and tea and fresh coffee maker. The philosophy in the contemporary restaurant is quality, fresh ingredients with uncomplicated presentation, and value for money. Classic and modern European dishes and daily specials are offered, and the home-made Sunday roast is a favourite. The pub is a popular for walkers and cyclists, tempted by the first-class beers and delicious meals.

Tilbury Lodge ♦♦♦♦

Map ref 3 - SP50
5 Tilbury Ln, OXFORD, OX2 9NB
A34 at junct A420 (Botley). Right at lights, past shopping centre. Turn right onto Eynsham Rd, 1st right Tilbury Ln

T 01865 862138
F 01865 863700
E tilburylodge@yahoo.co.uk
W www.oxfordcity.co.uk/hotels/tilbury

9 rooms, S £50-£55, D £65-£75, No smoking

You can expect a warm welcome and great hospitality at this refreshingly modern guesthouse set in a quiet Oxford suburb. Only 10 minutes from the city centre, you are also within a short walk of the River Thames, close to the historic village of Cumnor with two excellent pubs with restaurants, and near to a golf centre. The bedrooms at Tilbury Lodge are immaculate, with a modern style and an impressive range of extras. Breakfast is served in the dining room overlooking the large well-kept garden. There is ample off-street parking, enabling you to take the regular bus into Oxford. Special themed breaks are available.

RECOMMENDED IN THE AREA

Blenheim Palace; Farmore Reservoir; Vale of the White Horse

Shropshire

A selection of places to eat from the AA Restaurant & AA Pub guides

Restaurants

🏵 The Studio (British)
59 High Street, Church Stretton SY6 6BY
Tel 01694 722672

🏵🏵🏵🏵 Hibiscus (French)
17 Corve Street, Ludlow SY8 1DA
Tel 01584 872325

🏵🏵🏵 Mr Underhills (British)
Dinham Weir, Ludlow SY8 1EH
Tel 01584 874431

🏵🏵 The Waterdine (British)
Llanfair Waterdine LD7 1TU
Tel 01547 528214

🏵 Rosehill Manor (British, French)
Rosehill, Ternhill, Market Drayton TF9 2JF
Tel 01630 638532

Pubs

The Burlton Inn
Burlton SY4 5TB
Tel 01939 270284

The Crown Inn
Hopton Wafers, Cleobury Mortimer DY14 0NB
Tel 01299 270372

The Riverside Inn
Cound, Cressage SY5 6AF
Tel 01952 510900

The Malthouse
The Wharfage, Ironbridge TF8 7NH
Tel 01952 433712

The Roebuck Inn
Brimfield, Ludlow SY8 4NE
Tel 01584 711230

The Laurels ♦♦♦♦

Map ref 2 - SO79
Broadoak, Six Ashes,
BRIDGNORTH, WV15 6EQ

On right 5m from Bridgnorth travelling towards Stourbridge on the A458

T 01384 221546
E george@broadoak75.fsnet.co.uk
W www.thelaurelsbandb.co.uk

rooms, S £25, D £45-£50, No smoking, Closed Xmas, New Year

t the end of a long day exploring the Shropshire countryside, this naculate Victorian house located in a ely hamlet is a lovely spot to unwind. e Laurels' large patiois surrounded by nicured gardens overflowing with autiful flowers during the summer. The urbished bedrooms are furnished to a od homely standard, and are equipped with tea and coffee facilities and hairdryers, and some have bathrooms en suite. Three rooms are in a converted stable block. Breakfast is served in the conservatory-dining room, and a lounge and heated indoor swimming pool are available.

RECOMMENDED IN THE AREA

Ironbridge; Black Country Museum; Redhouse Cone

The Library House ♦♦♦♦♦

Map ref 2 - SJ60
11 Severn Bank, IRONBRIDGE,
TF8 7AN

50yds from Iron Bridge

T 01952 432299
F 01952 433967
E info@libraryhouse.com
W www.libraryhouse.com

4 rooms, S £55, D £65-£70,
No smoking

ocated just 60 yards from the famous Iron Bridge, this Grade II listed Georgian building is tucked ay in a pretty, peaceful thoroughfare yet close to nty of good pubs and restaurants. Hanging baskets window boxes enhance the creeper-covered walls e former library, and in the spring and summer the dens are immaculate. All of the bedrooms, which ude family rooms, are en suite, and each room has a vision with DVD, a small DVD library, and a hospitality tray. Excellent breakfasts are served in the pine-furnished dining room.

RECOMMENDED IN THE AREA

Ironbridge World Heritage Site; Telford International Exhibition Centre; Blists Hill Victorian Town

Top Farm House ♦♦♦♦

Map ref 5 - SJ32
KNOCKIN, SY10 8HN
In Knockin, past Bradford Arms & shop, past turning for Kinnerley
T 01691 682582
F 01691 682070
E p.a.m@knockin.freeserve.co.uk
W www.topfarmknockin.co.uk
3 rooms, S £35-£45, D £55-£60

Set in pretty gardens and retaining many original features, including a wealth of exposed beams and open log fires, Top Farm House combines traditional hospitality with elegant surroundings. The en suite bedrooms are equipped with many thoughtful extras. There is a relaxing beamed drawing room with a grand piano, and a spacious period dining room, which overlooks the garden, where imaginative and comprehensive breakfasts are served. The village of Knockin is one of the prettiest in this p of Shropshire, and the surrounding Welsh Marches form a quiet and unspoiled area of natural beauty.

RECOMMENDED IN THE ARI

Shrewsbury; Powys Castle (NT); Llanthaedr Waterfall

Angel House ♦♦♦♦

Map ref 2 - SO57
Bitterley, LUDLOW, SY8 3HT
On A4117 towards Kidderminster
T 01584 891377
E stay@angelhousecleehill.co.uk
W www.angelhousecleehill.co.uk
2 rooms, S £40-£65, D £65,
No smoking

With views over four counties, 17th century Angel House is a great place to take a break, whether visiting nearby Ludlow, exploring the historic sights, or walking the Shropshire Way. The views continue from the spacious modern bedrooms, which are thoughtfully equipped. There is a cosy dining room, a lounge, and a conservatory that looks out towards Ludlow. Breakfast is a highlight and sourced from the highest quality ingredients. Evening meals and packed lunches, also of a very high standard, can be orderec advance. You will be greeted on arrival at Angel Hous by the resident dog, Spencer, who welcomes other friendly and well-behaved canines. Children over five welcome.

RECOMMENDED IN THE AREA

Ludlow Castle; Stokesay Castle; Shropshire Way footpa

:okesay Castle near Craven Arms

Bromley Court B & B ♦♦♦♦♦

Map ref 2 - SO57
73 Lower Broad St, LUDLOW,
SY8 1PH
A49 onto B4361, over lights, 100yds on left

Ⓣ 01584 876996
Ⓔ phil@ludlowhotels.com
Ⓦ www.ludlowhotels.com

3 rooms, S £75-£110, D £95-£115, No smoking

Three tiny Tudor cottages have each been converted into a private suite, ›mplete with exposed oak beams, glenook fireplaces (in two) and a stylish ›corative theme. Each suite has a :ting room and bathroom en suite, ıtique bed with quality furnishings, and :cess to a lovely courtyard garden. :ter 25 years of running their guest ›use, Patricia and Philip Ross know at putting guests first and never skimping on quality guarantee to please everyone, including themselves. They offer a continental breakfast in the comfort of the suites (or the garden in warm weather), or a full English choice. All of Ludlow's AA Rosetted restaurants are within walking distance.

RECOMMENDED IN THE AREA

Ludlow town, castle & church; Woodland & riverside walks

The Clive Restaurant with Rooms ♦♦♦♦ 

Map ref 2 - SO57
Bromfield, LUDLOW, SY8 2JR
2m N of Ludlow on A49 in village of Bromfield

T 01584 856565
F 01584 856661
E info@theclive.co.uk
W www.theclive.co.uk

15 rooms, S £50-£75, D £70-£95, No smoking, Closed 25-26 Dec

RECOMMENDED IN THE AREA

Stokesay Castle, Craven Arms; Ludlow; Berringt Hall, Leominster (NT)

A stylish makeover of a former farmhouse has given The Clive a smart contemporary look. Food is the heart of the operation here with two dining options: the well-known restaurant or the less formal Cookhouse café and bar. In the former you can enjoy superb British cooking that uses fresh produce, including local meats, smoked products, vegetables and Cornish fish; service is friendly but not fussy. The relaxed brasserie-style Cookhouse with its backgroun music is ideal for families. Spacious en suite bedrooms have been refurbished to provide well-equipped accommodation. Paul and Barbara Brooks and their young team offer a sincere welcome and a warm atmosphere.

umber Twenty Eight ♦♦♦♦

ap ref 2 - SO57
 Lower Broad St, LUDLOW, SY8 1PQ
town centre. Over Ludford Bridge onto
wer Broad St, 3rd house on right
 01584 875466
 enquiries@no28ludlow.co.uk
 www.no28ludlow.co.uk
rooms, S £60-£80, D £80-£90,
 smoking, Closed Nov-Mar

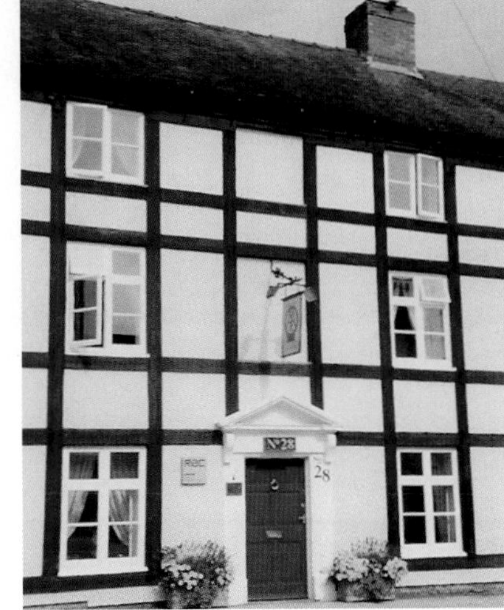

COMMENDED IN THE AREA
rington Hall (NT); Croft Castle (NT); Stokesay
tle

his Georgian house, built about 1770, lies near Ludlow's historic centre, and is close udford Bridge and Horseshoe Weir. Ludlow ket, the castle, pottery, craft and antique ps, and restaurants are just a short walk ay. Number Twenty Eight has charming, -equipped bedrooms that come with ne-made biscuits and hospitality trays. There cosy sitting room, or in fine weather you can relax in the pretty courtyard garden. For breakfast, freshly squeezed orange juice, fruit salad, local bacon, sausages, eggs and breads will set you up for exploring Ludlow or beautiful Whitcliffe Common, or longer excursions around south Shropshire or a trip to Ironbridge. No evening meals but you are close to many first-class restaurants, some of which are among the finest in the country.

Haywood Farm B & B ♦♦♦♦

Map ref 6 - SJ63

Haywood Ln, Cheswardine,
MARKET DRAYTON, TF9 2LW

3m S of Market Drayton. Off A529 for Cheswardine, over canal bridg 1st left

T 01630 661788
F 01630 661795
E haywoodfarm@hotmail.com

5 rooms, S £30, D £60, No smokir

Enjoy a traditional country break at this welcoming farmhouse, set in rolling countryside close to Goldstone Common. The 19th-century building has been renovated to provide comfortable accommodation with many pleasurable extras. Make use of the sauna and Jacuzzi, play table tennis, or enjoy a delightful local walk. The spacious en suite bedrooms have superb views of the garden and surroundings, and are attractively decorated and furnished. Breakfast is cooked to order on the kitchen Aga, served in the smart dining room, whil the stylish sitting room with its open f and comfy seating is perfect for unwinding after a busy day sightseeir

RECOMMENDED IN THE AR

Ironbridge World Heritage Site; Alton Towers; Chester

Pool Cottage ♦♦♦♦

Map ref 2 - SJ30

Gravels, MINSTERLEY, SY5 0JD

Off A488, signed Pool Cottage

T 01743 891621
E reservations@poolcottage.com
W www.poolcottage.com

3 rooms, S £27-£30, D £46-£50,
No smoking, Closed 24 Dec-2 Jan

This engaging cottage-style guesthouse has great charm, and is in an ideal spot for walking or birdwatching, or just relaxing. You can even bring your own horse and make use of the stables and grazing - there is direct access to Stapeley Common where you can ride the beautiful Shropshire hills. Well appointed in every detail, the modern accommodation has quite spacious bedrooms and includes a double aspect family room with stunning views - mo rooms are en suite or have private facilities. F English or continental breakfasts are served around one table in the cosy breakfast room.

RECOMMENDED IN THE AREA

The Long Mynd; Ludlow; Shrewsbury

͜rown Country Inn ♦♦♦♦

/lap ref 2 - SO58
/IUNSLOW, SY7 9ET
)ff B4368 into village
01584 841205
01584 841255
info@crowncountryinn.co.uk
www.crowncountryinn.co.uk
rooms, S £45, D £65-£70, No smoking, ;losed 25-Dec

ichard Arnold has been cooking professionally for many years, and in gust 2001 he and his wife Jane took over the own, an impressive Tudor inn located in an ea of Outstanding Natural Beauty between ich Wenlock and Craven Arms. Historic aracter is retained in the massive oak beams, gstone floors and a large inglenook fireplace he main bar area. Pine-furnished bedrooms in a converted Georgian stable block at the r of the inn. A double, twin and a family room available, all with facilities en suite, sitting eas, hospitality trays, fresh fruit and mineral ter. Traditional ales and food prepared from local produce are served in the bar and Corvedale Restaurant, and the day begins with a substantial English breakfast.

RECOMMENDED IN THE AREA

Ironbridge World Heritage Site; Discovery Centre, Craven Arms; Ludlow Castle

---

Abbey Court Guest House ♦♦♦♦

Map ref 2 - SJ41
134 Abbey Foregate,
SHREWSBURY, SY2 6AU
N of river off A5112
01743 364416
01743 358559
info@abbeycourt.biz
www.abbeycourt.biz
10 rooms, S £35-£40, D £55-£60

ocated within easy walking distance from the town centre, this Grade II listed former coaching inn vides a range of homely bedroom, some of which in an attractive extension. All rooms have a spitality tray, a shower room en suite and some also e a bath. Tempting, freshly cooked breakfasts are ved in the cosy dining room, and continental and getarian options are available. Val and Andy MacLeod ays give a warm welcome at Abbey Court, and are happy to recommend good restaurants nearby for an evening meal. This is an excellent base for visiting the attractions of Shropshire.

RECOMMENDED IN THE AREA

Shrewsbury Castle & Abbey; Attingham Park (NT); Ironbridge Gorge & museums

Fieldside Guest House ♦♦♦♦

Map ref 2 - SJ41
38 London Rd, SHREWSBURY, SY2 6NX
A5 onto A5064, premises 1m on le
🅣 01743 353143
🅕 01743 354687
🅔 robrookes@btinternet.com
🅦 www.fieldsideguesthouse.co.uk
4 rooms, S £38-£40, D £55-£60, No smoking

Fieldside, which dates back to 1835, is just 1 mile from the centre of Shewsbury and a five-minute walk from Shrewsbury Abbey. This delightful house is attractively furnished and decorated and offers both single and double/twin rooms, all en suite. The bedrooms feature period-style furniture and are equipped with tea and coffee facilities. Breakfast is served at individual tables in the spacious dining room. Traditional English or vegetarian or lighter options are available. There is ample private parking.

RECOMMENDED IN THE ARE

Shrewsbury Castle & Abbey; Attingham Park (NT); Ironbridge Gorge & museum

---

Avenue Farm Bed & Breakfast ♦♦♦♦

Map ref 2 - SJ60
Uppington, TELFORD, TF6 5HW
M54 junct 7, B5061 for Atcham, 2nd left signed Uppington. Right after sawmill, farm 400yds on right
🅣 01952 740253
🅕 01952 740401
🅔 jones@avenuefarm.fsnet.co.uk
🅦 www.
virtual-shropshire.co.uk/avenuefarm
3 rooms, S £35-£40, D £50-£55, No smoking in bedrooms or dining room, Closed Xmas

RECOMMENDED IN THE AREA

Ironbridge Gorge museums; Weston Park; Shrewsbury

The Jones family have farmed here since 1916, and are happy to share their 18th-century farmhouse and immaculate gardens with their guests. Magnificent views of the Wrekin and surrounding countryside can be enjoyed from the spacious en suite bedrooms, which are filled with thoughtful extras. Many original Georgian features have been kept in t impressive house, and there is fine period furniture. Wake up to a hearty farmhouse breakfast, served in an atmosphere of quality furnishings and decorative schemes, and the cosy sitting room is another plus.

Soulton Hall ♦♦♦♦

Map ref 6 - SJ52
Soulton, WEM, SY4 5RS
2m NE of Wem off B5065

T 01939 232786
F 01939 234097
E enquiries@soultonhall.co.uk
W www.soultonhall.co.uk

7 rooms, S £37.50-£56.50, D £70-£120,
No smoking

ECOMMENDED IN THE AREA
hester; Ironbridge; Shrewsbury

The Ashton family can trace their tenure of this impressive hall back to the 16th ntury, and much evidence of the building's e remains. The welcoming entrance lounge ads into the bar on one side and a restaurant the other, offering a good range of freshly epared dishes. The house has central heating well as log fires. The bedrooms reflect the aracter of the house with mullioned windows and exposed timbers; one room also has wood panelling. Five bedrooms are en suite, and two of these are in a converted coach house across the garden. Open farmland surrounds the house and you are welcome to explore the grounds. These include 1.5 miles of river and brook where guests can fish. There are also farm and woodland walks to explore.

Barley Mow House ♦♦♦♦

Map ref 2 - ST31
Aston Rogers, WESTBURY,
SY5 9HQ
2m S of Westbury. Off B4386 into Aston Rogers, house 400yds opp Aston Hall

T 01743 891234
E colinrigby@astonrogers.fsnet.co.uk
W www.stmem.com/barleymowhouse

2 rooms, S £26-£32, D £44-£56, No smoking

Dating from the 17th century, this property has been extended and restored to provide modern facilities with a cosy farmhouse style. It is surrounded by beautiful gardens, where you can enjoy tea and biscuits on the pretty patio. The Old Farmhouse bedroom is a large sunny room with a king-size bed and a bathroom en suite; the split-level studio bedroom, in the converted malt house with original beams, has a single and double bed and an adjoining room with a single bed, and a large bathroom. An Aga-cooked English breakfast is served in th spacious dining room. Westbury is a peaceful hamlet in an Area of Outstanding Natural Beauty.

RECOMMENDED IN THE ARE

Powis Castle (NT); Stiperstones Hills; Shrewsbury Castle & Abbey

Somerset

A selection of places to eat from the AA Restaurant & AA Pub guides

Restaurants

@@@ Royal Crescent Hotel - Pimpernels (British, Mediterranean)
16 Royal Crescent, Bath BA1 2LS
Tel 01225 823333

@ Truffles (European)
95 High Street, Bruton BA10 0AR
Tel 01749 812255

@@ The Crown Inn (British)
Exford TA24 7PP
Tel 01643 831554

@@@ Andrews on the Weir (British)
Porlock Weir, Porlock TA24 8PB
Tel 01643 863300

@ Brazz (British)
Castle Bow, Taunton TA1 1NF
Tel 01823 252000

Pubs

The Globe Inn
Appley TA21 0HJ
Tel 01823 672327

Woolpack Inn
Beckington BA11 6SP
Tel 01373 831244

The Wheatsheaf
Combe Hay BA2 7EG
Tel 01225 833504

The Horse & Groom
East Woodlands, Frome BA11 5LY
Tel 01373 462802

The Talbot 15th-Century Coaching In
Selwood Street, Mells, Frome BA11 3PN
Tel 01373 812254

Royal Oak Inn
Luxborough TA23 0SH
Tel 01984 640319

he Ayrlington ♦♦♦♦♦

ap ref 2 - ST76
-25 Pulteney Rd,
ATH, BA2 4EZ
1 onto A36, pass
olburne Museum, hotel
)0yds on right
01225 425495
01225 469029
mail@ayrlington.com
www.ayrlington.com
rooms, S £75-£175,
£100-£175,
o smoking,
osed 23 Dec-7 Jan

COMMENDED
THE AREA
Abbey;
rmal Bath Spa;
eum of East Asian Art

n impressive Grade II listed Victorian house of splendour, right in the rt of Bath, where owners on and Mee-Ling Roper western and eastern nes to stunning effect ughout. Asian antiques, vorks and fine fabrics sit nfortably alongside sical fireplaces, drapes seating. All of the spacious bedrooms are furnished and decorated to individual themes, including a Chinese room, an Empire room, and the Pulteney room that has a four-poster bed. Bathrooms are equipped with quality fixtures and fittings, and luxurious towels and toiletries, and some have a spa bath. You can enjoy superb views over the Oriental style walled gardens to the Abbey with your freshly cooked breakfast. There is also a bar and a welcoming lounge. This hotel offers a tranquil atmosphere and has ample parking. Simon and Mee-Ling also own the Lopburi Art & Antiques gallery, which is within walking distance.

*B*ailbrook Lodge Hotel ♦♦♦♦

Map ref 2 - ST76
35-37 London Rd West, BATH, BA1 7HZ
M4 junct 18, A46 S to A4 junct, left signec Batheaston, hotel on left

T 01225 859090
F 01225 852299
E hotel@bailbrooklodge.co.uk
W www.bailbrooklodge.co.uk

15 rooms, S £55-£85, D £70-£90,
No smoking

RECOMMENDED IN THE AREA

Pump Rooms & Roman Baths; Wookey Hole & Caves; Dyrham Park (NT)

Located on the east edge of Bath and only 10 minutes from junction 18 of the M4, this imposing property was built in 1821, The Grade II listed Georgian house stands in extensive tranquil gardens and has been redecorated in keeping with the Georgian period. The well-equipped bedrooms include some with four-poster beds and period furniture. Eight rooms overlook the gardens and the Avon valley, and the remaining rooms overlook the grounds. Service at Bailbrook Lodge is professional and efficient. There is a inviting lounge, decorated in country-house style with a small bar, and light snacks are available from noon until evening. Breakfast ir the elegant dining room is prepared using loc produce. In the grounds there is a very attrac riverside restaurant, The Waterwheel, only 500 yards from the house, where an excellen dinner is served in a beautiful setting complet with the original working waterwheel.

Aquae Sulis ♦♦♦♦

Map ref 2 - ST76
174-176 Newbridge Rd, BATH,
BA1 3LE
On A4 1.2m W of city centre
T 01225 420061
F 01225 446077
E enquiries@aquaesulishotel.co.uk
W www.aquaesulishotel.co.uk
13 rooms, S £55-£65, D £65-£99,
No smoking in bedrooms or dining room

Situated within easy reach of the city, yet away from the crowds, this ttractive Edwardian house offers a varm and genuine welcome. The en uite bedrooms are of a good size and ılly equipped with beverage trays, airdryers, direct-dial telephones, Sky elevision, radio alarms and trouser resses. Wireless broadband Internet ccess is available in all rooms, and iere are photocopying and fax facilities. here are two inviting lounges, one with a small but well-stocked bar, and another in which you may smoke. Traditional English or continental breakfasts are served in the dining room and the evening menu offers a good selection of dishes. There is a large, monitored car park, and a local shuttle service and doorstep bus service get you to the city centre in minutes. Close to beautiful riverside walks and areas of special wildlife interest, there is plenty to do nearby.

RECOMMENDED IN THE AREA
Roman Baths; Longleat; Cheddar Gorge & Caves

Beckfords B & B ♦♦♦♦

Map ref 2 - ST76
59 Upper Oldfield Park, BATH,
BA2 3LB
Off A36 Lower Bristol Rd onto Lower Oldfield Park at Green Park Tavern opp Renault, 3rd left
T 01225 334959
E post@beckford-house.com
W www.beckford-house.com
2 rooms, S £48-£60, D £65-£85,
No smoking, Closed Xmas

Anthony O'Flaherty maintains high standards of service at this spacious Victorian residence, which in a quiet location close to the attractions. The edrooms are well equipped, with unusual extras such s a binoculars to appreciate the views and a window iermometer to check the weather. The beds are king ze and the showers are twice the usual size. The reakfast room has French windows overlooking a mall, walled garden presided over by a statue of Pan. Local organic produce features wherever possible in the traditional English breakfast menu, accompanied with lots of toast and a remarkable range of preserves and spreads.

RECOMMENDED IN THE AREA
Georgian Bath; Wells; Dyrham Park (NT)

Brocks Guest House ♦♦♦♦

Map ref 2 - ST76
32 Brock St, BATH, BA1 2LN
Off A4 between The Circus & Royal Crescent

T 01225 338374
F 01225 334245
E marion@brocksguesthouse.co.uk
W www.brocksguesthouse.co.uk

6 rooms, S £55-£70, D £72-£88, No smoking, Closed 24-28 Dec, New Year

Built by John Wood the younger in 1765, this handsome house is ideally located between The Circus and Royal Crescent, some of Bath's finest Georgian architecture. The town centre, the Roman Baths and the Pump Room are just a short walk away. Bath is a World Heritage Site and has much to offer to the visitor. The interior of the house reflects the elegance of the period with beautifully furnished en suite bedrooms. A traditional breakfast is served in the large dining room, which has a lounge area where you can relax in easy chairs.

Recommended in the Area

Royal Crescent; Museum of Costume; Roman Baths

Cheriton House ♦♦♦♦♦

Map ref 2 - ST76
9 Upper Oldfield Park, BATH, BA2 3JX
A36 onto A367 Wells Rd, 1st right

T 01225 429862
F 01225 428403
E info@which.net
W www.cheritonhouse.co.uk

11 rooms, S £48-£60, D £68-£105, No smoking

Recommended in the Area

Cheddar; Wells; Longleat

This grand Victorian house has panoramic views over Bath and is only a short walk from the city. Expect a friendly welcome from proprietors Iris and John who work hard to achieve a relaxed atmosphere. The carefully restored en suite bedrooms are all charmingly individual with a mix of antiques and modern furniture, and include a two-bedroom suite in a converted coach house. A substantial breakfast is served in the large conservatory-breakfast room overlooking beautifully manicured gardens. Plan your day in the comfortable lounge, where you can browse the ample supply of brochures and guide books.

The County Hotel ♦♦♦♦♦

Map ref 2 - ST76

18-19 Pulteney Rd, BATH, BA2 4EZ

44 onto A36, pass Holburne Museum, 50yds on left

T 01225 425003

F 01225 466493

E reservations@county-hotel.co.uk

W www.county-hotel.co.uk

22 rooms, S £75-£80, D £112-£190, No smoking, Closed 21 Dec-9 Jan

ECOMMENDED IN THE AREA

man Baths; Thermae Bath Spa; Royal Crescent

This elegant house is perfectly placed to enjoy Bath. Looking out over the cricket d rugby grounds towards nearby Bath Abbey, e hotel is just around the corner from the nous Pulteney Bridge. The accommodation is ly outstanding, with beautifully decorated and nished rooms. The stylish Reading Room is eal for afternoon tea or just relaxing in, while e Cricket Bar is a quiet place for a bar lunch or evening drink. Bedrooms range from one with a four poster and others of superior quality to more standard rooms; all are comfortably furnished, and many have delightful views. Each room has a bathroom en suite, a Freeview television, and a connection for a computer. Breakfast is an impressive selection of fresh dishes, served in the fine dining room. This exceptionally caring hotel also has secure parking.

The Circus, Bath

Devonshire House ♦♦♦♦

Map ref 2 - ST76
143 Wellsway, BATH, BA2 4RZ
1m S of city centre. A36 onto A367 Wells Rd & Wellsway

Ⓣ 01225 312495
Ⓕ 01225 336676
Ⓔ enquiries@devonshire-house.uk.com
Ⓦ www.devonshire-house.uk.com

3 rooms, S £45-£65, D £55-£75, No smoking

Under new ownership, this charming house, built in 1880 and originally a grocer's shop, has kept its Victorian character. The friendly proprietors make every effort to ensure your stay is pleasant and memorable. The attractive en suite bedrooms have been refurbished to a high quality, and considerate extras include tea and coffee trays. After a day out in Bath you ca recharge your batteries in the pleasant Victoria sitting room. An excellent freshly cooked breakfast is served in the attractive dining roor Secure parking in the walled courtyard takes t hassle out of finding a space in the city, and th house is within walking distance of the city centre.

Recommended in the Area

Roman Baths; Longleat; Wells Cathdral

*D*orian House ♦♦♦♦♦

Map ref 2 - ST76
1 Upper Oldfield Park, BATH, BA2 3JX
A36 onto A367 Wells Rd, right onto Upper Oldfield Park, 3rd building on left

T 01225 426336
F 01225 444699
E info@dorianhouse.co.uk
W www.dorianhouse.co.uk

11 rooms, S £47-£95, D £60-£150, No smoking

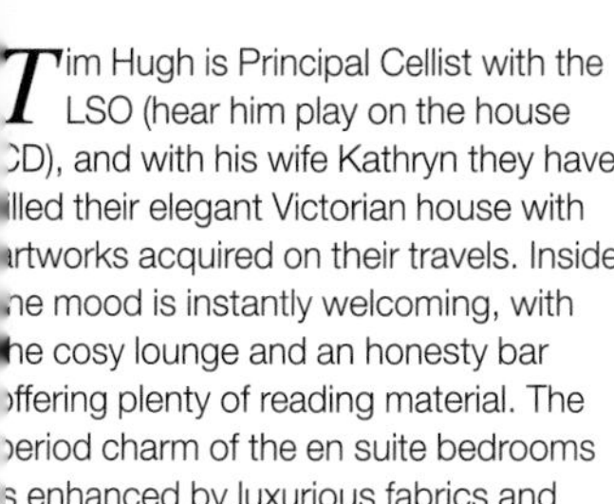

Tim Hugh is Principal Cellist with the LSO (hear him play on the house ⊃D), and with his wife Kathryn they have illed their elegant Victorian house with ırtworks acquired on their travels. Inside ne mood is instantly welcoming, with he cosy lounge and an honesty bar ›ffering plenty of reading material. The ›eriod charm of the en suite bedrooms s enhanced by luxurious fabrics and furnishings. Telephones, tea and coffee facilities and hairdryers are standard, and two rooms have oak four posters. There are lovely views across the city, and the centre is just a walk away. Breakfast is well worth getting up for.

RECOMMENDED IN THE AREA
Roman Baths & The Abbey; Royal Crescent & The Circus; Stourhead (NT)

---

*G*rove Lodge ♦♦♦♦

Map ref 2 - ST76
11 Lambridge, BATH, BA1 6BJ
0.6m NE of city centre. Off A4, 400yds W from junct A46

T 01225 310860
E stay@grovelodgebath.co.uk
W www.grovelodgebath.co.uk

5 rooms, S £38-£45, D £60-£72, No smoking, Closed Xmas, New Year

This Grade II listed Georgian property is reached by a winding stone path through attractive gardens ıith plenty of trees. Owners Isobel Miles, a former ɜacher, and her architect husband Peter Richards have ɜfurbished their beautiful home to highlight the period ɜatures. Bedrooms are spacious with high ceilings, ırge sash windows, and original marble or stone ʻeplaces. Furnishings blend modern and antique tyles, and all rooms have smart new bathrooms. Each room has a radio-alarm clock, king-size bed and a courtesy tray. Breakfast in the sunny dining room is largely organic with plenty of choice, and vegetarian and gluten free diets are happily catered for.

RECOMMENDED IN THE AREA
Georgian Bath; Roman Baths; Bath Abbey

Haydon House ♦♦♦♦♦

Map ref 2 - ST76
9 Bloomfield Park, BATH, BA2 2BY
A36 onto A367 Wells Rd, right onto Bloomfield Rd, 2nd right
T / F 01225 444919
E stay@haydonhouse.co.uk
W www.haydonhouse.co.uk
5 rooms, S £45-£75, D £65-£135, No smoking

Haydon House has been home to Gordon and Magdalene Ashman-Mark since 1988. They keep doves and also have two golden retrievers, Cloud and Cobweb, who are very much part of the establishment. The house is peacefully secluded but convenient for Bath. Reception areas are exquisitely furnished and the well-appointed bedrooms, including one four-poster room, are finished with Laura Ashley fabrics. Rooms are equipped with direct-dial telephones and thoughtful extras such as a decanter of sherry and home-made shortbread. Breakfasts are memorable, offering a good range and variety, with rum or Scottish whisky porridge as star attractions.

Recommended in the Area

Roman Baths; Stonehenge; Wells Cathedral

Marlborough House ♦♦♦♦

Map ref 2 - ST76
1 Marlborough Ln, BATH, BA1 2NQ
450yds W of city centre, on junct A4
T 01225 318175
F 01225 466127
E mars@manque.dircon.co.uk
W www.marlborough-house.net
7 rooms, S £45-£85, D £65-£95, No smoking

Marlborough House is an impressive Victorian stone house with lovely spacious rooms furnished with beautiful antiques. Built in 1867, the house lies in the heart of the city within walking distance of Bath's wonderful buildings. The bedrooms are handsomely furnished and have either an antique wood four-poster or a Victorian brass and iron bed. Each room is spotless and attention to detail is the key here. Sup on complimentary sherry or hot drinks, and sample home-baked cookies. Room service is available all day and evening. Breakfast, featuring the highest quality organic ingredients, is served either in the elegant parlour or lovely dining room. Light meals are available throughout the day.

Recommended in the Area

Roman Baths & Pump Room; Royal Crescent; Stonehenge

Monkshill Guest House ♦♦♦♦♦

Map ref 2 - ST76
Shaft Rd, Monkton Combe, BATH, BA2 7HL
2m SE of Bath in Monkton Combe. Off A36 into Monkton Combe, right opp school, up hill on left
T / F 01225 833028
E monks.hill@virgin.net
W www.monkshill.com
3 rooms, S £60-£75, D £75-£90, No smoking, Closed 2 wks Xmas-New Year

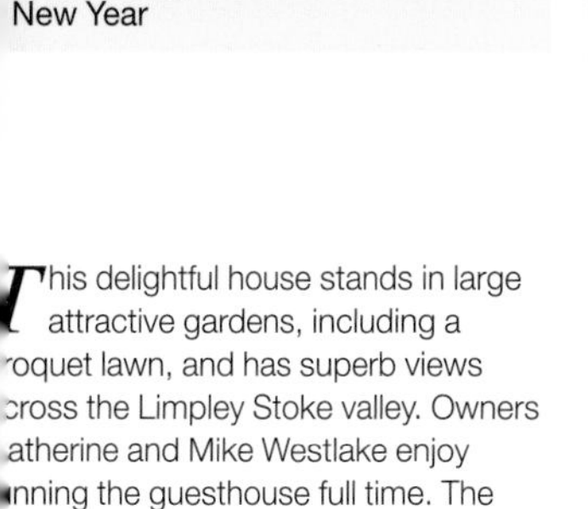

This delightful house stands in large attractive gardens, including a roquet lawn, and has superb views cross the Limpley Stoke valley. Owners atherine and Mike Westlake enjoy inning the guesthouse full time. The edrooms are spacious, and omfortably furnished in keeping with e character of the building. Two of the rooms are en suite and the third has a private bathroom. The attractive sitting room has a real homely feel and is the perfect place in which to relax. A choice of dishes is offered at breakfast, which is served in the elegant dining room at one large table.

RECOMMENDED IN THE AREA

Bath; Longleat; Wells Cathedral; Cheddar Gorge

Number 30 ♦♦♦♦

Map ref 2 - ST76
30 Crescent Gardens, BATH, BA1 2NB
0.5m from Queens Sq towards Bristol
T / F 01225 337393
E david.greenwood12@btinternet.com
W www.numberthirty.com
3 rooms, S £52-£69, D £69-£99, No smoking

RECOMMENDED IN THE AREA

Roman Baths; Royal Crescent; Jane Austen Centre

Number 30 is a friendly Victorian guesthouse with parking just a stroll from the city centre. The urbished accommodation represents housekeeping its best. The light and airy bedrooms have a ntemporary feel and all come with tea and coffee cilities. Each room is named after a famous person io contributed to the building and character of Bath. tail is paid to the cleanliness of the rooms, which ve been designed with allergy sufferers in mind.

Freshly prepared breakfasts, featuring home-made preserves, are served in the light, pleasant dining room, which has an original fireplace. The hosts are always happy to provide local information to help you make the most of your stay.

Oakleigh House ♦♦♦♦

Map ref 2 - ST76
19 Upper Oldfield Park, BATH, BA2 3JX
A36 onto A367 Wells Rd, 1st right
Ⓣ 01225 315698
Ⓕ 01225 448223
Ⓔ oakleigh@which.net
Ⓦ www.oakleigh-house.co.uk
3 rooms, S £50-£55, D £70-£85, No smoking, Closed phone for details

This large Victorian house, built from Bath stone, offers spacious accommodation in a quiet location just a 10-minute walk from the city centre. Jenny King is an enthusiastic host who soon makes her guests feel like old friends. The bedrooms are each equipped with a clock radio, tea and coffee facilities and a hairdryer. There is a pleasant, cosy lounge offering the chance to relax with the daily papers and plenty of books, games and local information. The attractive dining room is the venue for freshly cooked breakfasts. There are lovely views over Georgian Bath and the convenience of off-street parking.

Recommended in the Area

Roman Baths; Royal Crescent & The Circus

St Leonards ♦♦♦♦

Map ref 2 - ST76
Warminster Rd, BATH, BA2 6SQ
A4 onto A36, 1st exit at rdbt, over railway onto Warminster Rd, up hill 200yds on left
Ⓣ 01225 465838
Ⓕ 01225 442800
Ⓔ stleon@dircon.co.uk
Ⓦ www.stleonardsbath.co.uk
6 rooms, S £40-£75, D £65-£90, No smoking, Closed Xmas

From its vantage point high above Bath this well-maintained house has superb views over the city and the Avon valley. Despite a modern makeover the Victorian residence retains its original character. The en suite bedrooms are spacious and thoughtfully equipped, and have gleaming bathrooms. Wonderful country views can be savoured over a full English breakfast in the dining room, and there are lovely walks along the Kennet & Avon Canal near to the house, either into Bath or to a delightful 17th-century canalside pub. Most guests leave their cars safely behind in the private car park ar walk into the city.

Recommended in the Area

Thermae Bath Spa; Roman Baths; Bath Abbey

Clanville Manor ♦♦♦♦

Map ref 2 - ST63
CASTLE CARY, BA7 7PJ
A371 onto B3153, 0.75m entrance to Clanville Manor via white gate & cattle grid under bridge

Ⓣ 01963 350124
Ⓕ 01963 350719
Ⓔ info@clanvillemanor.co.uk
Ⓦ www.clanvillemanor.co.uk

4 rooms, S £30-£35, D £60-£70, No smoking, Closed 21 Dec-2 Jan

RECOMMENDED IN THE AREA
Glastonbury; Stourhead (NT); Wells Cathedral

Clanville Manor is a beef-rearing farm, and has been owned by the Snook family since 1898. Built in 1743 from local honey-colour Cary stone, its flagstone entrance hall and polished oak staircase lead up to individually decorated bedrooms, which retain much original character. Hearty breakfasts are served in the elegant dining room. Fresh golden-yolked eggs come from the farm's own hens, and the full English breakfast is cooked on the Aga - lighter alternatives are available from the breakfast menu. For the evening there are several excellent restaurants and pubs in the locality, or just unwind in the spacious drawing room. In summer you can make a splash in the outdoor heated swimming pool, or walk along the River Brue all year. Only assistance dogs are allowed.

SOMERSET

Batts Farm ♦♦♦♦♦

Map ref 2 - ST45
Nyland, CHEDDAR, BS27 3UD
A371 from Cheddar towards Wells, 2m right towards Nyland, Batts Farm 1m on left

T 01934 741469
E clare@batts-farm.co.uk
W www.batts-farm.co.uk

3 rooms, S £60-£70, D £70-£80,
No smoking

Batts Farm overlooks open farmland and moors at the foot of the Mendips Hills. The 200 year-old property is full of character, and owners Clare and John Pike make you feel at home . Clare's home-made biscuits and cakes are just part of the welcome here. The large bedrooms are all decorated and furnished to a high standard and include especially comfortable beds, one of which is a four-poster. Original sash windows, tiled floors and Victorian fireplaces have been retained. You can relax in the lounge or retreat to the walled garden with its summerhouse for a drink or a cream tea. Or else sit in the romantic formal garden and watch the birds in the water feature. Breakfast is a wide choice with home-made bread and local preserves. You can work off all the delicious goodies by some of the excellent walks in the vicinity.

Recommended in the Area

Cheddar Caves and Gorge; Wookey Hole Caves; Wells

Manor Farm ♦♦♦♦

Map ref 2 - ST40

Wayford, CREWKERNE, TA18 8QL

B3165 from Crewkerne to Lyme Regis, 3m in Clapton right onto Dunsham Ln, Manor Farm 0.5m up hill on right

T / F 01460 78865
W www.manorfarm.biz

5 rooms, S £30-£35, D £56-£60, No smoking

Built of local Ham stone and brick, this imposing farmhouse is on a working farm of 20 acres, including three stocked ponds where guests can fish. The views are wonderful, across open country to the Axe valley, and you can bring your own horses. The farm is on the Liberty Trail, an ancient footpath, and close to several National Trust properties. Bedrooms are comfortably furnished and have showers en suite, hospitality trays and ironing facilities. A self-catering apartment is also available. Breakfast is served in the cosy dining room, and a spacious lounge is provided.

Recommended in the Area

Cricket St Thomas Wildlife Park; Forde Abbey; Lyme Regis coast

---

Dollons House ♦♦♦♦♦

Map ref 2 - SS94

10-12 Church St, DUNSTER, TA24 6SH

Off A39 at lights onto A396 through High St onto Church St

T 01643 821880
E jmott@onetel.com

3 rooms, S £37.50, D £55, No smoking, Closed 25-26 Dec

Situated in the heart of one Exmoor's prettiest villages, Dollons House is a Grade II listed property, older than its 19th-century front suggests. The surrounding national park is ideal for walking, riding, fishing or golf. The house was originally two cottages and was at one time the village pharmacy. These days it provides a ground-floor gift shop, first-floor bed and breakfast accommodation, and an attractive garden at the rear. Bedrooms are full of character, two of them have views of the castle, and all are en suite. Walkers are especially welcome and drying facilities are available. Private parking nearby. Not suitable for children.

Recommended in the Area

Dunster Castle (NT); Exmoor National Park; Exmoor Heritage Coast

Willow Bridge Farms Country Guest House ♦♦♦♦♦

Map ref 2 - ST53
GLASTONBURY, BA5 1RZ
T 01458 835371
F 01458 834885
E julie@willowbridgefarm.co.uk
W www.willowbridgefarm.co.uk
5 rooms, S £45, D £65, No smoking

Recommended in the area

Glastonbury; Cheddar Gorge; Clarks Village, Street

If you love the idea of seeing a working farm in action then this is the place for you. Friendly owners Julie and Royston Andrews are happy to show you around. This is a spanking new property, and very nice too, with spacious en suite bedrooms all at ground level. Thoughtfully furnished and equipped with many extras, each room has French doors opening onto the patio overlooking the river from where you can see both Glastonbury Tor and The Mendips. Breakfast, featuring eggs from the hosts' own chickens and ducks and home-made preserves, is served in the light and airy dining room. The house is situated on the banks of the River Sheppey, which enables you to make the most of the peaceful Somerset Levels either on foot or by bike. There is accommodation especially designed for easier access.

The Old Rectory ♦♦♦♦♦

Map ref 2 - ST31

Cricket Malherbie, ILMINSTER, TA19 0PW

2.5m S of Ilminster. A303 onto A358 S towards Chard, after Donyatt left towards Ilminster, right to Cricket Malherbie, Old Rectory on left

T 01460 54364
F 01460 57374
E info@malherbie.co.uk
W www.malherbie.co.uk

5 rooms, S £60-£65, D £95-£105, No smoking, Closed 24-26 Dec

This Grade II listed house has been beautifully restored and is a lightful place to stay, with its thatched of, sandstone walls and grand ndows overlooking lawns. Your arming hosts Michael and Patricia Fry-ley take particular trouble to offer fine cal produce at breakfast and dinner, oked with flair and imagination. The bedrooms are well equipped, all are en suite and have tea and coffee facilities. The house is licensed and children over 16 can be accommodated, no dogs are allowed in the house except for guide dogs. There is plenty of parking.

RECOMMENDED IN THE AREA

Dorset Heritage Coast; Barrington Court (NT); Montacute House (NT)

Glendower House ♦♦♦♦

Map ref 2 - SS94

30-32 Tregonwell Rd, MINEHEAD, TA24 5DU

A39 into Minehead, last exit at minirdbt, 200yds right by school onto Ponsford Rd & Tregonwell Rd, hotel on left

T 01643 707144
F 01643 708719
E info@glendower-house.co.uk
W www.glendower-house.co.uk

12 rooms, S £35, D £60, No smoking, Closed mid Dec-Jan

friendly atmosphere fills this family-run establishment, occupying an Edwardian terrace not from the seafront, harbour and town centre. The nusiastic proprietors have been busy redecorating to vide elegantly furnished bedrooms with modern ower rooms en suite, and equipped with tea and ee facilities, radio alarms and hair dryers. There is a nely lounge or you can relax on the garden patio on a sunny day. Breakfast is served in the dining room. Ample parking to the rear is a bonus.

RECOMMENDED IN THE AREA

West Somerset Railway; Exmoor National Park; Dunster Castle (NT)

SOMERSET

Kenella House ♦♦♦♦

Map ref 2 - SS94
7 Tregonwell Rd, MINEHEAD, TA24 5DT
Off A39 onto Townsend Rd & right onto Ponsford Rd to Tregonwell Rd
T / F 01643 703128
E kenellahouse@fsmail.net
W www.kenellahouse.co.uk
6 rooms, D £60, No smoking, Closed 23 Dec-2 Jan

Steve and Sandy Poingdestsre welcome you to their elegant Victorian house. It is close to the town centre and combines modern comforts with original charm. The bedrooms are beautifully appointed with iron bedsteads and traditional furnishings. All are en suite and each has a beverage tray, radio alarm and luxury toiletries. Full English breakfasts are served at individual tables in the dining room, and traditional home-cooked meals are available by arrangement. Off-road parking is available, and walkers are well catered for, with maps books and lots of suggestions, plus heated cupboards for outdoor wear. No children or pets.

RECOMMENDED IN THE AREA
Exmoor National Park; West Somerset Railway; South West Coast Path

Cannards Grave Farmhouse ♦♦♦♦

Map ref 2 - ST64
Cannards Grave, SHEPTON MALLET, BA4 4LY
On A37 between Shepton Mallet & The Bath & West Showground, 100yds from Highwayman pub towards showground on left
T / F 01749 347091
E sue@cannardsgravefarmhouse.co.uk
W www.cannardsgravefarmhouse.co.uk
3 rooms, S £35-£50, D £50-£65, No smoking

Cannards Grave is a welcoming 17th-century farmhouse that has been refurbished to offer quality accommodation. New owner Sue Crockett is a charming host. She offers three delightful bedrooms, one with a four-poster bed, and all with modern en suites and hospitality trays. Mineral water, biscuits and mints are typically thoughtful extras, and the largest room has a fridge with fresh milk. Make yourself at home in the well-furnished lounge, and delicious breakfasts are served in the garden conservatory.

RECOMMENDED IN THE AREA
Bath & West Showground; Historic Wells; Glastonbury Tor

3arkham ♦♦♦♦

/lap ref 2 - SS73

'andyway, SIMONSBATH, EX36 3LU

)f A361 to North Molton, through village & nto moor signed Sandyway, left at x-rds 'gned Simonsbath, 400yds turn right

) / F 01643 831370

3 adie.exmoor@btinternet.com

) www.exmoor-vacations.co.uk

rooms, No smoking

ECOMMENDED IN THE AREA

'ington Court (NT); Dunkery Beacon; Quince ney Farm

This was one of the first farmhouses built in the Old Royal Park on Exmoor. The :ensive grounds include a steep wooded ey, pasture with a stream, and a large ehouse. Walks, riding, trout and salmon ing in season, are all close at hand. The wing room has an inglenook fireplace and nch windows opening onto the croquet /n. Bedrooms are satisfyingly simple, one has a bathroom en suite and a king-size double bed - the other rooms are en suite or have private facilities. Breakfast is served in the oak-panelled dining room. The premises are licensed. One of the barns has been converted into an art gallery where concerts take place. A number of courses are run at Barkham and it is a lovely setting for weddings and functions.

Greyhound Inn ♦♦♦♦

Map ref 2 - ST21
STAPLE FITZPAINE, TA3 5SP
Off A358 into village

T 01823 480227
F 01823 481117
E stay@the-greyhoundinn.com
W www.
the-greyhoundinn.fsbusiness.co.u

4 rooms, S £55, D £80, No smokin in bedrooms

Set in an Area of Outstanding Natural Beauty, this attractive 16th-century creeper-clad inn was formerly a hunting lodge. The building has been extended over the years and features a series of inter-connecting rooms with old timbers and exposed stone walls. An imaginative and varied choice of freshly prepared dishes using fine local produce are on offer, with fish fresh daily from Brixham in Devon and seasonal daily specials. A good selection of well-kept real ales is available (some locally brewed for The Greyhound) and traditional Somerset cider on hand pump. The delightful bedrooms are al en suite, and well-equipped with direct-dial telephones with modem, hairdryers, trouser presses and hospitality trays.

RECOMMENDED IN THE ARI

Quantocks; Exmoor National Park; Somerset Levels

Lower Farm ♦♦♦♦

Map ref 2 - ST22
Thornfalcon, TAUNTON, TA3 5NR
M5 junct 25, 2m SE on A358, left opp Nags Head pub, farm signed 1m on left

T / F 01823 443549
E lowerfarm@talk21.com
W www.somersite.co.uk

11 rooms, S £35-£40, D £55-£60, No smoking

A charming thatched 15th-century longhouse, full of character. Lovely gardens and open farmland surround this pretty property, where beamed ceilings and inglenook fireplaces testify to its age. The bedrooms include some in a converted granary, and all are either en suite or have private facilities. All rooms have high standards of furnishings - some bedrooms are ideal for families. A hearty breakfast is cooked on the Aga and served i the farmhouse kitchen, using quality local bacon and sausages, and free-range eggs from proprietor Doree Titman's own hens.

RECOMMENDED IN THE AREA

Hestercombe Gardens; Willow & Wetlands Visitors Cent Quantock Hills

ꓛrown & Victoria ♦♦♦♦

lap ref 2 - ST41
arm St, TINTINHULL, BA22 8PZ
n from Yeovil, off A303, follow signs for ntinhull Gardens
01935 823341
01935 825786
info@crownandvictoriainn.co.uk
www.crownandvictoriainn.co.uk
rooms, S £65-£75, D £85, No smoking in edrooms

ECOMMENDED IN THE AREA
inhull House; Montacute House (NT); Yeovil

The Crown and Victoria stands in the heart of the pretty village of Tintinhull. The inn has en refurbished to a high level of quality, and s standards of housekeeping and hospitality natch. The unfussy bedrooms are light and and very well equipped, and the staff ensure are well cared for. The contemporary bar d restaurant offer carefully presented dishes lunch and dinner, under the direction of head ef, London-trained Stephen Yates. The menu ranges from traditional English dishes such as steak and ale pie to the more elaborate pan-roasted breast of duck on a bed of spinach with a potato rösti, plum and port jus. The extensive wine list includes ten fine house wines. When the weather is kind, relax in the garden with a drink or enjoy a candlelit dinner in the conservatory with garden views.

Baggeridge Farmhouse ♦♦♦♦

Map ref 2 - ST75
WELLOW, BA2 8QP
6m S of Bath. Off A367 to Wellow, left at T-junct, pass Fox & Badger pub, down Mi Hill, over ford, left & right fork, farm at top hill

Ⓣ 01373 834687
Ⓕ 01373 834505
Ⓔ baggeridgefarmhouse@hotmail.com
Ⓦ http://home.btconnect.com/baggerid

3 rooms, D £50-£70, No smoking

RECOMMENDED IN THE AREA

American Museum, Holbourne Museum of Art, Bath Abbey (Bath)

It may not be the easiest place to get to, but the journey is well worth while. Look out for the two friendly black Labradors who will be delighted to see you. This gem of a farmhouse offers an escape from day to day living, in the middle of peaceful countryside. The farm has been in the same family ownership for more than 60 years, and Bridget Small's son still manages a herd of beef cattle as well as arable land. Guests are drawn back by the peaceful location, the traditional hospitality associated with a building that dates back over 500 year and bedrooms that are so comfortable that breakfast could be missed due to over-sleep New visitors will appreciate the inglenook fireplaces, flagstone floors, wooden beams a huge doors. The garden and views are acclaimed by all.

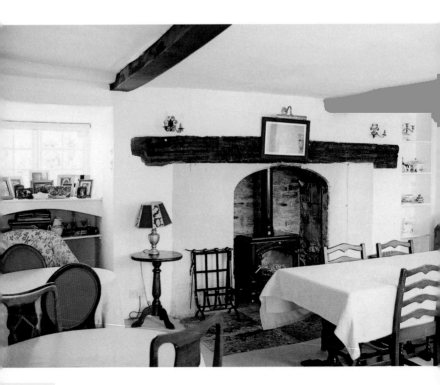

The Linhay B&B ♦♦♦♦

Map ref 2 - ST04
Williton Rd, WASHFORD, TA23 0NU
A39 towards Minehead, 2.5m after Williton
T 01984 641252
E thelinhay@aol.com
W www.linhay.co.uk
rooms, S £40, D £55-£60, No smoking

inhay is a comfortable barn conversion in the village of Washford the edge of the Exmoor National rk. It is convenient for coast and untry attractions and is well placed good walks. The hospitable owners sure your stay is memorable. e en suite bedrooms are particularly ll appointed, each having a tea and fee tray, DVD player, and a sitting a within the bedroom to relax. A hearty breakfast is served in the dining room and the patio leads to an attractive garden. A hot tub and sauna are available by arrangement for an additional charge.

RECOMMENDED IN THE AREA

Exmoor National Park; West Somerset Railway & Museum; Dunster Castle (NT)

Double-Gate Farm ♦♦♦♦

Map ref 2 - ST54
Godney, WELLS, BA5 1RX
A39 from Wells towards Glastonbury, at Polsham right signed Godney/Polsham, 2m to x-rds, continue to farmhouse on left after inn
T 01458 832217
F 01458 835612
E doublegatefarm@aol.com
W www.doublegatefarm.com
6 rooms, No smoking, Closed Dec-Jan

et amid the Somerset Levels, this fine stone farmhouse has a lovely view of Glastonbury Tor. akfast is served from an extensive menu at two ectory tables in the dining room, or on the patio in nmer. Other meals can be taken at local inns, uding the pub next door. A wide range of facilities udes a lounge, laundry, and a games room with a -size snooker table, table tennis and darts. ll-equipped en suite bedrooms feature hairdryers and complimentary tea and coffee. Also expect a warm welcome from the family cats and dogs - Jasper-Pilchards, Paddy 4 Paws, Laid-Back-Jack and Miss Jessops.

RECOMMENDED IN THE AREA

Wells (England's smallest city); Glastonbury; Cheddar Gorge

Beverley Guest House ♦♦♦♦

Map ref 2 - ST36
11 Whitecross Rd, WESTON-SUPER-MARE, BS23 1EP
Off A370 Beach Rd onto Ellenborough Park Rd & Whitecros Rd
T / F 01934 622956
E beverley11@hushmail.com
W www.beverleyguesthouse.co.uk
5 rooms, S £27-£35, D £50-£55, No smoking, Closed Xmas

Friendly hosts Mary and Peter Morgan offer holiday breaks at their charming Victorian guesthouse in a quiet residential area close to the beach. Children are warmly welcomed and this is an ideal seaside accommodation for the whole family. The en suite bedrooms are individually decorated and furnished, and each thoughtfully equipped with a beverage tray, shoe-cleaning kit and a torch. One double room is on the ground floor, and there is a family suite. Breakfast ingredients are sourced locally whene possible, and you are offered plenty o choice each morning in the dining roo The conservatory lounge is an appeal retreat.

RECOMMENDED IN THE ARE
Weston-Super-Mare beach; Clevedon Court (NT); Wookey Hole caves

Camellia Lodge ♦♦♦♦

Map ref 2 - ST36
76 Walliscote Rd, WESTON-SUPER-MARE, BS23 1ED
200yds from seafront
T / F 01934 613534
E dachefscamellia@aol.com
5 rooms, S £25-£27.50, D £50-£60

With the mile-long promenade and pier right on your doorstep, this is a great choice for a seaside break. The proprietors create a warm atmosphere that makes you want to return again and again - they are so pleased to have you stay they will even collect you from the train or bus stations. Inside their three-storey Victorian home you will find immaculate bedrooms well equipped for a long or sh stay. Most are a good size and have bathrooms en suite. Breakfast is a wide choice using local produce and evening meals are available. Both are served the dining room.

RECOMMENDED IN THE AREA
Weston Golf Club; Sea Life Centre; Cheddar Gorge

Karslake House ♦♦♦♦

Map ref 2 - SS93
Halse Ln, WINSFORD, TA24 7JE
Off A396 (Winsford). In village turn left beyond village stores signed Karslake House. Around corner 100yds on right
T / F 01643 851242
E enquiries@karslakehouse.co.uk
W www.karslakehouse.co.uk
6 rooms, S £53-£68, D £74-£108, No smoking, Closed Feb-Mar

Karslake is a small country hotel - very much a family home where guests are made to feel like old friends. It is surrounded by some of the most beautiful countryside in Exmoor and is ideal for a peaceful and relaxing break. Original beams and fireplaces feature and quality is evident in the furnishings throughout the house. The bedrooms are attractively decorated and thoughtfully equipped with hairdryers, complimentary toiletries, and tea, coffee and mineral water. Four bedrooms are en suite, including one with a four-poster bed. Food is a highlight, and interesting menus, home-baked bread, and home-made preserves are offered in the spacious restaurant, which has an AA Rosette award. Riding, fishing and shooting can be arranged. Dogs are welcome. No children under 12.

Recommended in the Area

Tarr Steps (medieval clapper bridge); Holnicote Estate (NT); Barle Valley Safaris (see the countryside by Landrover)

Staffordshire

A selection of places to eat from the AA Restaurant & AA Pub guides

Restaurants

@@ Moat House (British, Mediterranean)
Lower Penkridge Road,
Acton Trussell ST17 0RJ
Tel 01785 712217

@ Three Horseshoes Inn (International)
Buxton Road, Blackshaw Moor,
Leek ST13 8TW, Tel 01538 300296

@ Bratz (European)
Minster House, Pool Walk WS13 6QT
Tel 01543 253788

@ The Elms (Indian)
Snowhill, Shelton, Stoke-on-Trent ST1 4LY
Tel 01782 266360

@ Haydon House Hotel (European)
Haydon Street, Basford,
Stoke-on-Trent ST4 6JD
Tel 01782 711311

Pubs

The Old Boat
Alrewas DE13 7DB
Tel 01283 791468

The George
Castle Street, Eccleshall ST21 6DF
Tel 01785 850300

Ye Olde Royal Oak
Wetton, Leek DE6 2AF
Tel 01335 310336

The Hollybush Inn
Salt, Stafford ST18 0BX
Tel 01889 508234

Ye Olde Dog & Partridge Inn
High Street, Tutbury DE13 9LS
Tel 01283 813030

Blakelands Country House ♦♦♦♦

Map ref 2 - SO89
Halfpenny Green, BOBBINGTON, DY7 5DP
Off B4176 towards Halfpenny Gree & Bobbington, establishment signe 1.5m
T 01384 221000
F 01384 221585
E info@blakelands.com
W www.blakelands.com
15 rooms, S £51-£56, D £72-£82, No smoking in bedrooms or dining room, Closed 25 Dec-2 Jan

This Grade II listed country house dates from 1722 and stands in extensive grounds with a private fishing lake. Bedrooms are spread between various buildings, and range in size from suites with four posters and king-size beds to standard double rooms. Rooms in the main house have draped walls and oak floors, or exposed timbers and oak panels, while a further four are in the converted stables, and six more are in the lodge. All are exceptionally well equipped and attractive, with optional sunken whirlp bath and art-nouveau bathroom. A varied menu is served in the spacious restaurant, including delicious multi-choice breakfasts.

RECOMMENDED IN THE ARE
Ironbridge World Heritage Site; Black Country Living Museum, Dudley; Merry Hill Shopping Centre, Brierley Hill

---

Colton House ♦♦♦♦

Map ref 3 - SK01
Colton, RUGELEY, WS15 3LL
1.5m N of Rugeley Off B5013 into Colton, B&B 0.25m on right
T / F 01889 578580
E mail@colton-house.com
W www.colton-house.com
3 rooms, S £35-£60, D £48-£76, No smoking

This elegant Grade II* residence dates from the 1730s and has been restored to its original glory. Colton House stands in lovely grounds within the picturesque village of Colton on the edge of Cannock Chase. The grand interior features a carved stone fireplace in the hall, original oak panelling, and a stunning oak staircase rising from the hall. The bedrooms have their own distinctive style, from the Four Poster Room and the bright Summer Room, to beamed rooms at the top of the house. Nothing is too much trouble for owners Ron and Gay Lawrence, who are dedicated to ensuring you have ar enjoyable stay.

RECOMMENDED IN THE AREA
The Potteries; Cannock Chase; Shugborough (NT)

Haywood Park Farm ♦♦♦♦

Map ref 7 - SJ92
Shugborough, STAFFORD,
ST17 0XA
4m SE of Stafford off A513. Brown signs to Shugborough, B&B on right 400yds past Hall
T / F 01889 882736
E haywood.parkfarm@btopenworld.com
W www.haywoodparkfarm.co.uk
2 rooms, S £42-£45, D £60-£65,
No smoking

The attractive farmhouse stands on a 120-acre arable and sheep farm on Cannock Chase, part of Shugborough Estate. The large, attractively nished bedrooms have a host of extras such as fresh wers, fruit, tea facilities and shortbread. Large fluffy vels are provided in the luxury bathrooms, one with a -top bath. After a hectic day outdoors you can relax the fire in the pretty sitting room. Breakfast, using al produce, is served in the attractive lounge-dining room. The area is a paradise for walkers and cyclists with great opportunities for spotting wildlife. Fishing is offered in the lake, which is well stocked with carp and coarse fish.

Recommended in the Area

Shugborough Hall (NT); Wedgewood Museum; Alton Towers

---

arlaston Post Office ♦♦♦♦

Map ref 3 - SK20
Main Rd, Harlaston, TAMWORTH,
379 9JU
.5m N, off A513 into Harlaston illage
01827 383324
01827 383746
info@harlastonpostoffice.co.uk
www.harlastonpostoffice.co.uk
rooms, S £27.50-£30, D £48-£50,
No smoking

ECOMMENDED IN THE AREA

ayton Manor Theme Park; Lichfield thedral; National Memorial Arboretum, ewas

The Post Office is a row of traditional cottages that has been renovated to eate a desirable guesthouse. Still orporating a Post Office and stores, it nds opposite the church in an idyllic age, with pretty gardens behind. The suite bedrooms have been lividually decorated and furnished, d have comfy beds, bathrooms and hospitality trays, with plenty of thoughtful extras to help you feel at home. Other considerate touches are the guest kitchen, laundry and lounge, ideal for families with young children. Joyce Rowe is a delightful host, and her hearty cooked breakfasts have to be experienced.

Oak Tree Farm ♦♦♦♦♦

Map ref 3 - SK20
Hints Rd, Hopwas, TAMWORTH, B78 3AA
2m NW of Tamworth. Off A51 in Hopwas
T / F 01827 56807
E oaktreefarm1@aol.com
7 rooms, S £57-£100, D £75-£100, No smoking

RECOMMENDED IN THE ARE
Tamworth Snow Dome; Drayton Manor Pleasure Park; Lichfield Cathedral

This beautifully renovated farmhouse is on the edge of the village of Hopwas, north west of Tamworth. It is surrounded by spacious gardens and overlooks the River Thame. Two rooms are in the main house and the others are on the first and ground floors of a converted former grain store and farm building. All of them are en suite. There is an attractive breakfast room, where separate tables are provided. Other facilities include an indoor swimming pool and steam room. Mrs Lovett creates a friendly and relaxing atmosphere and really enjoys welcomi guests. Despite the tranquil rural location, the house is a convenient bas for visitors to Tamworth, Lichfield, Birmingham and the National Exhibitio Centre.

Suffolk

A selection of places to eat from the AA Restaurant & AA Pub guide

Restaurants

Swan House (British)
By The Tower, Beccles NR34 9HE
Tel 01502 713474

Fox & Goose Inn (British)
Fressingfield IP21 5PB
Tel 01379 586247

Hintlesham Hall (British)
Hintlesham IP8 3NS
Tel 01473 652334

Great House Restaurant (French)
Market Place, Lavenham CO10 9QZ
Tel 01787 247431

The Crown & Castle (International)
Orford IP12 2LJ
Tel 01394 450205

Pubs

Cornwallis Country Hotel
Brome IP23 8AJ
Tel 01379 870326

Red Lion
The Street, Icklingham,
Bury St Edmunds IP28 6PS
Tel 01638 717802

Angel Hotel
Market Place, Lavenham CO10 9QZ
Tel 01787 247388

St Peter's Hall
St Peter South Elmham NR35 1NQ
Tel 01986 783115

Crown Hotel
The High Street, Southwold IP18 6DP
Tel 01502 722275

The Toll House ♦♦♦♦

Map ref 4 - TM45
50 Victoria Rd, ALDEBURGH,
IP15 5EJ
B1094 into town until rdbt, B&B on right
T 01728 453239
W www.
tollhouse.travelbugged.com
7 rooms, D £70, No smoking

RECOMMENDED IN THE AREA
Minsmere Bird Sanctuary (RSPB); Concert Hall, Snape; Suffolk Heritage Coast

Expect a warm welcome at this delightful Victorian brick house, situated just a short walk from the seafront and 0.5 mile from the centre of Aldeburgh, with its associations with composer Benjamin Britten. This coastal area is a paradise for birdwatchers and walkers. Snape Maltings, 5 miles away, is a collection of traditional buildings nestling beside the River Alde with shops, galleries, restaurants and the world-class concert hall. The bedrooms at The Toll House - twins and doubles - all have bathrooms en suite, attractive coordinated fabrics and tea and coffee facilities. Breakfast is served at individual tables in the smart dining room that overlooks the pretty, secluded garden.

Earsham Park Farm ♦♦♦♦

Map ref 4 - TM38
Old Railway Rd, Earsham, BUNGAY,
NR35 2AQ
3m SW of Bungay on A143
T 01986 892180
F 01986 894796
E aa@earsham-parkfarm.co.uk
W www.earsham-parkfarm.co.uk
3 rooms, S £42-£60, D £62-£80,
No smoking

RECOMMENDED IN THE AREA
Bungay market town; Earsham Otter Trust; Suffolk Heritage Coast

The farmhouse has been refurbished by Bobbie and Simon Watchorn to retain its Victorian charm while providing modern comforts. Overlooking open countryside, the house is very much part of a working farm. An agricultural theme runs in the names of the three suites, which all feature antique furniture - there is a four poster in one room - and are beautifully decorated and fully equipped. Delicious breakfasts allow you to indulge in sausages and bacon from the farm's free-range pigs, accompanied by home-made breads and preserves. You can buy the pork produce and relive the farmhouse experience at home.

The Chantry Hotel ♦♦♦♦

Map ref 4 - TL86
8 Sparhawk St, BURY ST EDMUNDS, IP33 1RY
From cathedral S onto Crown St, left onto Sparhawk St
T 01284 767427
F 01284 760946
E chantryhotel1@aol.com
W www.chantryhotel.com
15 rooms, S £59-£79, D £79-£99, No smoking in bedrooms or dining room

RECOMMENDED IN THE AREA

Abbey Gardens & ruins; Theatre Royal (NT); Town centre restaurants

Built on the site of a 12th-century chapel, the hotel building is mainly Georgian, abutting a much older property. Part of a conservation area, it is Grade II listed and parking for each room is provided via a 19th-century carriage access. Bedrooms are decorated in period style, and the spacious superior double rooms (all non-smoking) feature antique beds. All the rooms are en suite and well equipped with direct-dial telephones and tea and coffee facilities. There is a cosy lounge bar, and breakfast and dinner are served in the smart restaurant. Dishes are home cooked and prepared from fresh ingredients.

Clarice House ♦♦♦♦♦

Map ref 4 - TL86
Horringer Court, Horringer Rd, BURY ST EDMUNDS, IP29 5PH
1m SW from town centre on A143 towards Horringer
T 01284 705550
F 01284 716120
E enquiry@clarice-bury.fsnet.co.uk
W www.clarice.co.uk
13 rooms, S £55-£70, D £85-£100, No smoking, Closed 24-26 Dec, 31 Dec-1 Jan

Clarice House is a large neo-Jacobean mansion set in 20 acres of pretty landscaped grounds a short drive from the historic centre of Bury St Edmunds. The family-run residential spa has spacious, well-equipped bedrooms with coordinated fabrics and many thoughtful touches. Public rooms include a smart lounge bar, an intimate restaurant, a further lounge and a conservatory. Superb leisure facilities feature a large swimming pool, sauna, steam room, spa, gym (assessment required), and a health and beauty salon, all at no extra charge. The restaurant offers a wide range of dishes with vegetarian options and a detox menu plan if desired.

RECOMMENDED IN THE AREA

Bury St Edmunds; Abbey Gardens; Ickworth House & Garden (NT)

83 Whiting Street ♦♦♦♦

Map ref 4 - TL86
83 Whiting St, BURY ST EDMUNDS,
IP33 1NX
In town centre
T 01284 704153
E gordon@83whitingst.fsnet.co.uk
3 rooms, S £36, D £58, No smoking

A lovely three-storey town-centre property, 83 Whiting Street is steeped in history. A wall painting, one of the best of its kind to be found in England, is thought to date back to 1330. The building was possibly once a hunting house. The en suite bedrooms are individually decorated, and feature fine furniture and tea and coffee facilities. Full English breakfasts are served in the beamed dining room with its open fireplace, which like all the public rooms is comfortable and inviting. Staying here you are well placed for shopping, but need to be circumspect about parking.

RECOMMENDED IN THE AREA
Abbey Gardens; Cathedral; West Stow Anglo-Saxon Village

The Three Kings ♦♦♦♦

Map ref 4 - TL86
Hengrave Rd, Fornham All Saints,
BURY ST EDMUNDS, IP28 6LA
2m NW of Bury. A14 junct 42, B1106 to Fornham, left at minirdbt, establishment on left
T 01284 766979
E the threekings@keme.co.uk
W www.the-three-kings.com
9 rooms, S £57.50, D £75,
No smoking

RECOMMENDED IN THE AREA
Bury St Edmunds Abbey & Gardens; West Stow Anglo-Saxon Village; Lavenham

The Kings Lodge is an attractive new building to the rear of the Three Kings, a 17th-century coaching inn situated in the pleasant village of Fornham All Saints. The Lodge contains the immaculate en suite bedrooms, which have an excellent range of facilities including minibars, bath or shower, radios, hairdryers, tea and coffee facilities, trouser presses, telephones and Internet access. You can unwind with a beverage in the friendly atmosphere of the lounge bar or conservatory in the Three Kings, where wholesome traditional English food is available. A Sunday carvery is served in the main restaurant.

Chippenhall Hall ♦♦♦♦♦

Map ref 4 - TM27
FRESSINGFIELD, IP21 5TD
8m E of Diss: 1.5m outside Fressingfield on B1116 to Framlingham

Ⓣ 01379 588180
Ⓕ 0870 831 5113
Ⓔ info@chippenhall.co.uk
Ⓦ www.chippenhall.co.uk

3 rooms, S £90-£105, D £95-£110, No smoking in bedrooms or dining room

RECOMMENDED IN THE AREA
Bressingham Garden Centre; Earsham Otter Trust; Norfolk Broads

A lovely 16th- and 17th-century house bursting with character, with plenty of original features. Walls and ceilings are heavily beamed, and a copper canopied inglenook fireplace that was once used for hanging game is now an honesty bar. Barbara and Jakes Sargent specialise in providing good food for dinner parties, and their home is also a popular wedding venue. Dinner and imaginative breakfasts are served at the antique refectory table in the dining room, and the brick-floored drawing room i a peaceful retreat. Spacious en suite bedrooms includ the high-vaulted Cheese Room, once part of the dairy which overlooks the duck pond and courtyard swimming pool.

Edge Hall ♦♦♦♦♦

Map ref 4 - TM04
2 High St, HADLEIGH, IP7 5AP
B1070 into Hadleigh. 1st property i High St on right

Ⓣ 01473 822458
Ⓕ 01473 827751
Ⓔ r.rolfe@edgehall-hotel.co.uk
Ⓦ www.edgehall-hotel.co.uk

10 rooms, S £45-£75, D £75-£95, No smoking

Known as the Cross when built in the 16th century, this imposing house is at the quiet end of High Street in the heart of Constable Country. Run by the same family for over 25 years, the proprietors have a good eye for detail. The flagstone hall and fine staircase give a superb first impression, and the rest of the house is just as pleasing. Spacious bedrooms are furnished in period style and the bathrooms have efficient showers - one room has a four-poster bed. Traditional breakfasts are served in the stately dining room and there is a comfortable lounge. In summer the walled garden is popular for afternoon tea or a game of croquet.

RECOMMENDED IN THE ARE
Sutton Hoo (NT); Flatford Mill; Beth Chatto Gardens

Lavenham Priory ♦♦♦♦♦

Map ref 4 - TL94
Water St, LAVENHAM, CO10 9RW
A1141 to Lavenham, turn by side of Swan onto Water St & right after 50yds onto private drive
T 01787 247404
F 01787 248472
E mail@lavenhampriory.co.uk
W www.lavenhampriory.co.uk
6 rooms, S £70-£85, D £90-£155, No smoking, Closed 21 Dec-2 Jan

Gilli and Tim Pitt have created a sumptuous haven in the midst of historic Lavenham, one of England's rettiest medieval villages. The building dates back to e 15th century and retains many fine early features, cluding an oak Jacobean staircase, leading to eautiful bedrooms with crown posts, Elizabethan wall aintings and oak floors. Each room has a spectacular ed, a four poster, lit bateau or polonaise; and all have suites and tea and coffee facilities. The house stands 3 acres of private grounds, all attractively landscaped d stocked with period herbs, plants and shrubs.

Breakfast is taken in the Merchant's Room at an imposing polished table. The great hall with its Tudor inglenook fireplace and an adjoining lounge are lovely places to relax and are well stocked with books.

Recommended in the Area

Lavenham Guildhall (NT); Sutton Hoo (NT); Kentwell Hall

The Garden Lodge ♦♦♦♦

Map ref 4 - TL66
11 Vicarage Ln, Woodditton,
NEWMARKET, CB8 9SG
3m S of Newmarket in Woodditton village
T 01638 731116
E swedishgardenlodge@hotmail.com
W www.gardenlodge.net
3 rooms, S £25-£30, D £40-£50, No smoking

There's a true home-from-home feel to this cabin annexe, due in no small part to the natural warmth and hospitality of Anna Tyler and Charles Smith. The Swedish-style building is in their lovely garden, and consists of three en suite bedrooms each equipped with a minibar-fridge and a hospitality tray. The rooms are comfortably furnished, and all are adaptable to doubles, twins or singles. Freshly cooked evening meals including wine are available in the main house, where the delicious full English or continental breakfasts are also served. Guests are given their own keys, and there is ample parking.

RECOMMENDED IN THE AREA

Newmarket Races; Cambridge University; Ely Cathedral

Bays Farm ♦♦♦♦♦

Map ref 4 - TM05
Forward Green, STOWMARKET,
IP14 5HU
A14 junct 50, onto A1120. 1m after Stowupland, turn right at sharp left hand bend signed Broad Green. Bays Farm 1st house on right
T 01449 711286
E information@baysfarmsuffolk.co.uk
W www.baysfarmsuffolk.co.uk
3 rooms, S £60, D £70, No smoking

A lavish restoration has turned this charming 17th-century farmhouse into a quality destination for discerning guests. A moat and 4 acres of mature gardens surround the property, while the interior is a wealth of oak beams, open fireplaces and exposed brickwork. The superb en suite bedrooms are furnished in coordinated colours and soft furnishings, and filled with generous extras. Afternoon tea with home-made cake is served in the drawing room. Home-made food also plays a part in the impressive breakfasts, served around a large polished table in the oak-beamed dining room.

RECOMMENDED IN THE AREA

Bury St Edmunds; Suffolk Heritage Coast; Constable Country

Long Springs B&B ♦♦♦♦♦

Map ref 4 - TM24
Woods Ln, Melton, WOODBRIDGE, IP12 1LN
Off A14 onto A12, at 7th rdbt turn right onto Woods Ln, B&B 500yds on left
T 01394 383646
F 01394 383905
E enquiries@longsprings.co.uk
W www.longsprings.co.uk
4 rooms, S £65-£95, D £95, No smoking in bedrooms

RECOMMENDED IN THE AREA
Sutton Hoo (NT); Orford Castle; Woodbridge Tide Mill

Long Springs is an Arts and Crafts country house set in mature landscaped grounds. Housed in a separate cottage, the lovely en suite bedrooms are decorated with natural colours and fabrics, and are well supplied with modern amenities. Public areas include a lounge with a large plasma screen television and a library with Internet access. Meals are served in the dining room or the informal conservatory. Other amenities include a tennis court, croquet lawn and indoor swimming pool within a log cabin. You can wander and relax in the gardens but tread carefully near the fish pond - Arthur the ghost carp is rumoured to eat children.

The Bull Auberge ♦♦♦♦♦

Map ref 4 - TM17
Ipswich Rd, YAXLEY, IP23 8BZ
On the A140 between Norwich & Ipswich at B1117 x-rds Eye/Stadbloke
T 01379 783604
F 01379 788486
E deestenhouse@fsmail.net
W www.the-auberge.co.uk
4 rooms, S £60-£70, D £80-£100, No smoking

RECOMMENDED IN THE AREA
Suffolk Heritage Coast; Cambridge; Newmarket

Convenient for the Suffolk and Norfolk coasts, this former pub sits in beautifully tended grounds and has been converted into a luxurious restaurant with rooms. Chef John Stenhouse and his wife Dee have successfully created a warm and intimate atmosphere, both in the restaurant and the elegant and spacious double bedrooms. There's a wealth of character, with exposed original brickwork and beams, and each bedroom is air-conditioned and furnished to a very high standard. The excellent restaurant offers a wide range of food, using fresh local produce wherever possible, and John will endeavour to accommodate special diets and requests.

A selection of places to eat from the AA Restaurant & AA Pub guide

Restaurants

Drakes on the Pond (British)
Dorking Road, Abinger Hammer RH5 6SA
Tel 01306 731174

La Luna (Italian)
10 Wharf Street, Godalming GU7 1NN
Tel 01483 414155

Bryce's at the Old School House (British, Seafood)
Ockley RH5 5TH
Tel 01306 627430

The Dining Room (British)
59A High Street, Reigate RH2 9AE
Tel 01737 226650

Kinghams (British)
Gomshall Lane, Shere GU5 9HE
Tel 01483 202168

Pubs

The Stephan Langton
Friday Street, Abinger Common RH5 6JR
Tel 01306 730775

The Crown Inn
The Green, Chiddingfold GU8 4TX
Tel 01428 682255

The Plough Inn
Coldharbour Lane, Coldharbour RH5 6HD
Tel 01306 711793

The Woolpack
The Green, Elstead GU8 6HD
Tel 01252 703106

The Inn @ West End
42 Guildford Road, West End GU24 9PW
Tel 01276 858652

Pembroke House ♦♦♦♦

Map ref 3 - SU96
Valley End Rd, CHOBHAM, GU24 8TB
A30 onto B383 signed Chobham, 3m right onto Valley End Rd, B&B 1m on left
T 01276 857654
F 01276 858445
E pembrokehouse@macunlimited.net
5 rooms, S £40-£50, D £80-£100, No smoking

Recommended in the Area

Windsor Castle; Wisley RHS Gardens; Shooting at Bisley

Julia Holland takes great pleasure in treating guests as friends at her beautifully appointed and spacious neo-Georgian home set among rolling fields. The elegant public areas include an imposing entrance hall and a dining room with views over the surrounding countryside. The bedrooms are filled with thoughtful extras and, along with the bathrooms, have been decorated for a restful stay. Two single rooms share a bathroom, while the other rooms are en suite, but all have a bath and power shower. The accent here is on sporting pursuits; there are many top-class golf clubs in the vicinity, as well as polo, horseracing and shooting. Or else saunter out to the tennis court in the attractive grounds.

Bentley Mill ♦♦♦♦♦

Map ref 3 - SU84
Bentley, FARNHAM, GU10 5JD
Off A31 Farnham-Alton road, opp Bull Inn, turn left onto Gravel Hill Rd
T 01420 23301
F 01420 22538
E ann.bentleymill@supanet.com
W www.bentleymill.com
4 rooms, S £50-£90, D £95-£120, No smoking, Closed Xmas, New Year

RECOMMENDED IN THE AREA
Jane Austen's House, Chawton; The Watercress Line, Alresford; Portsmouth Historic Dockyard

Hospitality knows no bounds here - Ann and David Hallett do everything in their power to ensure you njoy their wonderful country home, a former corn mill eside a river. You will be greeted with fresh flowers in ur room and luxury chocolates on your pillow. Set in acres of beautifully tended grounds, the two main ites are in the former mill where all the original beams rvive. The rooms are of superior quality featuring tiques and luxurious beds and deep sofas. Start your day with a delicious full breakfast cooked on the Aga or choose seasonal fruit, croissants or bagels. A room service menu is available 7pm-9pm providing hot and cold snacks.

Sussex

selection of places to eat from the AA Restaurant & AA Pub guides

estaurant

@@@ The Camellia Restaurant at South odge Hotel (British, Mediterranean)
righton Road, Lower Beeding RH13 6PS
el 01403 891711

Old Forge (Contemporary)
Church Street, Storrington RH20 4LA
el 01903 743402

@@ The Old House Restaurant (British, ench)
ffingham Road, Copthorne RH10 3JB
el 01342 712222

Sundial Restaurant (French)
erstmonceux BN27 4LA
el 01323 832217

@@ Terre à Terre (Vegetarian)
1 East Street, Brighton BN1 1HQ
el 01273 729051

Pub

Black Horse Inn
Nuthurst Street, Nuthurst RH13 6LH
Tel 01403 891272

George & Dragon
Burpham BN18 9RR
Tel 01903 883131

The Half Moon Inn
Kirdford RH14 0LT
Tel 01403 820223

Lickfold Inn
Lickfold GU28 9EY
Tel 01798 861285

The White Horse at Chilgrove
High Street, Chilgrove PO18 9HX
Tel 01243 535219

*F*arthings Farm ♦♦♦♦♦

Map ref 4 - TQ71
Catsfield, BATTLE, TN33 9BA
A271 W from Battle, left onto B2204 towards Catsfield, farm 1m on left on sharp S-bend & farmhouse 0.5m down lane

Ⓣ 01424 773107
Ⓔ penny.rodgers@btconnect.com
Ⓦ www.farthingsfarm.co.uk

3 rooms, D £60, No smoking, Closed 20-30 Dec

This elevated Edwardian farmhouse looks over 70 acres of unspoiled woodland, fields and lakes. Bedrooms in the renovated guest wing are finished with a modern minimalist feel, a careful mix of old and new hand-made furniture and paintings, while one room has a balcony. In the large lounge-dining room you can sink into comfy sofas, light a log fire, or else enjoy summer evenings on the garden terrace. A memorable traditional breakfast is served around a communal dining table. Historic Battle is a 20-minute walk away via the 1066 Country Walk, or drive to the South Downs and Beachy Head via Pevensey Castle.

RECOMMENDED IN THE AREA

Battle Abbey; Herstmonceux Castle; Bateman's (Kipling's house, NT)

---

*F*ox Hole Farm ♦♦♦♦

Map ref 4 - TQ71
Kane Hythe Rd, BATTLE, TN33 9QU
Off A271 onto B2096 farm 0.75m from junct on right

Ⓣ / Ⓕ 01424 772053
Ⓔ foxholefarm@amserve.com

3 rooms, S £35-£49, D £55-£65, No smoking, Closed Dec-Jan

RECOMMENDED IN THE AREA

Battle Abbey; Bodiam Castle (NT); Pashley Manor Gardens

No other house is visible from secluded Fox Hole Farm, an 18th-century woodcutter's cottage set in 40 acres of grounds surrounded by forest, close to the town of Battle. Bedrooms are traditional in style but well equipped with modern facilities, bathrooms en suite and hospitality trays. A three-course breakfast is served at individual tables in the dining room. Recommendations for nearby restaurants and pubs are gladly given. Relax in the sitting room, which has exposed beams and an inglenook fireplace with a wood-burning stove. There is no smoking in the farmhouse and well-tempered dogs can be accommodated.

White Barn Guest House ♦♦♦♦

Map ref 3 - SU80
Crede Ln, BOSHAM, PO18 8NX
A259 Bosham rdbt, turn S signed Bosham Quay, 0.5m to T-junct, left signed White Barn, 0.25m turn left signed White Barn, 50yds turn right
T / F 01243 573113
E chrissie@whitebarn.biz
W www.whitebarn.biz
3 rooms, S £40-£60, D £60-£90, No smoking

Some come to recharge their batteries with the peace and privacy, while thers enjoy meeting fellow guests and osts Chrissie and Terry. This delightful roperty is quietly located in the icturesque harbour village of Bosham. he coordinated bedrooms are bright nd inviting with many thoughtful extras. raditional English or continental breakfasts are a notable morning fixture, while the open-plan dining room is also the scene of hearty four-course dinners (by arrangement November to March). As it is unlicensed, you can bring your own wine and Terry and Chrissie will happily chill and open it for you.

Recommended in the Area

Goodwood; Chichester Harbour & Theatre; Portsmouth

Nineteen ♦♦♦♦

Map ref 3 - TQ30
19 Broad St, BRIGHTON & HOVE, BN2 1TJ
A23 to Brighton Pier, left onto, Broad St 3rd on left
T 01273 675529
F 01273 675531
E info@hotelnineteen.co.uk
W www.hotelnineteen.co.uk
8 rooms, D £90-£250, No smoking

Recommended in the Area

Brighton seafront; Royal Pavilion; South Downs

Only minutes from Brighton Pier, this trendy establishment is still in a quiet part of the resort. edrooms are appointed with pure white walls, wooden ors, silver blinds and contemporary artwork, and owned by glass beds illuminated by subtle blue hting. All rooms have flat-screen televisions, DVD and D players, and the en suites are stocked with Molton rown products. A unique addition is a bedroom mplete with hot tub in its own secluded courtyard. The continental breakfast (with complimentary Bloody Marys at weekends) is served in your bedroom. Pamper yourself with one of the beauty treatments offered in the privacy of your own room.

Judins ♦♦♦♦

Map ref 4 - TQ62
Heathfield Rd, BURWASH WEALD, TN19 7LA
A265 W from Burwash, pass filling station on right, house 0.6m on left
T 01435 882455
E sjudins@aol.co.uk
3 rooms, D £70-£85, No smoking

Nestled in 40 acres of countryside and with 2 acres of formal gardens, 300-year-old Judins is perfect for a relaxing break. The attractive bedrooms are mostly quite spacious, and each one is carefully furnished and thoughtfully equipped - the main bedroom has a king-size bed and lovely views. Public rooms include a sunny conservatory, a lounge and an elegant dining room. Breakfast is an excellent feast and your welcoming host Sandra Jolly uses the finest home-grown produce and free-range eggs and pork. Evening meals are available by arrangement. A summer highlight is the heated outdoor swimming pool available from May to September.

RECOMMENDED IN THE AREA
Bateman's (NT); Royal Tunbridge Wells; Battle Abbey

Royal Oak Inn ♦♦♦♦♦

Map ref 3 - SU80
Pock Ln, CHICHESTER, PO18 0AX
2m N of Chichester. Off A286 into East Lavant village centre
T 01243 527434
F 01243 775062
E ro@thesussexpub.co.uk
W www.thesussexpub.co.uk
6 rooms, S £50-£60, D £90-£120, No smoking in bedrooms or dining room

RECOMMENDED IN THE AREA
Chichester; South Downs; Goodwood

Located close to the Goodwood Estate and only 2 miles from Chichester, this stylish inn is full of character, with beamed ceilings, timber floors and open fires in the public areas. The en suite bedrooms, finished to a very high standard, are in the inn, a converted barn and a flint cottage - each room has a flat-screen television and CD player, a library of DVDs, and Sky television. The luxurious bathrooms are fitted with power showers. Home-made museli and local produce feature on the interesting breakfast menu. The popular restaurant serves a combination of French, Mediterranean and modern English cuisine with good wines to match. A lovely place to stay.

Yew House Bed & Breakfast ♦♦♦♦

Map ref 4 - TQ53
Crowborough Hill,
CROWBOROUGH, TN6 2EA
From High St over minirdbt, pass police station on left, Yew House on left

T 01892 610522
F 07789 993982
E yewhouse@yewhouse.com
W www.yewhouse.com

4 rooms, S £35-£55, D £55-£60, No smoking, Closed 25-Dec

A warm welcome is guaranteed at this new eco-friendly house offering pristine accommodation t minutes from local transport links and within easy ıch of many Sussex attractions. The bright spacious drooms have been finished to a high standard with e accessories. One room has a four-poster bed d a double shower. A delicious breakfast and me-cooked evening meals, by arrangement, are oyed in the pleasant dining room overlooking the garden. Packed lunches or picnic baskets are available on request. Local literary figures include Sir Arthur Conan Doyle and AA Milne, creator of Winnie the Pooh, with the famous Pooh sticks bridge in nearby Ashdown Forest.

RECOMMENDED IN THE AREA
Crowborough; Ashdown Forest; Royal Tunbridge Wells

Brayscroft House ♦♦♦♦

Map ref 4 - TV69
3 South Cliff Av, EASTBOURNE, BN20 7AH
2103 (Grand Parade) from pier in direction f Beachy Head, pass Grand Hotel, then ake right incline up South Cliff & 1st right nto South Cliff Av

01323 647005
brayscroft@hotmail.com
www.brayscrofthotel.co.uk

rooms, S £32-£35, D £64-£70, o smoking

Formerly an Edwardian family residence, the Brayscroft provides elegant commodation close to the seafront, pier, atres and town centre. Also nearby is the pular South Downs Way. The stylish drooms are all en suite and thoughtfully uipped with hospitality trays, clock radios, ers and shoe-cleaning kits. Fresh flowers are coming touches. A comfortable lounge is vided and evening meals are by angement. Owner William Carter is a keen dener, and most of the seasonal vegetables d in the kitchen are grown in the garden. The hotel has a residential licence and unrestricted street parking is available.

RECOMMENDED IN THE AREA
South Downs & Beachy Head; Seafront; Lawn tennis (international competitions)

The Manse B & B ♦♦♦♦♦

Map ref 4 - TV69
7 Dittons Rd, EASTBOURNE, BN21 1DW
A22 to town centre railway station, onto Old Orchard Rd, right onto Arlington Rd
T 01323 737851
E anne@themansebandb.co.uk
W www.themansebandb.co.uk
3 rooms, S £40-£50, D £64-£72, No smoking

RECOMMENDED IN THE ARE

South Downs & Beachy Head; Charlest Farmhouse (Bloomsbury group); Michelham Priory

This character home is in a quiet residential area only a 5-minute walk from the town centre. It was built as a Presbyterian manse in 1906 in the Arts & Crafts style, and retains many original features such as oak panelling and stained-glass windows. The beautifully decorated en-suite bedrooms are spacious and very comfortable, and come with armchairs, radios, tea and coffee trays and hairdryers. Anne Walker's breakfasts are very good, using a range of quality produce. If the traditional English is too much then try the Continental (smoked ham, cheese tomato and olives) or vegetarian optio or even a combination of your choice from the menu.

The Lawn Guest House ♦♦♦♦

Map ref 3 - TQ24
30 Massetts Rd, GATWICK AIRPORT (LONDON), RH6 7DF
M23 junct 9, signs to A23 (Redhill), at rdbt by Esso garage onto 3rd exit, Massetts Rd 300yds on right
T 01293 775751
F 01293 821803
E info@lawnguesthouse.co.uk
W www.lawnguesthouse.co.uk
12 rooms, S £40-£50, D £58-£60, No smoking

Handy for Gatwick airport, this imposing Victorian property benefits from a proprietor who uses his expertise in the hospitality business to provide an efficient well-run airport guesthouse. Thoughtful extras include an ice machine, scales to weigh luggage, airport parking, free airport transfers and an on-line computer. Bedrooms and bathrooms are fresh and bright, and include hairdryers, tea, coffee and chocolate facilities, direct-dial phones, early call system, fans and computer modem connections. A choice of hot and cold breakfast dishes is served in the attractive dining room, and there is a pretty garden. A good choice fo the international traveller.

RECOMMENDED IN THE AREA

Hever Castle; Chessington World of Adventure; Leonardslee Gardens

/ulcan Lodge Guest House ♦♦♦♦

lap ref 3 - TQ24
7 Massetts Rd, GATWICK
IRPORT (LONDON), RH6 7DQ
*l23 junct 9, A23 into Horley, off A23
righton Rd*
01293 771522
01293 775376
reservations@vulcan-lodge.com
www.vulcan-lodge.com
rooms, S £36-£40, D £55,
o smoking

's hard to believe this late 17th-century house is so convenient Gatwick Airport. Laid back from the n road in a third of an acre of neat dens, it gives the impression of being beautiful countryside. Established as a I and breakfast for more than a cade, each room is different but all are I equipped and have nice finishing ches - most are en suite. The nge-dining room comes with a cosy l-effect fire. A choice of breakfast, including vegetarian, is provided, and a continental breakfast can be brought to your room outside normal hours.

Recommended in the Area

Hever Castle; Wakehurst Place (NT); Box Hill (NT)

Parkside House ♦♦♦♦♦

Map ref 4 - TQ80
59 Lower Park Rd, HASTINGS &
ST LEONARDS, TN34 2LD
A2101 to town centre, right at rdbt, 1st right
T 01424 433096
F 01424 421431
E bkent.parksidehouse@talk21.com
5 rooms, S £30-£45, D £50-£65,
No smoking

Recommended in the Area

Battle Abbey; Bodiam Castle (NT); Michelham Priory

Parkside House is in a quiet conservation area opposite Alexandra Park, with its lakes, tennis rts and bowling green, yet is only a 15-minute k from the seafront. Four en suite bedrooms are red and another with private facilities. The rooms stylishly furnished, with many antique pieces, generously equipped with video recorders, dryers, tongs, toiletries, bathrobes, and beverage s with fresh milk and biscuits. A good choice of breakfast - English or Continental - is served at individual tables in the elegant dining room, and there is also an inviting lounge. The owner, Brian Kent, is more than happy to advise you on the places to see in this lovely area of southern England. The house is no smoking throughout.

*W*artling Place ♦♦♦♦♦

Map ref 4 - TQ61
Wartling Place, Wartling,
HERSTMONCEUX, BN27 1RY
Off A271 signed Wartling, Wartling Place on right opp St Mary Magdelan Church
T 01323 832590
F 01323 831558
E accom@wartlingplace.prestel.co.uk
W www.countryhouseaccomodation.co.uk
4 rooms, S £65-£95, D £90-£130,
No smoking

Recommended in the Area

Bodiam Castle (NT); Great Dixter; Bateman's, Burwash (NT)

Formerly a rectory, this Grade II listed Georgian country house has grand reception rooms furnished with antiques. The standard of the decor and furnishings is matched by equally high levels of service and hospitality. Each bedroom has a bath and shower en suite and features a superb king-size bed made up with quality linen; two rooms have four posters, and all are comprehensively equipped. Guests can relax in the stylish comfort of the drawing room, and a fine choice of breakfast is served in the elegant dining are overlooking the 2 acres of gardens with lawns and majestic trees. There are views across th Pevensey Levels to Eastbourne and the Sout Downs, and the house is ideally situated for visiting the many historic towns, castles, cour houses and gardens in Sussex. For dining ou the village inn and restaurant are within walkir distance, and there are a number of fine restaurants just a short drive away.

Vightingales ♦♦♦♦♦

Map ref 3 - TQ41
The Avenue, Kingston, LEWES, BN7 3LL
2m SW of Lewes. A23 onto A27 to Lewes, at rdbt exit for Kingston, right at 30mph sign, house 2nd from end on right
T / F 01273 475673
E jean.hudson@onetel.net
W www.users.totalise.co.uk/~nightingales
2 rooms, D £65-£70, No smoking

This modern bungalow is on a quiet country road, surrounded by well-kept gardens. You are free to plore the grounds, perhaps in the company of Ben, e resident black Labrador, who gives everyone a rm welcome. Both bedrooms are comfortably nished, and have facilities en suite and tea and coffee cilities. Jean Hudson thoughtfully provides a range of tras in the rooms, including fresh fruit, flowers, ocolate and sherry. Refreshments are offered on arrival, and you can relax in the conservatory, which is home to a wonderful pink bougainvillea and other exotic plants. Although dinner is not available, Jean is happy to recommend local restaurants, and a 15th-century pub serving real ale is nearby.

Recommended in the Area
Anne of Cleeves House Museum & Lewes Castle; South Downs Way; Battle Abbey

---

Racing Greens ♦♦♦♦

Map ref 3 - TQ00
70 South Ter, LITTLEHAMPTON, BN17 5LQ
A259 onto B2187 for Littlehampton seafront, brown signs to seafront, B&B faces the Greens and sea near Harbour Park Entertainment Centre
T 01903 732972
F 01903 719389
E racingreens@aol.com
W www.littlehampton-racing-greens.co.uk
2 rooms, D £60-£80, No smoking

Recommended in the Area
Littlehampton Blue Flag beach; Arundel; South Downs

ittlehampton Greens and the seafront form the main outlook from this torian terrace property, where owners en and Alan Thomas provide the small ches that make the difference to a y away from home. Their two drooms - one is on the ground floor but accessed by several steps - are fitted with wide beds and good mattresses, radios, alarm clocks and hairdryers; refreshment trays are also supplied. A selection of interesting ingredients contributes to the enjoyable breakfast, with speciality breads always available, and served in the sunny dining room.

Wellington House ♦♦♦♦

Map ref 4 - TQ82
Dixter Rd, NORTHIAM, TN31 6LB
Into Northiam from S, turn left after Post Office signed Great Dixter Gardens. B&B 50yds up Dixter Rd on left

T 01797 253449
E fanny@frances14.freeserve.co.uk

2 rooms, S £40, D £65, No smoking in bedrooms or dining room, Closed 15 Dec-15 Jan

Set in the quiet village of Northiam, this charming Victorian house with a pretty garden and well-appointed rooms is perfect for a tranquil break. The spacious en suite bedrooms offer a high level of comfort with thoughtful added extras such as home-made biscuits and hot water bottles cleverly disguised as teddy bears. The bathrooms have lots of pampering goodies. Enjoy afternoon tea by the open fire in the lounge. The hearty breakfast, served in the brick-floored dining room, features home-made breac local sausages and fish, and the freshest of free range eggs all served around one elegant table.

Recommended in the Area
Battle Abbey; Rye; Great Dixter House & Gardens

Orchard Mead ♦♦♦♦

Map ref 3 - TQ01
Toat Ln, PULBOROUGH, RH20 1BZ
Off A29 1m N of Pulborough onto Blackgate Ln, left onto Pickhurst Ln & right onto Toat Ln, Orchard Mead at end

T 01798 872640
E siggy.rutherford@ukonline.co.uk

2 rooms, No smoking, Closed Xmas, Etr

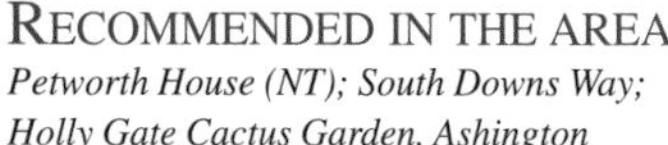

Recommended in the Area
Petworth House (NT); South Downs Way; Holly Gate Cactus Garden, Ashington

Orchard Mead is a comfortable home set in the heart of the Sussex Weald. The detached house is within easy reach of the local train station and within 30 minutes of Chichester. It is close to the village of Pulborough and only 15 minutes from the historic towns of Petworth and Arundel. John and Siggy Rutherford aim to make your stay a memorable one. Both bedrooms are well furnished with thoughtful touches, and attention to detail is evident with afternoon tea on arrival, and beds turnec down each evening and made each morning. There is lovely drawing room to relax in, an excellent breakfast and a delicious evening meal can be provided on request.

Jeake's House ◆◆◆◆◆

Map ref 4 - TQ92
Mermaid St, RYE, TN31 7ET
Approach from High St or The Strand
01797 222828
01797 222623
stay@jeakeshouse.com
www.jeakeshouse.com
1 rooms, S £39-£79, D £88-£120

ECOMMENDED IN THE AREA
diam Castle (NT); Battle;
singhurst Castle Garden (NT)

fine building in one of the most beautiful parts of Rye, Jeake's House dates from 39 and during its colourful history it has been th a wool store and a Baptist school. In the ly 20th century it was the home of American et and author Conrad Potter Aiken, and was setting for many literary get-togethers. The use is owned and run by Jenny Hadfield who ers accommodation of a high standard. The olic rooms include an oak-beamed lounge d a book-lined bar where you can relax over a drink. The original galleried chapel has been converted into a dining room where a traditional country breakfast is served. A vegetarian option is available. The bedrooms are individually styled with sumptuous furnishings. Nine rooms are en suite, and all offer telephones and hospitality trays. There is a private car park nearby.

Little Orchard House ♦♦♦♦♦

Map ref 4 - TQ92
West St, RYE, TN31 7ES
A259 into town via Landgate Arch & High St, 3rd left

T / F 01797 223831
E info@littleorchardhouse.com
W www.littleorchardhouse.com

2 rooms, S £50-£70, D £80-£100, No smoking

Recommended in the Area

Sissinghurst Castle & Great Dixter gardens; Saxon Shore Way; Lamb House, Rye (NT)

Both the house and the garden are full of character at this central property. The house, dating from around 1720, has been renovated and meticulously maintained. The proprietors create an informal atmosphere and guests are made to feel like old friends. There are views over the cobbled street or walled garden from beautifully appointed en suite rooms with four-poster beds. All have hospitality trays, fridges, hairdryers, radio alarms and hand-stitched quilts. The panelled book room has books and games, and in the sitting room you can relax by the fire and browse menus from local restaurants. Breakfast, served at a large table in the dining room, features local organic, free-range and home-made products. Off-street private parking available.

Manor Farm Oast ♦♦♦♦♦

Map ref 4 - TQ92
Windmill Ln, RYE, TN36 4WL
A259 Rye-Hastings road, from Rye in Icklesham pass church on left, left at x-rds onto Workhouse Ln. After sharp left bend, left into Orchards

T / F 01424 813787
E manor.farm.oast@lineone.net
W www.manorfarmoast.co.uk

3 rooms, S £54-£68, D £74-£84, No smoking, Closed 28 Dec-15 Jan

Recommended in the Area

Battle Abbey; Historic Rye; Ellen Terry's House (NT)

Built in 1860 and still surrounded by a working orchard on the edge of the Icklesham, Manor Farm Oast is ideal for quiet breaks and country walks. The oast house has been converted to keep the unusual original features both inside and out - the double bedroom in one of the oast towers is completely round. Kate Mylrea provides a very friendly welcome, and you can enjoy tea and home-made cake in one of the two lounges. Kate is also passionate about food: as well as a traditional English breakfast or a healthier alternative, she can prepare a top quality five-course dinner by arrangement, all exquisitely presented. Two of the rooms are en suite while the other has a private bathroom - thoughtful extras include bathrobes, home-made biscuits, bottled water and fresh flowers. Kate was an AA Landlady of the Year finalist in 2005.

Old Borough Arms Hotel ♦♦♦♦

Map ref 4 - TQ92
The Strand, RYE, TN31 7DB
A259 onto The Strand. Hotel at foot of Mermaid St overlooking Strand Quay
T / F 01797 222128
E info@oldborougharms.co.uk
W www.oldborougharms.co.uk
9 rooms, S £30-£55, D £60-£110, No smoking

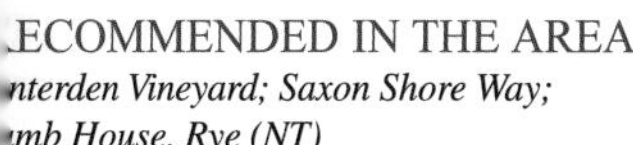
ECOMMENDED IN THE AREA
nterden Vineyard; Saxon Shore Way; mb House, Rye (NT)

There has been a hotel or inn on this site since the 15th century, and day the Arms is run by Lynn, Glynne d their family. The inn has an elevated sition at the foot of cobbled Mermaid reet, which winds up to Rye's parish urch. The bedrooms were pleasantly corated in 2004 and come in a variety sizes and styles - all are en suite and each one is well equipped. Breakfast is served in the charming dining room - Sussex bacon and sausages made to an exclusive recipe distinguish the full English, but there are Continental or Vegetarian selections too. There is a cosy lounge bar, and a coffee shop downstairs open during the day. A flower-decked patio overlooks the bustling Strand.

Avondale Hotel ♦♦♦♦

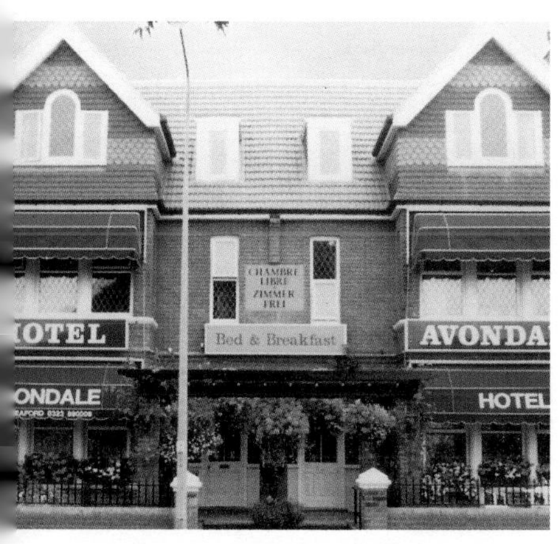

Map ref 3 - TV49
Avondale Rd, SEAFORD, BN25 1RJ
On A259 in town centre, opp town memorial
T 01323 890008
F 01323 490598
W www.avondalehotel.co.uk
16 rooms, S £22-£50, D £45-£65, No smoking

Guests frequently comment on how well they sleep in the centrally heated, spotlessly clean bedrooms the Avondale Hotel. The beds are certainly mfortable, but the friendly service and relaxed nosphere also play their part in the home-from-home perience. Bedrooms are accessible by stair lift, and are en suite. All are equipped with hospitality trays, dios and alarms. An inviting lounge is provided, and oyable home-cooked food is served in the attractive dining room, using fresh local produce wherever possible. The hotel is convenient for both the town centre and the seafront, and Seaford Leisure Centre is close by.

RECOMMENDED IN THE AREA
South Downs; Seven Sisters cliffs; Brighton

The Gallery ♦♦♦♦

Map ref 3 - TV49
Cliff Rd, SEAFORD, BN25 1BB
Off A259 onto Marine Parade, E along Esplanade to tower, left & 1st right
Ⓣ 01323 491755
Ⓔ jackie@wrightplace.info
Ⓦ www.wrightplace.info
3 rooms, S £35-£60, D £50-£75, No smoking

RECOMMENDED IN THE AREA

Seven Sisters Country Park, Seaford; Clergy House (NT), Alfriston; Brighton

The Gallery is only a stroll from the beach and a short walk from Seaford town centre. A warm welcome is guaranteed at this refurbished house with wonderful sea views and in a prime position for coastal walks, the South Downs and a golf course. Within a couple of miles is the South Downs Way long-distance path, which can take energetic walkers to Eastbourne. The bedrooms, themed after the French impressionists, are large and well appointed with tea and coffee facilities and DVD televisions. The king-size four-poster Monet room has beautiful sea views, as does the other canopied double room. Artwork by local artists adorns the walls of the breakfast room where an excellent meal is served. For a beautiful place to stay in a wonderful location The Gallery offers the ideal break. Off road parking is available.

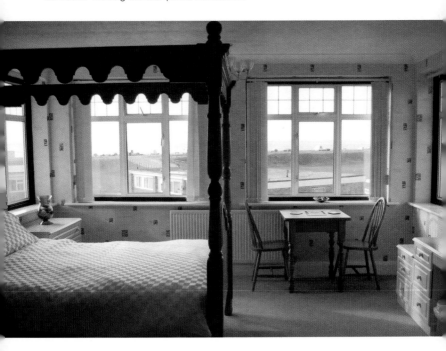

. selection of places to eat from the AA Restaurant & AA Pub guides

estaurants

Kings Court Hotel (European)
ings Coughton, Alcester B49 5QQ
el 01789 763111

Edmunds (British)
4 High Street, Henley-in-Arden B95 5BX
el 01564 795666

Simply Simpsons (French)
01-103 Warwick Road,
enilworth CV8 1HL
el 01926 864567

Mallory Court Hotel (European)
arbury Lane, Bishop's Tachbrook,
eamington Spa CV33 9QB
el 01926 330214

Solo (European)
3 Dormer Place,
eamington Spa CV32 5AA
el 01926 422422

The Fox and Goose Inn (British)
rmscote, Stratford-upon-Avon CV37 8DD
el 01608 682293

Pubs

The Bell
Alderminster CV37 8NY
Tel 01789 450414

The Golden Cross
Ardens Grafton B50 4LG
Tel 01789 772420

Kings Head
21 Bearley Road, Aston Cantlow B95 6HY
Tel 01789 488242

Fox & Hounds Inn
Great Wolford CV36 5NQ
Tel 01608 674220

The Boot Inn
Old Warwick Road, Lapworth B94 6JU
Tel 01564 782464

The Tilted Wig
11 Market Place, Warwick CV34 4SA
Tel 01926 410466

The Fox & Hounds Inn ♦♦♦♦

Map ref 3 - SP23
GREAT WOLFORD, CV36 5NQ
Off A3400, 1.5m to Great Wolford

T 01608 674220
F 01608 674160
E info@thefoxandhoundsinn.com
W www.thefoxandhoundsinn.com

3 rooms, S £45, D £70, No smoking in bedrooms, Closed 1st wk Jan

.ECOMMENDED IN THE AREA
ıtsford Arboretum; Cotswold Falconry ːntre; Stratford-upon-Avon

Set in glorious countryside on the edge of the Cotswolds, this 16th-ːntury village inn retains many original atures. The mellow stone walls ıcompass roaring log fires, and an ːeresting bar with blackboard menus, ːaditional ales and more than 180 ːrieties of whisky. Rustic furniture and emorabilia add to the character.

Converted outbuildings house the thoughtfully furnished en suite bedrooms, with complimentary toiletries and tea and coffee facilities. Paul and Veronica serve freshly prepared breakfasts before guests set out to explore the Cotswolds and Shakespeare country. No chidren 12 years or younger. Dogs welcome.

The Old Coach House ♦♦♦♦♦

Map ref 3 - SP23
GREAT WOLFORD, CV36 5NQ
Off A44 signed Great Wolford, B&B 1.25m, 1st on right
T 01608 674152
E theoldcoachouse2@aol.com
2 rooms, S £45-£70, D £70, No smoking

RECOMMENDED IN THE ARE
Chastleton House (NT); Hidcote Manor (NT); Royal Shakespeare Theatre, Stratfo

Only minutes from the thriving market town of Moreton-in-Marsh, this converted coach house is perfect for touring or walking in the north Cotswolds. The house provides high levels of comfort and facilities. Bedrooms are equipped with a wealth of thoughtful extras, and quality decor and furnishings enhance the intrinsic charm of the property. Exposed beams, a flagstone floor and wood-burning stove are features in the relaxing sitting room, which overlooks the delightful garden. All food is prepared using local produce and the pub next door serves excellent meals. The area is ideal for walkers, keen gardeners and antiques collectors.

Nolands Farm ♦♦♦♦

Map ref 3 - SP34
OXHILL, CV35 0RJ
1m E of Pillarton Priors on A422
T 01926 640309
F 01926 641662
E inthecountry@nolandsfarm.co.uk
W www.nolandsfarm.co.uk
8 rooms, S £30-£50, D £50-£65, No smoking in bedrooms or dining room, Closed Xmas, New Year

RECOMMENDED IN THE AREA

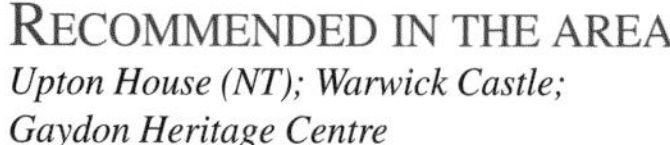

Upton House (NT); Warwick Castle; Gaydon Heritage Centre

Make yourself at home - that is the irresistible invitation from Sue Hutsby. A converted stable block houses the en suite bedrooms, most of them on the ground floor, and there is a choice of four poster, doubles, twins or singles, all with bathrooms. A small lounge bar with an open fire and a conservatory provide cosy places to relax with a book or a game, and dinner is served at separate tables in the spacious Granary Restaurant. The beautiful gardens are there to be enjoyed, and various activities can be arranged, including hot-air ballooning, fishing on the private lake, clay-pigeon shooting, cycling and badger watching.

Bubbenhall House ♦♦♦♦

Map ref 3 - SP36
Paget's Ln, LEAMINGTON SPA (ROYAL), CV8 3BJ
5m NE of Leamington. Off A445 at Bubbenhall S onto Pagets Ln, 1m on single-track lane (over 4 speed humps)
T / F 024 7630 2409
E wharrison@bubbenhallhouse.freeserve.co.uk
W www.bubbenhallhouse.com
3 rooms, S £45-£55, D £60-£75, No smoking in bedrooms or dining room

Located between Leamington Spa and Coventry, this large Edwardian house stands in 5 acres of woodland and extensive grounds with an abundance of wildlife. Carpeted with bluebells in spring, the woods are home to one of Britain's two dormouse sanctuaries. The carefully restored house features oak beams, a fine Jacobean-style staircase, an elegant dining room and a choice of sumptuous lounges. Thoughtful extras are provided in the large en suite bedrooms, each with its own individual character and with splendid views across the gardens and woods. In addition you will find a championship surface hard tennis court, plenty of parking, pet friendly owners, first-class breakfasts, and tasty dinners to order.

Recommended in the Area
Stoneleigh Abbey; Ryton Organic Gardens; Warwick Castle

Holly End Bed & Breakfast ♦♦♦♦

Map ref 3 - SP24
London Rd, SHIPSTON ON STOUR, CV36 4EP
0.5m S of Shipston on Stour on A3400
T 01608 664064
E enquiries@holly-end.co.uk
W www.holly-end.co.uk
3 rooms, S £45-£70, D £65-£90, No smoking

Top-drawer accommodation on the edge of the Cotswolds Whether your preferences lie with country hikes and quaint Cotswold villages or the history and culture of Shakespeare country, this bed and breakfast is suitably placed for both. The modern detached family house, immaculately maintained and spotlessly clean, is just a short walk from the town centre. Spacious rooms with subtle soft furnishings and decor have shower-baths en suite, while dormer windows add to the character - pamper yourself with the Sanctuary spa products provided in each room. A comprehensive freshly cooked English breakfast uses the best of local produce (organic wherever possible). Afternoon tea or sherry and snacks are offered on arrival.

Recommended in the Area
Stratford-upon-Avon; Hidcote Manor (NT); Warwick Castle

Ambleside Guest House ♦♦♦♦

Map ref 3 - SP25
41 Grove Rd, STRATFORD-UPON-AVON, CV37 6PB
On A4390 Grove Rd, opp Firs Park
T 01789 297239
F 01789 295670
E ruth@amblesideguesthouse.com
W www.amblesideguesthouse.com
8 rooms, S £22-£33, D £46-£80, No smoking

RECOMMENDED IN THE AREA
Shakespeare's birthplace;
Royal Shakespeare Theatre;
Anne Hathaway's Cottage

Ambleside is a comfortable guesthouse in the heart of town, where owners Ruth Rogers and Peter Halford provide a warm welcome. A recent refurbishment has left the house in sparkling condition, and the accommodation can suit every need. Choose from a family room, a double or twin, or one on the ground floor, and there is even a four-poster bed. Many rooms have shower rooms en suite, and each one is equipped with a hairdryer and a hospitality tray. Ironing facilities are also available. The choice at breakfast ensures that no one will go hungry, and the full English and vegetarian options are freshly cooked. Breakfast is served the bright and spacious dining room, which looks over the charming front patio garden. Standing opposite Firs Park, Ambleside is just a stroll into the town, where there is a good choice of restaurants, cafés and inns.

Cross o'th' Hill Farm ♦♦♦♦

Map ref 3 - SP25

Broadway Rd, STRATFORD-UPON-AVON, CV37 8HP

0.5m S of Stratford. A3400 S from Stratford for Shipston, 0.75m onto B4632, farm signed 0.25m on right, farmhouse 200yds

T 01789 204738
E decimanoble@hotmail.com
W www.crossothhillfarm.com

3 rooms, S £55, D £70-£74, No smoking, Closed 25 Dec-Feb

Recommended in the area

Hidcote Manor Garden (NT); Warwick Castle; Charlecote Park (NT)

You can see the Royal Shakespeare Theatre from this lovely old farmhouse, and Holy rinity Church where the Bard was buried is just short walk through fields. There has been a ırm here since the 15th century, though the resent property was built in 1860. Decima and)avid Noble share their relaxing and elegant ome with discerning guests, and encourage ıem to try the baby grand piano in the drawing ɔom. Here and in the dining room, full-length ash windows open onto the garden where a unken croquet lawn and orchards merge into pasture. In this peaceful setting it is easy to unwind, and the spacious bedrooms and bathrooms are warm and inviting. Attractive furnishings and decorations are combined with many practical and homely additions. A low-fat cooked breakfast is served with granary bread and local and organic produce whenever possible, and home-made preserves ensure a delicious start to the day.

Victoria Spa Lodge ♦♦♦♦

Map ref 3 - SP25
Bishopton Ln, Bishopton, STRATFORD-UPON-AVON, CV37 9QY

A3400 1.5m N to junct A46, 1st left onto Bishopton Ln, 1st house on right

T 01789 267985
F 01789 204728
E ptozer@victoriaspalodge.demon.co.uk
W www.stratford-upon-avon.co.uk/victoriaspa.htm

7 rooms, S £50, D £65, family rooms available, No smoking

Opened in 1837 by Princess Victoria, whose coat-of-arms is built into the gables, this attractive house is in a peaceful country setting on the edge of town. The Grade II listed building was once the home of cartoonist Bruce Bairnsfather, and many original features still grace the property. The beautifully appointed bedrooms offer spacious comfort with quality furniture, stylish fabrics and thoughtful touches (family rooms by arrangement). The dramatic drawing room has a stripped hardwood floor and inviting furniture. Expect a warm welcome and high standards of service. Stratford is a gentle 20-minute walk away.

Recommended in the Area

Warwick Castle; Shakespeare theatres & properties; The Cotswolds

---

Loxley Farm ♦♦♦♦

Map ref 3 - SP25
Loxley, STRATFORD-UPON-AVON, CV35 9JN

4m SE of Straford. Off A422 to village T-junct, left, 3rd house on right

T 01789 840265
F 01789 840645
E loxleyfarm@hotmail.com

2 rooms, S from £45, D from £70, No smoking, Closed Xmas, New Year

Easily reached via the M40 and a short drive from Stratford, this thatched former farmhouse stands in attractive cottage gardens in the peaceful village of Loxley. The thoughtfully equipped bedrooms are in a converted 17th-century shieling or cart barn, and each room has an adjacent sitting area. The hostess is a very nice lady who looks after her guests. Tasty breakfasts are served around a family table in the main house dining room.

Recommended in the Area

Warwick Castle; Shakespeare sites in Stratford; The Cotswolds

West Midlands

A selection of places to eat from the AA Restaurant & AA Pub guides

Restaurants

Bank Restaurant & Bar (European)
4 Brindley Place, Birmingham B1 2JB
Tel 0121 633 4466

Chung Ying Garden (Chinese)
17 Thorp Street, Birmingham B5 4AT
Tel 0121 666 6622 or 0121 622 1668

La Toque d'Or (French)
27 Warstone Lane, Hockley,
Birmingham B18 6JQ, Tel 0121 233 3655

Nuthurst Grange Country House Hotel (British, French)
Nuthurst Grange Lane,
Hockley Heath B94 5NL
Tel 01564 783972

The Fairlawns at Aldridge (British)
178 Little Aston Road, Aldridge,
Walsall WS9 0NU, Tel 01922 455122

Pubs

The Malt Shovel
Barston Lane, Barston B92 0JP
Tel 01675 443223

The Peacock
Icknield Street, Forhill, nr King's Norton,
Birmingham B38 0EH
Tel 01564 823232

The Rose and Castle
Ansty, Coventry CV7 9HZ
Tel 024 76612822

Waggon & Horses
17A Church Street, Oldbury B69 3AD
Tel 0121 5525467

Beacon Hotel
129 Bilston Street, Sedgley DY3 1JE
Tel 01902 883380

The Vine
Roebuck Street, West Bromwich B70 6RD
Tel 0121 5532866

Black Firs ♦♦♦♦

Map ref 3 - SP08
113 Coleshill Rd, Marston Green,
BIRMINGHAM, B37 7HT
M42 junct 6, A45 W, onto B4438, signs for Marston Green
T / F 0121 779 2727
E julie@b-firs.co.uk
W www.b-firs.co.uk
6 rooms, S £59-£89, D £69-£89,
No smoking

The location in a mainly residential area on the edge of the NEC makes this majestic house a popular choice. Being close to Birmingham International Airport and the city centre are also bonuses. Black Firs is beautifully maintained and spotlessly clean, and has a range of individually furnished bedrooms - double, single and family rooms - with pretty coordinated fabrics and smart shower rooms. Memorable breakfasts are served in a dining room that overlooks immaculate gardens. The lounge is a restful area for a chat or a quiet read, and French doors open onto a large patio.

Recommended in the area

Belfry golf course; Warwick; Stratford-upon-Avon

Acacia Guest House ♦♦♦♦

Map ref 3 - SP37
11 Park Rd, Cheyles More,
COVENTRY, CV1 2LE
Off city ring road junct 6 to railway station & left
T / F 024 7663 3622
E acaciaguesthouse@hotmail.com
14 rooms, S £27.50-£35, D £40-£60
Closed Xmas

The Acacia lies just outside city centre ring road and is within easy walking distance of the train station, university and main sights and amenities. This constantly improving establishment is very well maintained and spotlessly clean, and provides a range of carefully furnished bedrooms, many of which are on the ground floor. A range of popular dishes is served in an attractive dining room and a cosy lounge bar is also available.

Recommended in the are

Kenilworth Castle; Coventry Cathedral; Warwick

Wiltshire

A selection of places to eat from the AA Restaurant & AA Pub guide

Restaurants

◎◎ The Tollgate (British, Mediterranean)
Bradford-on-Avon BA14 6PX
Tel 01225 782326

◎◎ The Pear Tree at Purton (British)
Church End, Purton SN5 4ED
Tel 01793 772100

◎ George & Dragon (European)
High Street, Rowde SN10 2PN
Tel 01380 723053

◎ The Linnet (British)
Great Hinton, Trowbridge BA14 6BU
Tel 01380 870354

◎◎ The Pear Tree Inn (British, Italian)
Top Lane, Whitley SN12 8QX
Tel 01225 709131

Pubs

The Crown
Alvediston SP5 5JY
Tel 01722 780335

The Beckford Arms
Fonthill Gifford SP3 6PX
Tel 01747 870385

The Smoking Dog
62 The High Street, Malmesbury SN16 9AT
Tel 01666 825823

The Kings Arms
Monkton Farleigh BA15 2QH
Tel 01225 858705

The Vine Tree
Froxley Road, Norton SN16 0JP
Tel 01666 837654

The Angel Inn
Upton Scudamore, Warminster BA12 0AG
Tel 01985 213225

The Close ♦♦♦♦

Map ref 3 - SU23 (6.5m NE of Salisbury)
Tidworth Rd, BOSCOMBE, SP4 0AB
Off A338 towards Boscombe Church. The Close is next to church
T 01980 611989
E theclose@moocowco.com
W www.moocowco.com/theclose
2 rooms, S £40, D £60, No smoking, Closed 24-26 Dec

Suited to both business and leisure visitors, the spacious bedrooms at this Grade II listed 17th-century former farmhouse are carefully furnished and come with fresh fruit and flowers, teas, chocolate and fresh coffee, and a range of pampering toiletries. There is a relaxing drawing room, where a log fire burns in the inglenook fireplace, creating an inviting atmosphere on cooler evenings and during warmer weather, French doors open onto the pretty cottage garden. Great pride is taken in using quality fresh local food, and breakfast is served round a communal table in the smart dining room. No evening meals but there is a pub a brisk walk away.

Recommended in the Area
Salisbury Cathedral; Old Sarum; Stonehenge

White Smocks ♦♦♦♦♦

Map ref 2 - ST86
Ashley, BOX, SN13 8AJ
A4 1m W of Box turn opp The Northy, at T-junct White Smocks right of thatched cottage
T 01225 742154
F 01225 742212
E whitesmocksashley@hotmail.com
W www.whitesmocks.com
2 rooms, S £40-£45, D £65-£70, No smoking

Located in the pleasant village of Ashley, White Smocks offers a relaxing escape. You are encouraged to enjoy the pleasant garden in the summer, real fires in the winter, and the Jacuzzi all year round. Angela and Paul Berry look forward to making you feel at home, and they can also advise on visits to surrounding attractions. The two bedrooms and bathrooms are immaculately presented and comfortably furnished, as befits Angela's other occupation of interior designer. There is also a welcoming lounge. The tasty, well-cooked meals are enhanced by fresh ingredients.

Recommended in the Area
Bath; Lacock; Castle Combe

Forester Inn ♦♦♦♦

Map ref 2 - ST92

Lower St, DONHEAD ST ANDREW, SP7 9EE

A30 towards Salisbury, through Ludwell, take left signed Donheads, turn left at T-junct and continue to B&B

T 01747 828038
F 01747 828050
E enquiries@foresterinndonheadstandrew.co.uk
W www.foresterinndonheadstandrew.co.uk

2 rooms, S £55-£75, D £65-£110,
No smoking in bedrooms or dining room

RECOMMENDED IN THE AREA

Wardour Castle; Salisbury Cathedral; Shaftesbury Gold Hill

Located 4 miles from the hilltop town of Shaftesbury, the 16th-century thatched inn is an ideal base for touring Dorset and Wiltshire. It has been carefully refurbished to preserve its character and original features, while quality and modern comforts abound. Bedrooms are equipped with fresh milk for tea and coffee, and are suited for business or leisure. They feature 5ft wide antique iron beds with Egyptian linen. The bathrooms have power showers and complimentary toiletries. Freshly prepared lunch and dinners are available in the informal bar-restaurant, where service is attentive and friendly. The restaurant has a growing following for both its food and the comprehensive wine list. A continental breakfast is available and includes freshly baked croissants and pastries. The inn is has a pleasant garden and patio where food is served in fine weather.

At the Sign of the Angel ♦♦♦♦♦

Map ref 2 - ST96
6 Church St, LACOCK, SN15 2LB
Off A350 into Lacock, follow Local Traffic sign
T 01249 730230
F 01249 730527
E angel@lacock.co.uk
W www.lacock.co.uk
10 rooms, S £72-£85, D £105-£155, No smoking in bedrooms, Closed 23-30 Dec

Log fires, oak panelling, low beams and squeaky floorboards create a wonderful atmosphere in this 15th-century former wool merchant's house. There really is a feeling of going back in time in the National Trust village of Lacock, where television aerials, overhead cables and yellow lines have been banished. The same family has owned this inn for over half a century and the restaurant is internationally renowned for its traditional cooking, using herbs and vegetables from the garden. Lunch is available every day except Monday; there is a daily changing menu and full à la carte, by candlelight, in the evening. All of the bedrooms are en suite - four are in the cottage across the footbridge over a stream. Furnished with antiques, one has an enormous bed that was owned by the Victorian engineer Isambard Kingdom Brunel, another has a four poster, and a third room has a French tented bed.

Recommended in the Area

Lacock Abbey (NT); Fox Talbot Museum; Bowood House & Gardens

Chetcombe House ♦♦♦♦

Map ref 2 - ST83
Chetcombe Rd, MERE, BA12 6AZ
Off A303
T 01747 860219
F 01747 860111
E mary.butchers@lineone.net
5 rooms, S £36, D £55, No smoking

Recommended in the Area

Stourhead (NT); Stourton House; Longleat

Looking across an acre of well-tended gardens towards Gillingham and the Blackmore Vale, Chetcombe House, built in 1937, oozes elegance and charm. The property, just a few minutes from the centre of Mere, is a good base from which to explore the many local attractions. Chetcombe is pleasantly spacious and extremely comfortable. The en suite bedrooms, one of which is a family room, are equipped with tea and coffee facilities, and the attractive dining room, overlooking the garden and surrounding countryside, is the venue for a substantial breakfast. Pubs and restaurants nearby provide plenty of options for evening meals.

The Old Farmhouse ♦♦♦♦♦

Map ref 3 - SU08
Bagbury Ln, Restrop, PURTON, SN5 4LW
M4 junct 16, signs for Purton, right at 1st x-rds, Bagbury Ln 1st left
T 01793 770130
E stay@theoldfarmhouse.net
W www.theoldfarmhouse.net
6 rooms, D £65-£120, No smoking

The 18th-century Old Farmhouse is a wonderful place, set in tranquil countryside only a short distance from Swindon and the M4. Style and quality abound here, and the hospitality and housekeeping are also great strengths. Each bedroom is individually styled and very comfortable, and all are provided with a host of thoughtful nick-knacks. Soft furnishings and bed linen are sumptuous, and the bath soaks verge on the sensual. An impressive continental breakfast is served in each room - ingredients are local, home made or organic. There are no public areas, but there is a private, nine-hole golf course here for guests, and its free.

Recommended in the Area

Cotswold Water Park, Ashton Keynes; Wiltshire chalk horses; Avebury

Cathedral View ♦♦♦♦

Map ref 3 - SU12
83 Exeter St, SALISBURY, SP1 2SE
200yds E of cathedral. Off A338 ring road onto Exeter St, signs for Old George Mall
T 01722 502254
E wenda.rampton@btopenworld.com
W www.smoothhound.co.uk/hotels/tamar.html
4 rooms, S £50, D £60, No smoking

Cathedral View is less than a minute walk from St Anne's Gate, one of the entrances to the beautiful Cathedral Close. (You can see the cathedral spire from the house.) It's an ideal location for visitors to the city, and there is always a warm welcome. The Grade II listed Georgian house has been carefully modernised to offer well-equipped en suite bedrooms with shower rooms, and tea and coffee facilities, and thoughtful extras make you feel at home. Breakfast includes a hearty full English made from local produce, and served around a large table in the dining room; home-made museli and preserves, and smoked salmon and scrambled eggs are among the lighter options. Parking is available.

Recommended in the Area

Salisbury Cathedral; Stonehenge; Old Sarum

The Old House ♦♦♦♦

Map ref 3 - SU12
161 Wilton Rd, SALISBURY, SP2 7JQ
On A36 1m W from city centre
Ⓣ 01722 333433
Ⓕ 01722 335551
7 rooms, S £35-£50, D £55, No smoking

Charming accommodation is offered at this 17th-century house, located n the Wilton road within walking istance of the city centre. Ground-floor reas are beautifully furnished in tune ith the building's period character. The ature gardens are a lovely surprise, ith three distinct areas providing rivacy on summer evenings. Bedrooms have been tastefully decorated and equipped with modern facilities, including bath or shower rooms en suite. There are two rooms at ground floor level and one room with a splendid four-poster bed, all with hairdryers and hospitality trays.

RECOMMENDED IN THE AREA
Stourhead (NT); Heale Garden; Wilton House

Stratford Lodge ♦♦♦♦

Map ref 3 - SU12
4 Park Ln, off Castle Rd, SALISBURY, SP1 3NP
0.6m N of city centre. Off A345 Castle Rd onto Park Ln, an unadopted road between Victoria Park & Co-op shop
Ⓣ / Ⓕ 01722 325177
Ⓔ enquires@stratfordlodge.co.uk
Ⓦ www.stratfordlodge.co.uk
8 rooms, S £55-£62, D £65-£82, No smoking

an and Jacqueline Lawrence have been running Stratford Lodge since 1997. Despite its secluded cation in a quiet lane by Victoria Park, the house is ose to the city centre and has a lovely garden with a ge car park to the rear. The bedrooms, including one ur-poster room, are all en suite and decorated in soft laxing shades with pretty coordinated fabrics. A cosy unge is provided, and a traditional English breakfast is rved in the conservatory, along with alternatives such as mushrooms on toast or poached eggs. Fruits, cereals, yoghurts and local honey also feature. Dinner is available during the winter.

RECOMMENDED IN THE AREA
Salisbury Cathedral; Stonehenge; Old Sarum

Ardecca ♦♦♦♦

Map ref 3 - SU18

Fieldrise Farm, Kingsdown Ln, Blunsdon, SWINDON, SN25 5DL

Off A419 at Turnpike rdbt for filling station, left onto Turnpike Rd, 1st right

T 01793 721238
E chris-graham.ardecca@fsmail.net
W www.ardecca-bedandbreakfast.co.uk

4 rooms, S £30-£35, D £50-£55, No smoking

RECOMMENDED IN THE AREA

Cotswold Water Park; Avebury stone circle; Marlborough & Savernake Forest

Ardecca is an amalgamation of the names Rebecca and Richard, the owners' children, and it has been the family home for over 25 years. The large modern bungalow is immaculate inside and out and sits in 16 acres of pastureland on the edge of Blunsdon village, a quiet spot with easy access to Swindon and the Cotswolds. A great find and an asset to the area, the house offers spacious first-class accommodation in a friendly atmosphere. All rooms are on the ground floor, larger than average and equipped with modern amenities. A full breakfast is provided and freshly cooked dinners are available by arrangement. No children under 6 years. Credit cards not accepted.

Newton Farmhouse ♦♦♦♦

Map ref 3 - SU22
Southampton Rd, WHITEPARISH, SP5 2QL
7m SE of Salisbury on A36 1m S of A27 junct
T 01794 884416
E newtonfarmhouse1@aol.com
W www.newtonfarmhouse.co.uk
9 rooms, S £40-£55, D £70-£90, No smoking, Closed 24-27 Dec

Once part of the Trafalgar Estate, this historic farmhouse has been oughtfully restored. Modern amenities ave been added while original beams, gstones, an inglenook fireplace and, in e conservatory, a well have all been tained. The en suite bedrooms are ed with fresh flowers and home-made scuits are sure to please. Suzi and John Lanham thrive on guest satisfaction, and go out of their way to recommend the delights of the Salisbury area. Their sumptuous breakfasts with free-range eggs, seasonal fruits, and home-made bread and preserves are the stuff of dreams, and delicious dinners by arrangement are well worth sampling.

RECOMMENDED IN THE AREA

Salisbury Cathedral, Stonehenge, New Forest NP

The Woodfalls Inn ♦♦♦♦

Map ref 3 - SU12
The Ridge, WOODFALLS, SP5 2LN
A338 onto B3080 to village
T 01725 513222
F 01725 513220
E woodfallsi@aol.com
W www.woodfallsinn.co.uk
10 rooms, S £49.95-£53.95, D £69.95-£77.95, No smoking in bedrooms or dining room

RECOMMENDED IN THE AREA

New Forest National Park; Salisbury Cathedral; Broadlands, Romsey

Woodfalls Inn has been providing hospitality to travellers since 1870. Its position on the northern ge of the beautiful New Forest National Park makes it rfect for outdoor pursuits and there is a ampionship golf course just 2 miles away. efurbished, the inn also has additional new commodation. The rooms are nicely decorated in glish country style and each is named after a flower the forest. All rooms are en suite and some have four-posters. Eating is a pleasure at Woodfalls, whether it is the full English breakfast, lunch in the bar or conservatory, or a picnic for your day out. Excellent ales and wines are available, and for dinner try the intimate Lover's Restaurant.

A selection of places to eat from the AA Restaurant & AA Pub guides

Restaurants

Lygon Arms (International)
High Street, Broadway WR12 7DU
Tel 01386 852255

Grafton Manor Restaurant (British, Indian)
Grafton Lane, Bromsgrove B61 7HA
Tel 01527 579007

Riverside Hotel (European)
The Parks, Offenham Road,
Evesham WR11 8JP, Tel 01386 446200

Cottage in the Wood (British)
Holywell Road, Malvern Wells,
Malvern WR14 4LG, Tel 01684 575859

Glass House Restaurant (International)
Church Street, Worcester WR1 2RH
Tel 01905 611120

Pubs

Horse & Jockey
Far Forest, Bewdley DY14 9DX
Tel 01299 266239

Walter de Cantelupe Inn
Main Road, Kempsey WR5 3NA
Tel 01905 820572

The Talbot at Knightwick
Knightwick WR6 5PH
Tel 01886 821235

The Red Lion
4 St Ann's Road, Malvern WR14 4RG
Tel 01684 564787

Peacock Inn
Tenbury Wells WR15 8LL
Tel 01584 810506

Number Thirty ♦♦♦♦♦

Map ref 2 - SO77
30 Gardners Meadow, BEWDLEY,
DY12 2DG
Off High St onto Lax Ln, right at T-junct
T / F 01299 402404
E info@numberthirty.net
W www.numberthirty.net
4 rooms, S from £50, D from £70,
No smoking

Number Thirty is a smart modern house close to the River Severn in the lovely town of Bewdley. The house, overlooking the cricket ground, has been refurbished to provide luxury accommodation complemented by excellent service. Contemporary meets traditional in the beautifully appointed bedrooms, which include complimentary sherry and fresh flowers. Jenny Paddock, ably assisted by husband Geoff, was a runner-up for AA Landlady of the Year 2005. The couple search out the best of local ingredients for their generous breakfasts with superb family-made sausages and free-range eggs. Savour your meal in the attractive dining room overlooking the sun deck or relax in the elegant lounge.

Recommended in the Area

Severn Valley Railway; West Midlands Safari Park; Wyre Forest

Leasow House ♦♦♦♦

Map ref 3 - SP03
Laverton Meadows, BROADWAY, WR12 7NA
2m SW of Broadway. Off B4632 towards Wormington, 500yds on right

T 01386 584526
F 01386 584596
E leasow@hotmail.com
W www.leasow.co.uk

7 rooms, S £37-£57, D £57-£67, No smoking, Closed Xmas, New Year

Leasow House is situated south-west of Broadway in a peaceful rural etting. Parts of the building date from ne 1600s and renovation has ensured nat much of the original character is etained. The en suite bedrooms are well quipped with central heating, direct-dial elephones and hospitality trays. Some ave low beams set off by pretty decor. wo bedrooms are in a converted barn. elicious breakfasts are served in the ttractive dining room, which overlooks the gardens. The library lounge is a comfortable room where you can enjoy a complimentary glass of sherry. Barbara and Gordon Meekings delight in welcoming guests, many of whom return regularly to their lovely home.

Recommended in the Area

Warwick Castle; Hidcote Manor Garden (NT); Sudeley Castle

The Dell House ♦♦♦♦

Map ref 2 - SO74
Green Ln, Malvern Wells, MALVERN, WR14 4HU
2m S of Great Malvern on A449. Turn left off A449 onto Green Ln. House at top of road on right

T 01684 564448
F 01684 893974
E burrage@dellhouse.co.uk
W www.dellhouse.co.uk

3 rooms, S £33-£42, D £56-£64, No smoking

One of the oldest houses in Malvern Wells, The Dell House was built around 1820 when one of lalvern's famous healing springs was diverted to its rounds. Nowadays the ancient spring has slowed to a ickle, but the restorative qualities of the house and ardens are enduring. Located on the sheltered slopes of e Malvern Hills, it was a holiday destination for Ian and elen Burrage before they bought it in 2002. They offer oacious, individually styled en suite bedrooms where period elegance is combined with homely comforts; two rooms have wonderful views to the Cotswolds. Breakfast is served in the impressive Morning Room with superb views over the Severn valley.

Recommended in the Area

Three Counties Showground; Malvern Hills; Malvern Theatre

Garden Cottages ♦♦♦♦

Map ref 2 - SO87
Stoney Ln, Crossway Green,
STOURPORT-ON-SEVERN,
DY13 9SL
3m SE of Stourport off A449 rdbt
T / F 01299 250626
E accommodation@mamod.co.uk
W www.gardencottages.co.uk
4 rooms, S £35-£40, D £65-£70,
No smoking, Closed Xmas

A pretty L-shape cottage set in the beautiful countryside within easy reach of the cathedral city of Worcester. The traditional oak-beamed property has been modernised to a high standard without spoiling the original character. Bedrooms are well equipped with en suites or private bathrooms, refreshment trays, clock radios and good toiletries. There is also a twin-bed log cabin with a kitchen and shower room. You will feel at home in the beamed lounge with its log fire. Breakfast is served in the smart dining room, using freshly laid eggs and local farm produce Gardens, a sun lounge and sun terrace add to the pleasures.

Recommended in the Area

Severn Valley Railway; Elgar Birthplace Museum; Worcester Cathedral

Yorkshire

A selection of places to eat from the AA Restaurant & AA Pub guides

Restaurants

The Three Hares Inn & Restaurant (British, French)
Main Street, Bilsbrough YO23 3PH
Tel 01937 832128

The Dining Room (European)
20 St James Square,
Boroughbridge YO51 9AR
Tel 01423 326426

The Worsley Arms Hotel (British)
High Street, Hovingham YO62 4LA
Tel 01653 628234

The Yorke Arms (European)
Ramsgill HG3 5RL
Tel 01423 755243

Blue Bicycle
34 Fossgate, York YO1 9TA
Tel 01904 677688

Pubs

Crab & Lobster
Asenby YO7 3QL
Tel 01845 577286

The General Tarleton
Boroughbridge Road, Ferrensby HG5 0PZ
Tel 01423 340284

The Buck Inn
Buckden BD23 5JA
Tel 01756 760228

The Boars Head Hotel
Ripley Castle Estate, Harrogate HG3 3AY
Tel 01423 771888

The Angel
Hetton BD23 6LT
Tel 01756 730263

Shallowdale House ♦♦♦♦♦

Map ref 8 - SE57
West End, AMPLEFORTH,
YO62 4DY
Off A170, near village centre
T 01439 788325
F 01439 788885
E stay@shallowdalehouse.co.uk
W www.shallowdalehouse.co.uk
rooms, S £65-£75, D £82-£99,
No smoking, Closed Xmas-New Year

Shallowdale House was opened in 1998 by owners Anton van der Horst d Phillip Gill who wanted to provide 'a ecial place to stay, with the highest ndards of hospitality, attention to detail, d quality of food'. In this architect-signed 1960s house they have hieved all this and more. The house is in tunning location, on a sheltered hillside n more than 2 acres of gardens, erlooking an Area of Outstanding tural Beauty. The spacious south-facing drooms (two en suite and one with a vate bathroom) have huge picture ndows and lovely views, and the atmosphere is relaxed and friendly. The four-course dinners are a highlight, featuring local and seasonal produce, and equal care is taken with breakfast, which can feature Whitby kippers and local sausages, as well as home-made preserves. Complimentary tea and excellent home-baked delicacies are offered in the afternoon.

RECOMMENDED IN THE AREA
Castle Howard; Rievaulx Abbey; Nunnington Hall (NT)

Elmfield House ♦♦♦♦

Map ref 7 - SE28
Arrathorne, BEDALE, DL8 1NE
4m NW of Bedale. A684 from Bedale for Leyburn, right after Patrick Brompton towards Richmond, B&B 1.5m on right
T 01677 450558
F 01677 450557
E stay@elmfieldhouse.co.uk
W www.elmfieldhouse.co.uk
7 rooms, S £45-£49, D £70-£78,
No smoking

The former gamekeeper's cottage has been extended to provide spacious, well-equipped drooms with tea and coffee facilities. Two rooms ve four-poster beds and two have easier access. The ractive public rooms are also well proportioned and mprise a pleasant lounge area with an honesty bar, a nservatory-lounge and a games room. Relax in the rdens or stroll to the 14-acre wood and fishing lake sightings of deer and kingfishers. The full English breakfast using local produce is a highlight and home-cooked evening meals can be ordered by arrangement.

RECOMMENDED IN THE AREA
Bedale; Richmond; Yorkshire Dales & Moors

The Castle Arms Inn ♦♦♦♦

Map ref 7 - SE28
Snape, BEDALE, DL8 2TB
2m S of Bedale. Off B6268 into Snape

T 01677 470270
F 01677 470837
E castlearms@aol.com

9 rooms, S £51, D £67.50, No smoking in bedrooms or dining room

The former coaching inn stands in the quiet village of Snape on the edge of the North Yorkshire Dales. The accommodation is full of character, with bedrooms in a converted barn. Rooms are comfortably furnished and well equipped. While some bathrooms are modest in size, they are well fitted and practical with quality fixtures. A good selection of fine ales is served in the restaurant and bar, along with an interesting selection of freshly prepared dishes.

RECOMMENDED IN THE ARE
Bedale Museum; Brimham Rocks; Theakston Brewery & Visitor Centre

Five Rise Locks Hotel & Restaurant ♦♦♦♦

Map ref 7 - SE13
Beck Ln, BINGLEY, BD16 4DD
Off Main St onto Park Rd, 0.25m left onto Beck Ln

T 01274 565296
F 01274 568828
E info@five-rise-locks.co.uk
W www.five-rise-locks.co.uk

9 rooms, S £50, D £72, No smoking in bedrooms or dining room

Named after the historic locks on the nearby Leeds and Liverpool Canal, this fine Victorian house has an attractive terraced garden and delightful country views. Expect a genuine welcome and good service tailored to your needs. The practical en suite bedrooms provide plenty of space - each one comes with a bathroom, trouser press, hospitality tray and a hairdryer. The hotel is furnished with period pieces, interesting artworks and comfy sofas, and its relaxed air makes it easy to feel at home. You can sample imaginative food in the restaurant, and enjoy breakfast in the pretty breakfast room.

RECOMMENDED IN THE AREA
Bronte Country, Haworth; Saltaire World Herita Site; Keighley & Worth Valley Railway

Marton Grange ♦♦♦♦♦

Map ref 8 - TA16
Flamborough Rd, Marton cum Sewerby, BRIDLINGTON, YO15 1DU
On B1255 600yds from Links golf club
T / F 01262 602034
E martongrange@talk21.com
W www.marton-grange.co.uk
11 rooms, S £40-£48, D £64-£76, No smoking, Closed Dec-Feb

Stuart Nelson gave up a long career in the footwear industry to renovate this anquil property and turn it into a esirable hotel. He has never looked ack, and his ongoing labour satisfies iscerning guests. The TLC lavished on ıe bedrooms has made them very 'elcoming, with one or two thoughtful xtras designed to make everyone feel at home. Stuart serves a substantial breakfast in the elegant dining room. There are views of the garden from the lounges, making them ideal places in which to relax.

RECOMMENDED IN THE AREA
RSPB Bempson Cliffs & Flamborough Head; Bridlington Links Golf Club

---

Sunflower Lodge ♦♦♦♦

Map ref 8 - TA16
24 Flamborough Rd, BRIDLINGTON, YO15 2HX
Signs to Leisure World, past church on right, Lodge just past Alexandra Walk
T 01262 400447
E rosie4infosunlodge@fsmail.net
W www.sunflower-lodge.co.uk
4 rooms, S £35-£45, D £58-£78

Comfort and practicality are top priorities at this guesthouse, just a troll from the seafront. The bedrooms 'e attractively furnished and decorated individual styles, with impressive levels f equipment and thoughtful additions ‹e fridges, flowers, chocolates and ine. Bathrooms are even more plendid, with luxury toiletries and wels. Jerry and Rosie Banks began refurbishing this property six years ago. Jerry cooks a substantial breakfast in the mornings, while Rosie, a former florist, is behind the floral names of the bedrooms, and the pretty displays in the bedrooms.

RECOMMENDED IN THE AREA
Forum Cinema; Beside the Seaside Museum; Sewerby Hall & Gardens

The Downe Arms Inn ♦♦♦♦

Map ref 8 - NZ60
3 High St, CASTLETON, YO21 2EE
4m S off A171 in village centre
T / F 01287 660223
E thedownearms@yahoo.co.uk
W www.thedownearms.co.uk
3 rooms, S £35, D £60-£70,
No smoking in bedrooms or dining room

Phil and Susie offer a warm welcome to their country inn, set in the beautiful upper Esk valley in Heartbeat country. The North York Moors National Park Centre at Danby is just a short walk away, and there are plenty of opportunities for walking, horse riding and cycling. The refurbished bedrooms are of a high standard and come with complimentary toiletries, crisp white linen, and hospitality trays with mineral water and chocolates. Relax in the lounge bar with its open log fire, original beamed ceiling and exposed stone walls. The resident chef uses local and organic produce to create English classics and exotic meals.

Recommended in the Area
Danby; Whitby; York

Flaneburg Hotel & Restaurant ♦♦♦♦

Map ref 8 - TA27
North Marine Rd, FLAMBOROUGH, YO15 1LF
From Flamborough signs to North Landing
T / F 01262 850284
14 rooms, S £37.50, D £65

It might take its name from the Old English form of Flamborough, but there is nothing old fashioned about this hotel. It is cosy and warm even when chill winds blow across the North Sea, with modern en suite bedrooms, direct-dial telephones with personal voice mail, room and laundry service, and complimentary toiletries. Hairdryers, radio alarms and hospitality trays are standard. Well-cooked traditional meals are served in the bar and smart restaurant, along with a good range of drinks and wines.

Recommended in the Area
Bempton RSPB Nature Reserve; Flamborough Head; Numerous golf courses

Ashfield House Hotel ♦♦♦♦♦

Map ref 7 - SE06
Summers Fold, GRASSINGTON,
BD23 5AE
B6265 to village centre Main St, left onto Summers Fold
T / F 01756 752584
E sales@ashfieldhouse.co.uk
W www.ashfieldhouse.co.uk
7 rooms, D £85-£95, No smoking

Resident owners Joe Azzopardi and Elizabeth Webb provide a warm welcome at Ashfield House, tucked away down a lane just off the cobbled village square. Furnishings and decor throughout the ground floor highlight the original features of the 17th-century building. A wood-burning stove and large open fires create a cosy atmosphere in winter, while in summer there is an attractive walled garden. The en suite bedrooms are all equipped with thoughtful extras. Dinner menus are imaginative and breakfasts are the business before exploring the Dales.

RECOMMENDED IN THE AREA
Bolton Abbey; Stump Cross Caverns; Aysgarth Falls

Grassington Lodge ♦♦♦♦♦

Map ref 7 - SE06
8 Wood Ln, GRASSINGTON,
BD23 5LU
B6265 into village centre
T / F 01756 752518
E relax@grassingtonlodge.co.uk
W www.grassingtonlodge.co.uk
8 rooms, D £40-£45, No smoking, Closed 25-Dec

Built in 1898, this country house in a picturesque Yorkshire Dales village provides first-class hospitality and service. Refurbished in a contemporary style, the bedrooms offer practical extras such as DVD players and free loan of recent films. A comprehensive breakfast menu makes use of local produce and is served in the modern breakfast room. On chilly days a log fire blazes in the lounge. Outside you can experience the dramatic scenery that was made famous by the film Calendar Girls - the cobbled village square, quaint streets, fine old pubs, as well as interesting shops, cafes and restaurants. A good stop for hikers.

RECOMMENDED IN THE AREA
Yorkshire Dales NP; Harrogate; Settle (scenic railway to Carlisle)

The Kings Head Hotel & Restaurant ♦♦♦♦

Map ref 8 - NZ61
The Green, Newton under Roseberry, nr GUISBOROUGH, TS9 6QR
A171 towards Guisborough, at rdbt onto A173 to Newton under Roseberry, under Roseberry Topping landmark

T 01642 722318
F 01642 724750
E info@kingsheadhotel.co.uk
W www.kingsheadhotel.co.uk

8 rooms, S £55-£95, D £69.50-£95, No smoking, Closed 25-Dec

Built from a row of traditional cottages, this family-owned establishment offers modern accommodation with original character. The stylish bedrooms are thoughtfully equipped, including hot beverage facilities - for special occasions there is a four-poster bedroom. The restaurant, next door, serves quality food with produce sourced from the local area. There is a comprehensive list of wines and beer and in summer you can take a drink on the patio. A full English or continental breakfast is served in the glass-roofed breakfast area with unspoiled views of Roseberry Topping, a hill known locally as the Matterhorn of Cleveland.

RECOMMENDED IN THE AREA

Cleveland Way; North York Moors National Park; Whitby

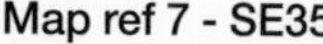

Alexa House & Stable Cottages ♦♦♦♦

Map ref 7 - SE35
26 Ripon Rd, HARROGATE, HG1 2JJ
On A61 0.25m from junct A59

T 01423 501988
F 01423 504086
E alexahouse@msn.com
W www.alexa-house.co.uk

13 rooms, S £45-£52.50, D £75-£85, No smoking in bedrooms or dining room

With its town centre location and the International Conference Centre and Exhibition Halls just a 4-minute walk away, this small hotel is a perfect base for business and leisure travellers. Bedrooms are split between the main house and the cottage rooms, and all have direct-dial telephones, hospitality trays and en suites. An honesty bar in the elegant sitting room is a focal point in the evenings, and dinners are cooked for groups by arrangement. Light meals are served daily in the bright dining room. The enthusiastic owners are engaging hosts.

RECOMMENDED IN THE AREA

RHS Harlow Carr Garden; The Royal Pump Museum; Harewood House

Fountains B & B ♦♦♦♦

Map ref 7 - SE35
27 Kings Rd, HARROGATE,
HG1 5JY
500yds N of town centre. Off A59 Skipton Rd onto Kings Rd, 0.75m on right

T 01423 530483
F 01423 705312
E dave@fountains.fsworld.co.uk
W www.fountainsharrogate.co.uk

10 rooms, S £38-£55, D £65, No smoking, Closed 24 Dec-2 Jan

Fountains is just a short walk from the Harrogate International Centre and the town centre with its fine restaurants and exclusive shops. Overlooking a wooded coppice, the house was built in 1891 and was finally converted into a guesthouse in the mid 1990s. Welcoming owners Dave and Nell Giles have combined original Victorian splendour with modern day facilities. The bedrooms are stylish and individually decorated, and have bathrooms en suite and extensive hospitality trays. Two bedrooms are on the ground floor for easier access. Home cooking is a speciality and breakfast, using produce from local suppliers, is served in the elegant dining room.

RECOMMENDED IN THE AREA

Betty's Café Tea Rooms, Harrogate; Yorkshire Dales; Fountains Abbey (NT)

Laskill Grange ♦♦♦♦

Map ref 8 - SE58
Hawnby, HAWNBY, YO62 5NB
6m N of Helmsley on B1257

T 01439 798268
F 01439 798498
E suesmith@laskillfarm.fsnet.co.uk
W www.laskillgrange.co.uk

4 rooms, D £60-£70, No smoking, Closed 25-Dec

RECOMMENDED IN THE AREA

Rievaulx Abbey; Castle Howard; Nunnington Hall (NT)

Laskill is a country lover's paradise, a charming 19th-century house in the North York Moors National Park. There are splendid walks in the surrounding countryside and fishing in the River Seph, which runs through the grounds. Or there are historic houses and abbeys, picture postcard villages and traditional market towns to visit. The elegant house has exposed beams and open fireplaces, and the immaculate bedrooms are decorated to a very high standard and come with hot-drink trays and flowers. The generous breakfast portions are prepared using home-grown produce wherever possible. Across the courtyard from the farmhouse are converted barns for self-catering. There is an activity centre for children too.

Helmsley Castle

Plumpton Court ♦♦♦♦

Map ref 8 - SE68
High St, Nawton, HELMSLEY, YO62 7TT
A170 from Helmsley into Beadlam & Nawton, 3rd left (Plumpton Court signed), 60yds on left

T 01439 771223
E mail@plumptoncourt.com
W www.plumptoncourt.com

9 rooms, S £40-£45, D £52-£62, No smoking, Closed Dec-Jan

RECOMMENDED IN THE AREA

North Yorkshire Moors Railway; Rievaulx Abbey; Castle Howard

Plumpton Court is situated in the pretty village of Nawton between Helmsley and Kirbymoorside in the foothills of the North Yorkshire Moors. It is well placed for some wonderful walks and for exploring the unspoiled countryside. Chris and Sarah Braithwaite offer a warm welcome to their delightful 17th-century stone house. The bedrooms include two luxury king-size rooms, one with a four-poster bed. Each room is en suite, and all are well fitted out and have tea and coffee trays. The lounge with open fire and well-stocked bar is a cosy place to relax with a drink. To the rear of the house is a secure car park and a secluded garden.

The Huddersfield Central Lodge ♦♦♦♦

Map ref 7 - SE11
11-15 Beast Market, HUDDERSFIELD, HD1 1QF
In town centre off Lord St. Signs for Beast Market from ring road
Ⓣ 01484 515551
Ⓕ 01484 432349
Ⓔ enquiries@centrallodge.com
Ⓦ www.centrallodge.com
22 rooms, S £45, D £62

RECOMMENDED IN THE AREA

Huddersfield University; Lawrence Batley Theatre; Kingsgate Shopping Centre

The Lodge is a former textile mill located on a restored lane made from Yorkshire stone cobbles and only 500 yards from Huddersfield's main amenities. This smart operation is run by the Marsden family and offers spacious en suite bedrooms with modern bathrooms, hospitality trays, trouser presses, toiletries and ironing facilities. There is Internet connection in every room, making the Lodge ideal for business travellers. Some rooms are in the main building, while new rooms with kitchenettes are situated across a courtyard. Public rooms include a bar and a conservatory. Breakfast, served in the refurbished lounge, is prepared using organic and local Yorkshire produce, and many ingredients are from farm shops- choose from vegetarian or meat options, healthy starters and wholesome traditional English. For evenings the staff can recommend local restaurants. Secure free on-site parking right in the centre of Huddersfield is an added bonus.

The Weavers Shed Restaurant with Rooms ♦♦♦♦

Map ref 7 - SE11

Knowl Rd, Golcar, HUDDERSFIELD, HD7 4AN

3m W of Huddersfield. A62 onto B6111 to Milnsbridge & Scar Ln to Golcar, right onto Knowl Rd, signed Colne Valley Museum

T 01484 654284
F 01484 650980
E info@weaversshed.co.uk
W www.weaversshed.co.uk

5 rooms, S £70, D £90, Closed Xmas-New Year

Recommended in the Area

Royal Armouries Museum; National Museum of Film & Television; National Coal Mining Museum

Converted from a cloth-finishing mill in the 1970s, with original features making an interesting talking point, the Weavers Shed continues to impress. Chef-patron Stephen Jackson and his wife Tracy have achieved their ideal of providing a near self-sufficient restaurant, where guests can retire after a superb meal for a luxurious night's sleep. His superior bedrooms are a blend of traditional and classic styles with modern comforts. All rooms, named after local textile mills, are en suite. The restaurant, where the delicious breakfasts including home-made preserves are served, specialises in modern British cooking and simply presented dishes. The kitchen garden supplies virtually all of the fruit, herb and vegetable requirements, and allows the chef to offer excellent seasonal menus. South-west France dominates the wine list, with less well-known vineyards that produce small-yield quality wines.

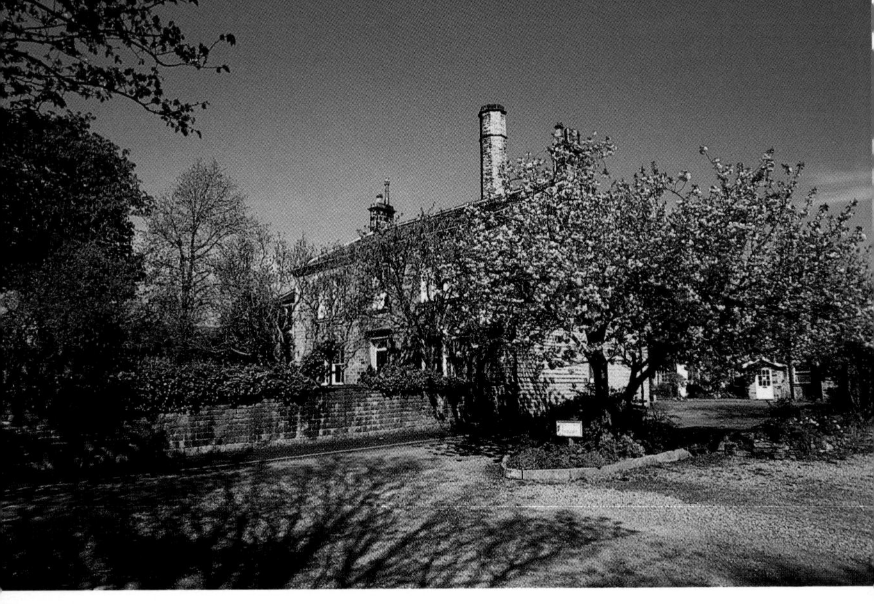

Brickfields Farm ♦♦♦♦

Map ref 8 - SE68
Kirby Mills, KIRKBYMOORSIDE, YO62 6NS
A170 E from Kirbymoorside, 0.5m right into Kirby Mills (signed), farm 1st right
Ⓣ 01751 433074
Ⓔ janet@brickfieldsfarm.co.uk
Ⓦ www.brickfieldsfarm.co.uk
3 rooms, S £38-£48, D £64-£75, No smoking

Janet Trousdale inherited the family farm and has since turned it into a ghly successful guesthouse. The furbished bedrooms have been dividually styled and filled with plenty of omely and luxury extras. Some rooms ave antique French beds, others have xposed beams that were discovered uring renovation, and all have quality furniture. Modern showers and fluffy bathrobes add to the comfort. Sheep graze beyond the conservatory where appetizing breakfasts are served. Delicious home-cooked dinners are available by arrangement.

RECOMMENDED IN THE AREA
Rievaulx Abbey; Castle Howard; North Yorkshire Moors Railway

Gallon House ♦♦♦♦ 

Map ref 8 - SE35
47 Kirkgate, KNARESBOROUGH, HG5 8BZ
Next to railway station
Ⓣ 01423 862102
Ⓔ gallon-house@ntlworld.com
Ⓦ www.gallon-house.co.uk
3 rooms, S £70, D £90, No smoking in bedrooms or dining room

RECOMMENDED IN THE AREA
Leeds; York; Fountains Abbey (NT)

Quality rooms in an elegant house with fabulous views Situated overlooking Nidd Gorge, in one of e most scenic parts of Yorkshire, Gallon House is pular for its welcoming atmosphere and first-class commodation. This delightful Tudor-style building ers very stylish bedrooms, each named after the view at it offers. The rooms are individually furnished with any extras, including CD players, bathrobes and perb refreshment trays. Rick Hodgson's culinary delights are not to be missed and he places strong emphasis on local ingredients. Dinner, by arrangement, features quality local bread, pates and chutneys and the beef casserole is prepared using local Yorkshire ale.
A stay at Gallon House is the perfect antidote to a corporate hotel experience.

Newton House ♦♦♦♦

Map ref 8 - SE35
5-7 York Place, KNARESBOROUGH, HG5 0AD
On A59 in Knaresborough, 500yds from town centre
T 01423 863539
F 01423 869748
E newtonhouse@btinternet.com
W www.newtonhousehotel.com
11 rooms, S £45, D £80-£100, No smoking in bedrooms or dining room, Closed 1 wk Xmas

RECOMMENDED IN THE AREA

Harewood House; Fountains Abbey; Knaresborough Castle

Newton House is a former coaching inn, built in the 18th-century of honey-colour stone that reputedly comes from nearby Knaresborough Castle. The River Nidd and the town's picturesque maze of streets and alleys are only a stroll away. Entry to the lovingly restored hotel is through an archway into a courtyard. Modern, individually decorated bedrooms are well equipped with irons, hairdryers and tea and coffee facilities, and some include four-posters and king-size doubles - all but one of the rooms is en suite. Children are welcome and family rooms are available. There is an inviting lounge, and individually cooked breakfasts are served in an attractive dining room. The menu offers a wide selection from full English to smoked salmon with scrambled eggs or croissants. Bread straight from the oven and home-made muffins are a feature, and vegetarians are welcome. Proprietors Kevin and Sara Earl work hard to ensure you have an enjoyable stay.

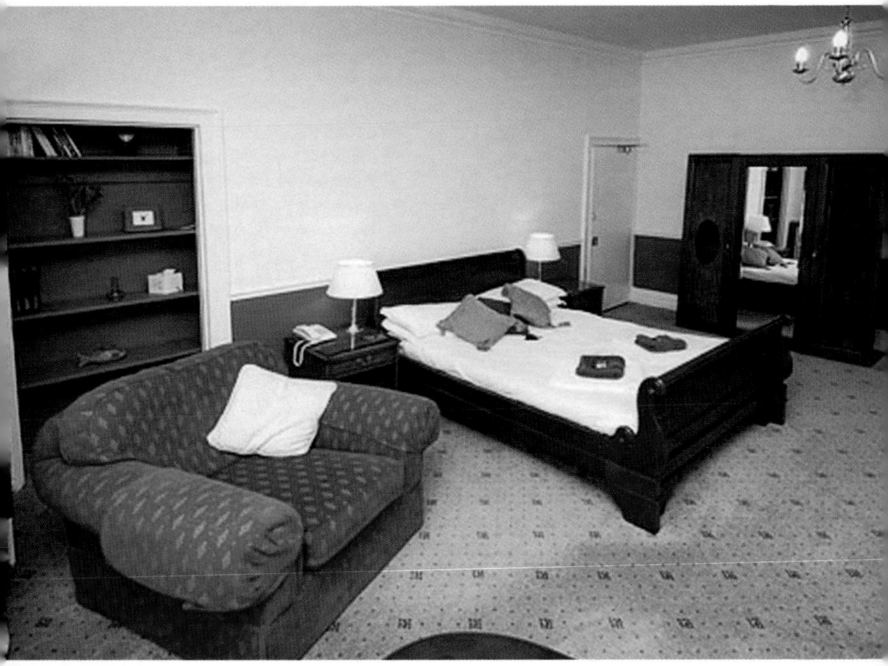

River House Hotel ♦♦♦♦

Map ref 7 - SD96
MALHAM, BD23 4DA
Off A65, 7m N to Malham
T 01729 830315
E info@riverhousehotel.co.uk
W www.riverhousehotel.co.uk
8 rooms, S £30-£45, D £50-£60, No smoking

A warm welcome awaits you at this attractive Victorian house close to the Pennine Way. The superb surrounding countryside is excellent for walking, golf, mountain biking and horse riding. The bedrooms are bright and well equipped and some have original fireplaces - one room on the ground floor has easier access. The public areas include a cosy lounge, with a wood burning stove for cooler months, and a large, well-appointed dining room. The owners provide exceptional breakfasts, including scrumptious sausages and black pudding from the local butcher. Delicious dinners also feature local produce. Pets are welcome.

Recommended in the Area

Settle to Carlisle Railway; Skipton; Pennine Way

Bank Villa Guest House ♦♦♦♦

Map ref 7 - SE28
MASHAM, HG4 4DB
Enter on A6108 from Ripon, property on right
T 01765 689605
E bankvilla@btopenworld.com
W www.bankvilla.com
6 rooms, S £45-£60, D £50-£85, No smoking

With a background in the hospitality industry proprietors Graham and Liz Howard-Barker have created a welcoming atmosphere in their charming Georgian home, a great base for exploring the Dales. Relax in the lovely terraced gardens, in one of two comfortable lounges, or the conservatory, all of which have plenty of character. Individually decorated bedrooms feature beams, stripped pine period furniture and the luxury of crisp white linens. Liz's cooking uses home-grown and local produce when-ever possible, served in the relaxed atmosphere of the licensed restaurant. Packed lunches and snacks are also available.

Recommended in the Area

Black Sheep & Theakstons breweries; Rievaulx & Fountains abbeys; Yorkshire Dales

The Moorlands Country House ◆◆◆◆◆

Map ref 8 - SE78
Levisham, PICKERING, YO18 7NL
A169 N from Pickering 6m, left to Lockton & Levisham

T 01751 460229
F 01751 460470
E ronaldoleonardo@aol.com
W www.moorlandslevisham.co.uk

7 rooms, S £55-£75, D £110-£130, No smoking, Closed Dec-Feb

There are stunning views from this elegant Victorian house set in mature gardens and woodland in the heart of the North Yorkshire Moors. Inside, the atmosphere is welcoming and homely. (You can even bring your own horse.) The en suite bedrooms in this former vicarage are luxuriously appointed, with stylish decoration. Each one has a bathroom or shower, and a refreshment tray. You can relax in the spacious lounge. Hearty breakfasts are served by the Gill and Ron Leonard in the dining room. Delicious dinners can also be prepared.

RECOMMENDED IN THE AREA

Heartbeat country; Castle Howard; Harrogate

Bay Tree Farm ◆◆◆◆

Map ref 7 - SE37
Aldfield, RIPON, HG4 3BE
4m W, S off B6265

T / F 01765 620394
E btfarm@ppcmail.co.uk
W www.baytreefarm.co.uk

6 rooms, S £35-£50, D £65-£75, No smoking

Bay Tree Farm covers 400 acres of beef and arable land. Situated between the Yorkshire Dales and the North York Moors, there is ample opportunity to explore the countryside or to visit Fountains Abbey nearby. The farmhouse itself is in the quiet village of Aldfield, near Ripon, with spacious accommodation in a converted barn. Family and ground-floor rooms are available, all en suite with tea and coffee facilities. Dinner is available and the wholesome farm fare uses fresh local produce. There is a comfortable lounge where a wood-burning stove is lit in colder weather. Valerie and Andrew Leeming are attentive hosts.

RECOMMENDED IN THE AREA

Studley Park; Brimham Rocks; Yorkshire Dales

St George's Court ♦♦♦♦

Map ref 7 - SE37
Old Home Farm, Grantley, RIPON, HG4 3PS
B6265 W from Ripon, right signed Grantley & Winksley, up hill 1m past Risplith sign & next right
T / F 01765 620618
E stgeorgescourt@bronco.co.uk
W www.stgeorges-court.co.uk
5 rooms, S £45-£55, D £60-£75, No smoking

Warm hospitality is the hallmark at this renovated farmhouse complex the edge of Wensleydale, close to ountains Abbey World Heritage Site. e elegant 18th-century house is set in acres that includes a small lake, me to numerous waterfowl. The ound-floor rooms, each with their own nt door, are located around a pretty ntral courtyard, and are well equipped h quality beds, refreshment trays and acious bathrooms. One unit with two bedrooms is ideal for families. Imaginative breakfasts, using the farm's own free-range eggs and finest local ingredients, are served in the conservatory-dining room, which has splendid views of the surrounding countryside.

RECOMMENDED IN THE AREA
Fountains Abbey (NT); Brimham Rocks; Newby Hall

Low Skibeden Farmhouse ♦♦♦♦

Map ref 7 - SD95
Marrogate Rd, SKIPTON, BD23 6AB
At E end of Skipton bypass off A65/A59, 1m on right
T 01756 793849
W www.yorkshirenet.co.uk/accgde/lowskibeden/index.html
5 rooms, S £36-£48, D £52-£60, No smoking

Yorkshire hospitality at its best is just part of the appeal of this lovely stone farmhouse. You are eted with tea and cakes on arrival, and there are nty of other home comforts. The traditionally corated and furnished bedrooms are equipped with of thoughtful extras, and the bathrooms are dern. There is a comfy lounge, while in the evening ather Simpson serves suppertime drinks. Breakfast n occasion, when hearty full English dishes are served in the dining room. Outside there are lovingly tended gardens to enjoy and the beautiful Dales to be explored. No children or pets.

RECOMMENDED IN THE AREA
Harrogate; Ingleton waterfalls; Bronte Parsonage, Howarth

The Blackwell Ox Inn ♦♦♦♦

Map ref 8 - SE56
Huby Rd, SUTTON-ON-THE-FOREST, YO61 1DT
Off A1237, onto B1363 to Sutton-on-the-Forest. Left at T-junct, 50yd on right

T 01347 810328
F 01904 691529
E info@blackwelloxinn.co.uk
W www.blackwelloxinn.co.uk

5 rooms, S £90, D £90, No smoking

Picturesque Sutton-on-the-Forest is only 7 miles from York, making it a good base for exploring the city and the surrounding countryside. The refurbished inn offers attractive, individually designed bedrooms and pleasing public rooms. The cooking is well worth seeking out and the staff are very keen and friendly. Chef Steven Holding prepares excellent dishes in the restaurant using local produce to create French-inspired dishes such as cassoulet of saddleback pork with chorizo and gar sausage. Spain is also well represente as Steven recreates the bold flavours the Catalan region. Tasty puddings round off the experience. Children welcome but only guide dogs please.

RECOMMENDED IN THE ARE

Castle Howard; Yorvic Centre, York; Railway Museum, York

Spital Hill ♦♦♦♦♦

Map ref 8 - SE48
York Rd, THIRSK, YO7 3AE
1.5m SE of town. House set back 200yds from A19, driveway marked by 2 white posts

T 01845 522273
F 01845 524970
E spitalhill@amserve.net
W www.spitalhill.co.uk

5 rooms, S £57-£66, D £84-£96, No smoking

Robin and Ann Clough warmly welcome guests to their beautiful home, a fine country house set in its gardens and parkland surrounded by open countryside. The atmosphere is very relaxing. There is a lovely lounge and meals are taken house-party style at one large table in the dining room. Ann produces an excellent set dinner each evening as an optional extra, using good fresh produce, much of which comes from the garden. The well-prepared breakfast is also highlight. Bedrooms are furnished with quality and st and thoughtfully equipped with bathrobes, fresh fruit shortbread, mineral water, books, alarm clocks and hairdryers. There is no tea making equipment as Anr prefers to offer tea as a service.

RECOMMENDED IN THE AREA

Herriott Centre, Thirsk; Byland Abbey; York Minster

Woodhouse Farm ♦♦♦♦

Map ref 8 - SE76
WESTOW, YO60 7LL
Off A64 to Kirkham Priory & Westow. Right at T-junct, farm drive 0.5m out of village on right
T / F 01653 618378
E stay@wood-house-farm.co.uk
W www.wood-house-farm.co.uk
2 rooms, S £30-£40, D £50-£65, No smoking, Closed Xmas, New Year, Mar-mid Apr

Make yourself at home at this family-run mixed farm set in open ›untryside. The 18th-century Grade II ted farmhouse combines original oak ›ams and log fires with up-to-date ›mforts. The two well-equipped en ›ite bedrooms have king-size beds, ›throoms, robes and hospitality trays. ›e cosy lounge comes with books and games, and you can use the fridge in the dining room. Delicious breakfasts are cooked in the farmhouse kitchen from home-grown produce, and home-made bread, preserves and other local goodies are served.

RECOMMENDED IN THE AREA
Castle Howard; North Yorks Moors Railway; York

Corra Lynn ♦♦♦♦

Map ref 8 - NZ81
28 Crescent Av, WHITBY, YO21 3EW
Corner A174 & Crescent Av
T / F 01947 602214
5 rooms, S £23, D £50, Closed 21 Dec-5 Jan

Bruce and Christine Marot have a passion for what they do, mixing traditional values with trendy ›le. The house has a prominent corner position on the ›est Cliff and is within easy walking distance of the ›wn and its picturesque harbour. Bedrooms are ›oughtfully equipped, individually furnished and ›lourfully decorated. The delightful dining room with a ›rner bar and a wall adorned with clocks really ›tches the eye. Breakfasts are hearty, with a vegetarian option, and the menu changes with the seasons.

RECOMMENDED IN THE AREA
Whitby Abbey; Captain Cook Memorial Museum; Robin Hood's Bay

Netherby House Hotel ♦♦♦♦

Map ref 8 - NZ81
90 Coach Rd, Sleights, WHITBY, YO22 5EQ
In village of Sleights, off A169 Whitby-Pickering road
T / F 01947 810211
E info@netherby-house.co.uk
W www.netherby-house.co.uk
11 rooms, S £34-£38.50, D £68-£77
No smoking, Closed 21-26 Dec

For owners Lyn and Barry Truman their bed and breakfast business is a labour of love - look no further than the beautifully kept gardens and the delightful day rooms and bedrooms, all of which contribute to a restful stay. Hospitality is another strength of Netherby House, and imaginative evening meals using fresh garden produce are served in the candlelit dining room. Choose between the en suite twin, double and family rooms, with a four poster for extra luxury. There is a lounge-bar and conservatory for relaxing in, and there are exceptional views from the summer house.

Recommended in the area

Historic Whitby; North Yorkshire Moors National Park; North Yorkshire Moors Railway

---

Barbican House ♦♦♦♦

Map ref 8 - SE65
20 Barbican Rd, YORK, YO10 5AA
Signs to city centre, premises 100yds from Barbican Leisure Centre near junct A19 & A1079
T 01904 627617
F 01904 647140
E info@barbicanhouse.com
W www.barbicanhouse.com
7 rooms, S £60-£66, D £70-£80,
No smoking

Adrian and Ann Bradley ensure a friendly welcome and attentive service at their delightful ine Victorian house built in 1888. Overlooking the medieval city walls, Barbican House is only a short walk from all York's main attractions, and the splendid Barbican Leisure Centre with pool and concert hall is only 100 yards away. The house is very well furnished throughout and has attractive bedrooms decked out to complement the Victorian property. All rooms come with hospitality trays, four have king-size beds, and all are en suite. An excellent hearty Yorkshire breakfast is served in the cosy dining room and features local outdoor-reared bacon and sausages (well the pigs were).

Recommended in the area

Jorvik Viking Centre; National Railway Museum; York Minster

Ascot House ♦♦♦♦

Map ref 8 - SE65
80 East Parade, YORK, YO31 7YH
0.5m NE of city centre. Off A1036 Heworth Green onto Mill Ln, 2nd left
T 01904 426826
F 01904 431077
E admin@ascothouseyork.com
W www.ascothouseyork.com
15 rooms, S £28-£65, D £56-£75, No smoking in bedrooms or dining room, Closed 21-28 Dec

RECOMMENDED IN THE AREA

Jorvik Viking Centre; National Railway Museum; York Minster

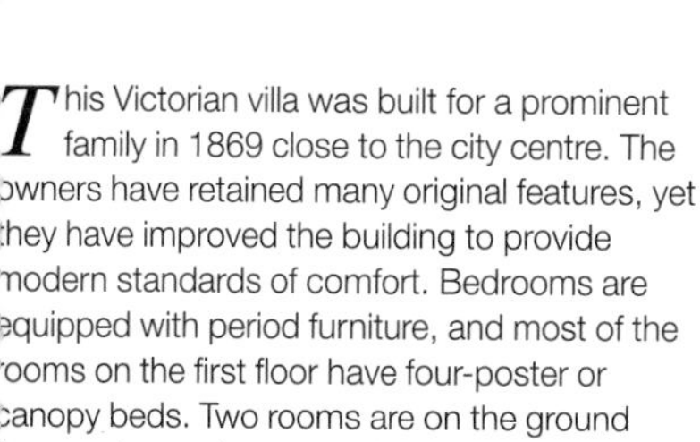

This Victorian villa was built for a prominent family in 1869 close to the city centre. The owners have retained many original features, yet they have improved the building to provide modern standards of comfort. Bedrooms are equipped with period furniture, and most of the rooms on the first floor have four-poster or canopy beds. Two rooms are on the ground floor, and most have en suites along with hospitality trays and more. The curved stained-glass window on the landing is particularly attractive. Ascot House is a welcoming property that can be reached from the city by bus in just a few minutes, or by a short brisk walk. It has an enclosed car park, and the public park next door has two tennis courts and two bowling greens.

Isle of Man

A selection of places to eat from the AA Restaurant & AA Pub guides

Restaurants

Sefton Hotel (European)
Harris Promenade, Douglas IM1 2RW
Tel 01624 645500

Pubs

The Creek Inn
Station Place, Peel IM5 1AT
Tel 01624 842216

Falcon's Nest Hotel
The Promenade, Station Road,
Port Erin IM9 6AF
Tel 01624 834077

Dreem Ard ♦♦♦♦

Map ref 5 - SC37
Ballanard Rd, DOUGLAS, IM2 5PR
From St Ninian's Church along Ballanard Rd for 1m, over Johnny Watterson Ln x-rds, past farm on left, Dreem Ard on left
T / F 01624 621491
3 rooms, S £30-£40, D £50-£60, No smoking

Cliff and Rosemary Walters are semi-retired teachers whose philosophy is 'to make people happy and feel at home'. Their elegant house stands above the wooded slopes of the Glass River Valley, just a few minutes from Douglas. Calming views of the glens and a high degree of privacy are guaranteed to relax even the most stressed city dweller. Splendid breakfasts and evening meals served around a circular table are a feature here, and the en suite bedrooms are homely as well as stylish. Some rooms also have seating areas (the family room has a separate lounge), and hospitality trays are provided.

Recommended in the Area

Manx Museum; Gaiety Theatre; Superb countryside

Aaron House ♦♦♦♦♦

Map ref 5 - SC26
The Promenade, PORT ST MARY, IM9 5DE
Signs for South & Port St Mary, left at Post Office, house in centre of Promenade overlooking harbour
T 01624 835702
W www.aaronhouse.co.uk
4 rooms, S £49-£88, D £70-£98, No smoking, Closed 21 Dec-3 Jan

Aaron House, on The Promenade at Port St Mary, transports you back in ne. This family-run establishment vingly recreates the property's original ctorian style, with exquisite interior esign, cast-iron fireplaces in the public oms, sparklingly polished period rniture, and lovingly collected ic-a-brac. Quality is the watchword, ident from the delicious home-made kes served on arrival to the luxurious edrooms with details such as a ot-water bottle placed in your bed at ght. Breakfast is a great treat, with ome-made breads and preserves, freshly cooked dishes, squeezed juices and a vast selection of fresh fruits. Evening meals are offered in the winter only (Monday-Friday). Smoking and alcohol are not permitted, and children and pets cannot be accommodated. Free parking 70 yards away.

Recommended in the Area

Cregneash Folk Village; Victorian Steam Railway; Sound & Calf of Man (bird sanctuary)

The River House ♦♦♦♦♦

Map ref 5 - SC49
RAMSEY, IM8 3DA
T / F 01624 816412
3 rooms, S £46.50-£58.50, D £73-£93, Closed Feb-Mar

Nicely situated in over 3 acres of mature gardens beside the River Sulby, this Georgian house is a fect place to unwind. From here you can explore the cinating island with its own parliament and currency. ere are wonderful walks, superb stretches of spoiled coast and many attractions to visit. The acious accommodation has luxurious facilities - all oms come with bathrooms en suite and overlook the r. The breakfast room, also with good river views, is a lovely place to savour the delicious food on offer. The hospitality here is spontaneous and friendly, which explains why guests return again and again.

Recommended in the Area

Manx Electric Railway; Millennium Way long-distance path; Ramsey Bay

Channel Islands

A selection of places to eat from the AA Restaurant & AA Pub guides

Restaurants

La Frégate (British, French)
Les Cotils, St Peter Port, Guernsey GY1 1UT
Tel 01481 724624

Le Nautique (International)
Quay Steps, St Peter Port, Guernsey GY1 2LE
Tel 01481 721714

The Village Bistro (British, Mediterranean)
Gorey Village, Gorey, Jersey JE3 9EP
Tel 01534 853429

Green Island Restaurant (Mediterranean)
Green Island, St Clement, Jersey JE2 6LS
Tel 01534 857787

Longueville Manor (British)
St Saviour, Jersey JE2 7WF
Tel 01534 725501

La Sablonnerie (International)
Sark GY9 0SD
Tel 01481 832061

Pubs

Hotel Hougue du Pommier
Hougue du Pommier Road, Catel, Guernsey GY5 7FQ
Tel 01481 256531

Castle Green Pub and Bistro
La Route de la Cote, Gorey, Jersey JE3 6DR
Tel 01534 853103

Old Court House Inn
St Aubin's Harbour, St Aubin, Jersey JE3 8AB
Tel 01524 746433

La Pulente Hotel
La Route de la Pulente, St Brelade, Jersey JE3 8HG
Tel 01534 744487

Hotel Petit Champ ♦♦♦♦

Map ref 13
SARK, GY9 0SF
Signs from the Methodist Chapel
T 01481 832046
F 01481 832469
E info@hotelpetitchamp.co.uk
W www.hotelpetitchamp.co.uk
10 rooms, S £57.50-£66.50, D £111-£129, Closed Nov-Etr

The sea views and sunsets from this small hotel are magnificent. Set on the car-free, feudal island of Sark, its splendid position overlooking the sea and the neighbouring Channel islands is matched by very high standards of hospitality and service. Chris and Caroline followed a dream to run this hotel, and they guarantee to send you home refreshed and happy. The en suite bedrooms have no televisions (there is a television lounge) and morning tea or coffee is brought to your room. Breakfasts and the five-course dinners make excellent use of fresh loc produce, and there is a well-stocked wine cellar.

RECOMMENDED IN THE ARE

La Seigneurie Gardens; Horse & Carria tours; Boat trips

The Panorama ♦♦♦♦

Map ref 13
La Rue du Crocquet, ST AUBIN, JE3 8BZ
In village centre
T 01534 742429
F 01534 745940
E info@panoramajersey.com
W www.panoramajersey.com
14 rooms, S £35-£58, D £70-£116,
No smoking, Closed mid Oct-mid Apr

A genuine warm welcome and spectacular views across St Aubin's Bay can be expected at this aptly named hotel in a pretty seafront street. Savour the glorious outlook from the sunny terrace or relax in the public areas with their seaward vistas. Antiques feature here, in particular the elegant fireplaces, and the hotel is notable for its collection of teapots - over 500 at the last count. A hallmark of the bedrooms is the luxury pocket-sprung beds, most of which are well over six feet long. Breakfast is excellent, with each meal individually cooked to order. Dishes such as Grand Slam and Elegant Rarebit are long-time favourites. The area is well served with restaurants, many within walking distance, and the owners are happy to make recommendations. This is a good base for walking, cycling or travelling around the island by bus. No children.

RECOMMENDED IN THE AREA

Picturesque village of St Aubin; Railway Walk to Corbiere; Beauport and Les Creux Country Park

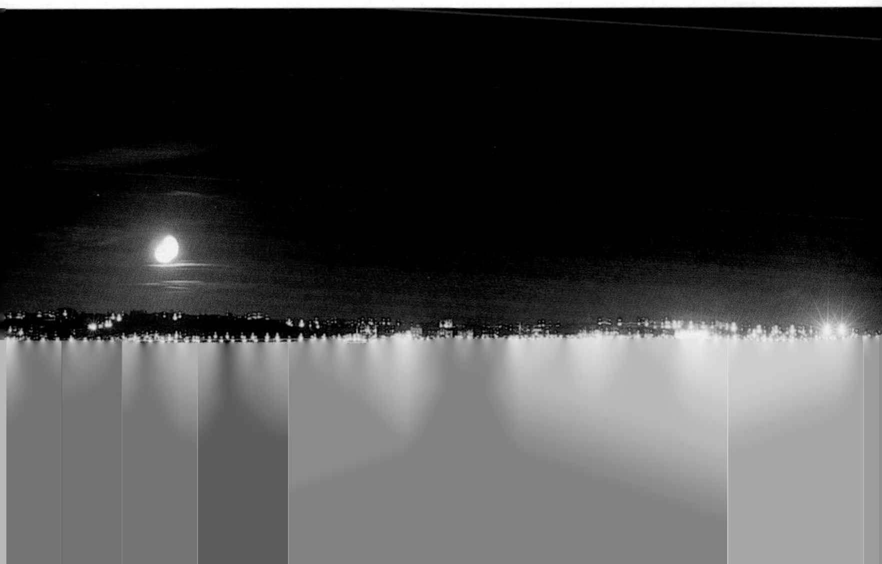

Millbrook House Hotel ♦♦♦♦

Map ref 13

Rue de Trachy, Millbrook, ST HELIER, JE2 3JN

1.5m W of town off A1

T 01534 733036
F 01534 724317
E millbrook.house@jerseymail.co.uk
W www.millbrookhousehotel.com

27 rooms, S £39-£43, D £78-£86, No smoking in bedrooms or dining room, Closed Oct-early May

RECOMMENDED IN THE AREA

Coastal walks; Elizabeth Castle; WWII German Underground Hospital

The gracious Georgian mansion stands in 10 acres of gardens and parkland overlooking the sea. George and Philippa Pirouet's hospitality reflects the friendly Jersey atmosphere and with good food too. They have been doing this successfully for well over 20 years, and Millbrook House is ideal for the independent traveller seeking an establishment of character at an acceptable price. It has been in the same island family since 1848, with extensions providing modern accommodation on three floors to the rear. The grounds have a five-hole pitch and putt golf course, as well as ample parking. Each of the bedrooms has a private bathroom, and most of them have sea and garden views. Direct-dial telephones and hospitality trays are provided, and there is a lift to all floors. In the dining room, an imaginative menu is supported by an extensive wine list.

Scotland

A selection of places to eat from the AA Restaurant & AA Pub guides

Restaurants

The Silver Darling (French, Seafood)
'ocra Quay, North Pier, Aberdeen
AB11 5DQ
Tel 01224 576229

Loch Melfort Hotel (European)
Arduane, Argyll & Bute PA34 4XG
Tel 01852 200233

The Harbour Inn (International)
Bowmore, Isle of Islay,
Argyll & Bute PA43 7JR
Tel 01496 810330

Restaurant Martin Wishart
(Modern European)
The Shore, Leith, Edinburgh EH6 6RA
Tel 0131 553 3557

Seafood Bar & Restaurant (Seafood)
16 West End, St Monans, Fife KY10 2BX
Tel 01333 730327

The Buttery (International)
652 Argyle Street, Glasgow G3 8UF
Tel 0141 221 8188

Quigley's
158 Bath Street, Glasgow G2 4TB
Tel 0141 3314060

Ubiquitous Chip (Traditional
Scottish)
12 Ashton Lane, Glasgow G12 8SJ
Tel 0141 334 5007

Three Chimneys Restaurant
(Modern Scottish)
Colbost, Isle of Skye, Highland IV55 8ZT
Tel 01470 511258

Hotel Eilean Iarmain (Scottish)
Isle Ornsay, Isle of Skye, Highland IV43 8QR
Tel 01471 833332

Killiecrankie House Hotel
(Scottish, International)
Killiecrankie, Perth & Kinross PH16 5LG
Tel 01796 473220

Burts Hotel (European)
The Square, Melrose,
Scottish Borders TD6 9PL
Tel 01896 822285

Champany Inn (British)
Champany, Linlithgow,
West Lothian EH49 7LU
Tel 01506 834532

Pubs

Prince of Wales
7 St Nicholas Lane, Aberdeen AB10 1HF
Tel 01224 640597

Cairnbaan Hotel & Restaurant
Cairnbaan, Lochgilphead,
Argyll & Bute PA31 8SJ
Tel 01546 603668

Creggans Inn
Strachur, Argyll & Bute PA27 8BX
Tel 01369 860279

Creebridge House Hotel
Minnigaff, Newton Stewart,
Dumfries & Galloway DG8 6NP
Tel 01671 402121

Doric Tavern
15-16 Market Street, Edinburgh EH1 1DE
Tel 0131 225 1084

Applecross Inn
Shore Street, Applecross,
Highland IV54 8LR
Tel 01520 744262

Cawdor Tavern
The Lane, Cawdor, Highland IV12 5XP
Tel 01667 404777

Dundonell Hotel
Dundonell, Highland IV23 2QR
Tel 01854 633204

Moorings Hotel
Banavie, Fort William, Highland PH33 7LY
Tel 01397 772797

The Plockton Hotel
Harbour Street, Plockton,
Highland IV52 8TN
Tel 01599 544274

Plockton Inn & Seafood Restaurant
Innes Street, Plockton,
Highland IV52 8TW
Tel 01599 544222

Shieldaig Bar
Shieldaig, Highland IV54 8XN
Tel 01520 755251

Lomond Country Inn
Kinnesswood, Perth & Kinross KY13 9HN
Tel 01592 840253

SCOTLAND

Callater Lodge Guest House ♦♦♦♦

Map ref 12 - NO19
9 Glenshee Rd, BRAEMAR,
Aberdeenshire AB35 5YQ
Next to A93, 300yds S of Braemar centre

T 013397 41275
F 013397 41345
E hampsons@hotel-braemar.co.uk
W www.hotel-braemar.co.uk

6 rooms, S £27-£32, D £50-£58,
No smoking in bedrooms or dining room,
Closed Xmas, New Year

RECOMMENDED IN THE AREA
Balmoral Castle; Cairngorms National Park; Glenshee Ski Centre, Cairnwell

Callater Lodge, built of local granite in 1861, stands in spacious and attractive grounds at the south end of this pretty village with its royal connections. A warm welcome is assured at any time, but especially in the winter when this beautifully kept house is heated round the clock. Sink into deep leather chairs in the lounge after a day walking, climbing, golfing, cycling, fishing or skiing. The library with its inglenook fireplace and licensed bar is another peaceful option. The individually styled en suite bedrooms have lovely soft furnishings and the bathrooms contain a good selection of toiletries. Breakfast is served in the bright dining room and offers a wide choice. Later, soup of the day, snacks and a variety of tasty sandwiches are served until 9 pm. Surrounded by fine hills, the magnificent Braemar Castle can be reached by one of many pretty walks.

Kirkton House ♦♦♦♦♦

Map ref 9 - NS37
Darleith Rd, CARDROSS,
Argyll & Bute G82 5EZ
.5m N of village. Turn N off A814 onto Darleith Rd at W end of village. Kirkton House 0.5m on right

T 01389 841951
F 01389 841868
E aa@kirktonhouse.co.uk
W www.kirktonhouse.co.uk

5 rooms, S £37.50-£40, D £50-£60, No smoking in bedrooms or dining oom, Closed Dec-Jan

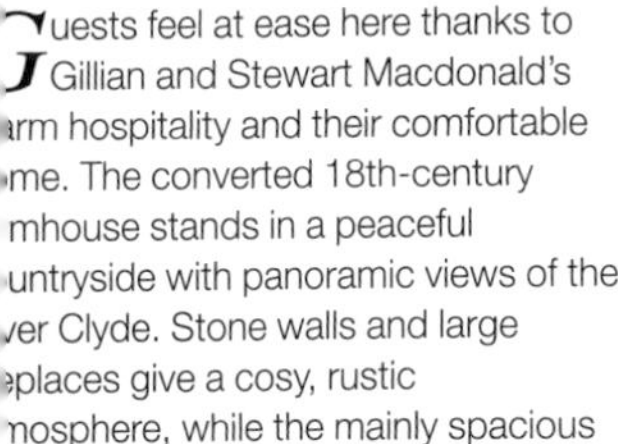

Guests feel at ease here thanks to Gillian and Stewart Macdonald's arm hospitality and their comfortable me. The converted 18th-century mhouse stands in a peaceful untryside with panoramic views of the ver Clyde. Stone walls and large eplaces give a cosy, rustic mosphere, while the mainly spacious bedrooms are individually styled. Plenty of homely extras enhance the good facilities. Easy access ground-floor rooms and rooms for families are available, and also stabling for horses. The full Scottish breakfast is another high point.

Recommended in the Area

Loch Lomond; The Hill House, Helensburgh (NTS); Burrell Collection, Glasgow

Ards House ♦♦♦♦

Map ref 9 - NM93
CONNEL, Argyll & Bute PA37 1PT
On A85, 4m N of Oban

T 01631 710255
F 01631 710857
E info@ardshouse.com
W www.ardshouse.com

4 rooms, S £45-£60, D £60-£80, No smoking, Closed Dec-Jan

Expectations are sure to be satisfied at this Victorian house in a truly stunning setting. With the Firth of rn and the Morven Hills spread out before it, and the enic Loch Etive just a few miles away, the outlook re than justifies a visit. The house itself is warm and lcoming, and owner Margaret Kennedy has added nty of stylish touches since taking over. An open fire d plenty of games and books feature in the spacious awing room, and the en suite bedrooms are well equipped. Delicious breakfasts made from fresh local produce are worth setting the alarm for.

Recommended in the Area

Dunstaffnage Castle, Oban; Bonawe Iron Furnace; Arduaine Garden

Coylet Inn ♦♦♦♦

Map ref 9 - NS17
Loch Eck, DUNOON, Argyll & Bute
PA23 8SG
9m N from Dunoon on A815
T / F 01369 840426
E reservations@coylet-locheck.co.uk
W www.coylet-locheck.co.uk
4 rooms, S £40-£42.50, D £70-£75

RECOMMENDED IN THE AREA
Dunoon; Benmore Botanical Gardens; Quadmania Outdoor Adventure Centre

Coylet means wooded inlet and this charming 17th-century coaching inn on the shore of Loch Eck is an ideal spot for hill walking, golf, water sports and pony trekking, and boats are available for fishing on the loch. The bedrooms have been upgraded to a high standard of comfort - one room has an enormous bath in the window, perfect for supping champagne and watching the world go by. Access to the rooms is by an original spiral staircase. The cosy well-stocked bar - including a large selection of malt whiskies - comes with a log fire, and delicious and imaginative food using the finest of local produce is served in the spacious dining room. Special breaks and wedding packages are available.

Lethamhill ♦♦♦♦♦

Map ref 9 - NS28
West Dhuhill Rd, HELENSBURGH, Argyll & Bute G84 9AW
A82 onto B831, left onto B832, follow sign for Hillhouse. 2nd right after 30mph sign, over minor x-rds, 3rd entrance on right
T / F 01436 676016
E Lethamhill@talk21.com
W www.lethamhill.co.uk
3 rooms, S £45-£55, D £60-£70, No smoking

This large spacious property with lovely well-tended gardens is a showcase for Douglas Johnston's collection of antiques and bric-a-brac, which is always a talking point. Superb hospitality and impressive bedrooms ensure that guests return time and again, and Jane's delicious breakfasts made from fresh Scottish produce are another lure. The rooms come with superb bathrooms, great beds and flat-screen televisions, along with many thoughtful extras. Public areas are equally comfortable, with a spacious lounge and a delightful dining room that looks out to the garden. Minimum stay two nights.

RECOMMENDED IN THE AREA
The Hill House, Helensburgh (NTS); Loch Lomond; Glasgow Airport

Glenburnie House ♦♦♦♦

Map ref 9 - NM82
The Esplanade, OBAN, Argyll & Bute
PA34 5AQ
On Oban seafront. Follow signs for Ganavan
Ⓣ / Ⓕ 01631 562089
Ⓔ graeme.strachan@btinternet.com
Ⓦ www.glenburnie.co.uk
14 rooms, S £35-£45, D £70-£90,
No smoking, Closed Nov-Mar

From its prime position on the Esplanade, this handsome stablishment has dazzling views across e Firth of Lorne to the Isle of Mull. The ouse has been lovingly restored by the trachan family, who greet guests on rival with tea and shortbread. The en uite bedrooms, including a superior ur-poster and a mini-suite, are eautifully decorated, comfortably rnished, and equipped with modern cilities. There is a lovely sitting room ith a fire for cooler evenings. Delicious reakfasts featuring the best of local produce and home-made preserves are served in the attractive dining room. The Strachans are happy to advise you on the many restaurants in the town centre, which is just a stroll away. AA Landlady of the Year finalist 2004-2005. Private parking is available.

Recommended in the Area

Crarae & Arduaine gardens; Fishing & golf; Boat hire & cruises

---

Douglas House ♦♦♦♦

Map ref 5 - NX76
63 Queen St, CASTLE DOUGLAS,
Dumfries & Galloway DG7 1HS
A75 W, left at rdbt signed Castle Douglas, over minirdbt, 2nd left next rdbt, B&B 500yds on left
Ⓣ / Ⓕ 01556 503262
Ⓔ steve@douglas-house.com
Ⓦ www.douglas-house.com
4 rooms, S £27-£30, D £60-£80,
No smoking

Recommended in the Area

Threave Gardens (NTS); Threave Castle; Red Kite feeding station

Douglas House offers quality accommodation and high levels of personal attention just off the town entre. On arrival at this elegantl house built in 1825 you ill be greeted with drinks and refreshments. The dividual bedrooms range from the cosy single to the pacious ground-floor double or twin with a magnificent athroom. Complimentary toiletries and refreshments ay are standard in every room. The lounge-breakfast om has comfy leather sofas and a substantial Scottish breakfast is served round the communal table. Evening meals are by arrangement. Douglas House is in the right place for golf, fishing, walking or just relaxing.

Rivendell ♦♦♦♦

Map ref 5 - NX97
105 Edinburgh Rd, DUMFRIES, Dumfries & Galloway DG1 1JX
On A701 Edinburgh Rd, 400yds S from A701/A75 junct

T 01387 252251
F 01387 263084
E info@rivendellbnb.co.uk
W www.rivendellbnb.co.uk

5 rooms, S £25-£40, D £48-£54, No smoking

Recommended in the Area

Solway coast; Robert Burns Heritage Trail; Caerlaverock Castle

This striking Arts and Crafts mansion is within a mile of Dumfries town centre. The house, set in substantial landscaped gardens, has been refurbished to a very high standard with 1920s decoration complementing the original features. The bedrooms are thoughtfully equipped and most are spacious, and all have state of the art showers, tea and coffee facilities, and some are furnished with antiques. Traditional breakfasts are served in the smart dining room, and overall Rivendell provides excellent quality and a high level of service. Outside in the lovely grounds there is a tennis court and a rotating summer house, and to the rear of the house there is a large, secure and illuminated car park. The Nith Estuary National Scenic Area just south of Dumfries is great for wildlife and birdspotting and has some impressive heritage sites. Laundry service available. No pets.

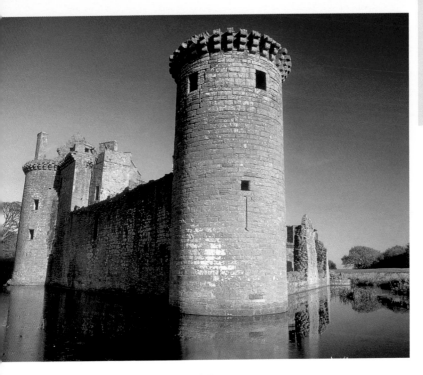

Caerlaverock Castle near Dumfries, Dumfries & Galloway

Wallamhill House ♦♦♦♦♦

Map ref 5 - NX97
Kirkton, DUMFRIES, Dumfries & Galloway DG1 1SL
Off A701 signed Kirkton, 1.5m on right
Ⓣ 01387 248249
Ⓔ wallamhill@aol.com
Ⓦ www.wallamhill.co.uk
3 rooms, S £28-£30, D £50, No smoking

Hospitality is a real strength at Wallamhill House, a very nice house set in well-tended gardens and peaceful countryside 3 miles from Dumfries. The large bedrooms are extremely well equipped, plus there is a drawing room, and a mini health club with sauna, steam shower and gym equipment. Evening meals (by arrangement) are served in the dining room around one large table, and you can bring your own wine. The breathtaking views from both front and rear are an invitation for great walking (follow the footsteps of Rabbie Burns along the nearby River Nith), cycling, or mountain biking in the Ae and Mabie forests.

RECOMMENDED IN THE AREA

Nithdale; New Abbey (Sweetheart); Caerlaverock Castle

Hart Manor ♦♦♦♦♦

Map ref 5 - NY29
ESKDALEMUIR, Dumfries & Galloway
DG13 0QQ
1m S of village on B709 Langholm road
T 013873 73217
E visit@hartmanor.co.uk
W www.hartmanor.co.uk
5 rooms, S £77.50-£80.50, D £135-£141,
No smoking, Closed Xmas, New Year

Recommended in the Area

Kagyu Samye Ling Tibetan Centre; Langholm walks; Grey Mare's Tail Waterfall

Hart Manor is set in grounds just 1 mile from the lovely village of Eskdalemuir, surrounded by gentle hills that are ideal for walking. The house has been refurbished to provide stylish modern accommodation. All the bedrooms are en suite, have tea facilities, and there are two superior rooms, one double and one with twin beds. Downstairs are two dining rooms, one for breakfast, one for dinner, and you can relax with coffee or after-dinner drinks in either the lounge or the library. Food is a great attraction here - British country fare - and everything, including the bread, is home made.

Baytree House ♦♦♦♦♦

Map ref 5 - NX65
110 High St, KIRKCUDBRIGHT, Dumfries & Galloway DG6 4JQ
Off main street onto St Cuthbert's St & Castle St
T / F 01557 330824
E jackie@baytreekirkcudbright.co.uk
W www.baytreekirkcudbright.co.uk
3 rooms, No smoking

Choose from the gorgeous romantic room with the four-poster bed, or he two slightly more prosaic win-bedded ones, but whichever, your stay here is sure to be memorable. Jackie Callander's cheerful manner permeates this restored Georgian house. Upstairs, a magnificent drawing oom with vaulted ceiling and original marble fireplace makes guests feel like royalty, while Jackie's superb breakfasts served in the garden dining room show off her great cooking skills. The three bedrooms come with bath and shower en suite and are as thoughtfully equipped as the rest of the house.

RECOMMENDED IN THE AREA
Threave Gardens; Broughton House; Tolbooth Art Centre

Limetree House ♦♦♦♦

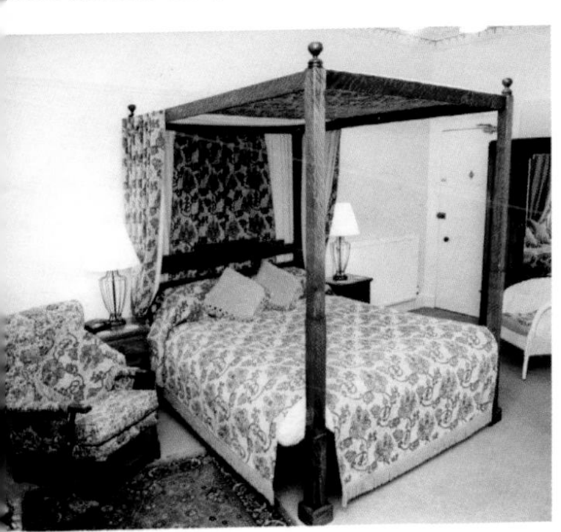

Map ref 10 - NT00
Eastgate, MOFFAT, Dumfries & Galloway DG10 9AE
Off High St onto Well St, left onto Eastgate, house 100yds
T 01683 220001
E info@limetreehouse.co.uk
W www.limetreehouse.co.uk
6 rooms, S £29-£37, D £48-£65, No smoking

Renovation of this quiet listed property near Moffat's High Street has achieved high standards of accommodation and kept many original features. <atherine and Derek make you feel as comfortable as possible, and the lounge has newspapers, games and a music centre - but no television. The en suite rooms, ncluding one with a four-poster bed, are smartly urnished in pine. Refreshment trays and hairdryers are provided in the rooms. Derek's legendary pancakes and a wide choice of buffet and cooked dishes are sure to meet with approval at breakfast time.

RECOMMENDED IN THE AREA
Craigieburn Gardens; Grey Mare's Tail waterfall; St Mary's Loch

Blinkbonnie Guest House

Map ref 0 - NW95
School Brae, PORTPATRICK, DG9 8LG
From A77, pass parish church on left. Next left on School Brae. 2nd house on left

Modern coastal villa standing within landscaped gardens The charmingly named Blinkbonnie stands in manicured, well-kept gardens on an elevated position overlooking the picturesque village and harbour. Friendliness is a strength here and nothing is too much trouble. All the bedrooms have facilities en suite and all are on the ground floor. Each room is individually decorated, double glazed and has a refreshment tray. The delightful lounge, with a 12ft window, has a wonderful view over the rooftops of Portpatrick towards the Irish Sea and is a great place to view the sunset. The cosy dining room also has fine sea views, the perfect place to start your day with a nourishing breakfast.

Recommended in the Area
Portpatrick Harbour; Southern Upland Way; Logan Botanic Gardens

---

Faussetthill House ♦♦♦♦♦

Map ref 10 - NT48
20 Main St, GULLANE, East Lothian EH31 2DR
Off A1 onto A198 to Gullane
T / F 01620 842396
E faussetthill@talk21.com
3 rooms, S £50, D £70-£72, No smoking, Closed Nov-Mar

George and Dorothy Nisbet welcome you to their delightful home, which stands in well-tended gardens in the picturesque village of Gullane. Immaculately maintained, the house is both comfortable and inviting. Bedrooms are well proportioned and attractively decorated. Three rooms are en suite, and all have tea and coffee facilities. There is a first-floor lounge with well-filled bookshelves, and breakfast is served at one table in the elegant dining room. From Gullane, North Berwick is just 10 minutes away, Edinburgh 30 minutes by car, and there are many places of interest to visit in the area. Keen golfers can note that there are 19 golf courses within easy reach, with five in the village itself, including Muirfield. Children under 10 are not accommodated and dogs are not premitted in the rooms. This is a non-smoking house.

Recommended in the Area
Beautiful walks around Gullane beach; Scottish Seabird Centre; Dirleton Castle & Gardens

*D*unstane House Hotel ♦♦♦♦♦

Map ref 10 - NT27
4 West Coates, Haymarket, EDINBURGH, EH12 5JQ
On A8 between Murrayfield Stadium and Haymarket railway station. 5 mins from city centre 15 mins from airport

T 0131 337 6169
F 0131 337 6060
E reservations@dunstanehousehotel.co.uk
W www.dunstane-hotel-edinburgh.co.uk

16 rooms, S £55-£85, D £98-£138, No smoking in bedrooms or dining room

RECOMMENDED IN THE AREA

Edinburgh Castle; Edinburgh International Conference Centre; Murrayfield Stadium

Enjoy a country house atmosphere within walking distance of the city centre. The impressive Grade B listed Victorian property stands in the valley of the Water of Leith, within mature gardens filled with attractive shrubs and flowers. From its elevated position there are fine views of the Pentland Hills. The original fireplaces, panelling and stained-glass windows give the house a baronial atmosphere. The smart en suite bedrooms have plenty of quality extras - business guests will appreciate the direct-dial telephones with fax and modem points. Delicious meals are served the stylish Skerries Seafood Restaurant, where many of the ingredients are from Orkney and Shetland (the charming hosts are Orcadians). The friendly bar stocks a huge variety of malt whiskies and serves lighter meals.

Ellesmere House ♦♦♦♦

Map ref 10 - NT27
11 Glengyle Ter, EDINBURGH,
EH3 9LN
S of city centre off A702
T 0131 229 4823
E celia@edinburghbandb.co.uk
W www.edinburghbandb.co.uk
4 rooms, S £33-£45, D £66-£90

RECOMMENDED IN THE AREA
Edinburgh Castle & Royal Mile; Princes Street; Palace of Holyroodhouse

Ellesmere House is part of a handsome Victorian terrace overlooking Bruntsfield Links. The latter was once an 18-hole golf course - reputedly the oldest in the world. The location is convenient for the city centre and all the major tourist attractions, including the castle, Princes Street, the Royal Mile, the Edinburgh International Conference Centre, the universities and the museums. The en suite bedrooms are individually designed and vary in size; there is a single, twin, double and a family room, and one room features a four-poster bed. All come with tea and coffee facilities. Breakfast is prepared from the best of local produce and is served in the lounge-dining room.

Elmview ♦♦♦♦♦

Map ref 10 - NT27
15 Glengyle Ter, EDINBURGH,
EH3 9LN
A702 S along Lothian Rd, 1st left past Kings Theatre onto ValleyField St, one-way to Glengyle Ter
T 0131 228 1973
E nicki@elmview.co.uk
W www.elmview.co.uk
3 rooms, D £80-£110, No smoking, Closed Dec-Feb

RECOMMENDED IN THE AREA
Edinburgh Castle; Edinburgh Old Town; Museum of Scotland

This substantial Victorian property offers superior bed and breakfast accommodation 1 mile from Edinburgh Old Town. The constantly upgraded decor and facilities appeal to both tourist and business travellers. The bedrooms have stylish bathrooms en suite and a good level of comfort, which compensates for the absence of a lounge. The rooms are exceptionaly well equipped, including thoughtful extras such as wine glasses and a fridge with fresh milk. Nicki and Robin Hill are always on hand when needed. The highlight of your stay will be the excellent breakfasts taken at one large, elegantly appointed table.

*K*ew House ♦♦♦♦♦

Map ref 10 - NT27
1 Kew Ter, Murrayfield,
EDINBURGH, EH12 5JE
On A8 Glasgow road, 1m W of city centre, close to Murrayfield Rugby Stadium

Ⓣ 0131 313 0700
Ⓕ 0131 313 0747
Ⓔ info@kewhouse.com
Ⓦ www.kewhouse.com

6 rooms, S £70-£75, D £80-£140,
No smoking

RECOMMENDED IN THE AREA

Edinburgh Castle; Edinburgh International Conference Centre; Murrayfield Rugby Stadium

Kew House forms part of a terrace dating from around 1869, located 1 mile west of the city centre, convenient for Murrayfield Rugby Stadium, and just a 15-minute walk from Princes Street. The house is ideal for both business travellers and holidaymakers, with secure private parking. While period features have been retained, the interior design is contemporary, and the standards of housekeeping are superb. Expect complimentary sherry and chocolates on arrival, and you can order supper in the lounge and bar. Full Scottish breakfast is included in the room tariff, and light snacks, with room service, are available all day. Bedrooms, including some on the ground floor, are en suite and well equipped with direct-dial telephones, modem points, hairdryers, trouser presses, and tea and coffee facilities. Kew House also offers serviced apartments accommodating one to five people.

Kildonan Lodge Hotel ♦♦♦♦♦

Map ref 10 - NT27
27 Craigmillar Park, EDINBURGH, EH16 5PE
From city by pass (A720), exit A701 city centre, continue 2.75m to large rdbt straight on, located 6 buildings on right

Ⓣ 0131 667 2793
Ⓕ 0131 667 9777
Ⓔ info@kildonanlodgehotel.co.uk
Ⓦ www.kildonanlodgehotel.co.uk

12 rooms, S £56-£89, D £78-£145, No smoking, Closed Xmas

An elegant Victorian property, beautifully restored and offering comfortable accommodation. Holiday and business guests are equally well catered for, and there is plenty of tourist information available. The en suite bedrooms are of a very high standard, and include some with four posters and Jacuzzis for complete luxury. Radio alarms, hair dryers, hospitality trays and lots of homely extras add to the comfort, and there are also rooms for families. An honesty bar provides drinks and breakfast is another high spot. Hospitality and service match the quality of the accommodation, and there is a car park too.

RECOMMENDED IN THE AREA

Edinburgh Castle; Dynamic Earth; Palace of Holyrood House

The International Guest House ♦♦♦♦

Map ref 10 - NT27
37 Mayfield Gardens, EDINBURGH, EH9 2BX
On A701 1.5m S of Princes St

Ⓣ 0131 667 2511
Ⓕ 0131 667 1112
Ⓔ intergh1@yahoo.co.uk
Ⓦ www.accomodation-edinburgh.com

9 rooms, S £30-£65, D £50-£120

This attractive stone terrace house is on the south side of the city, 1.5 miles from Edinburgh castle. There is ample private parking, and it is on a main bus route to the city centre. The high ceilings and large windows, wooden staircase, and decor with ornate plasterwork embody the splendour of the Victorian period. All the bedrooms, decorated and fitted in matching period floral prints, have fresh flowers and modern en suites. Some rooms have magnificent views across to the extinct volcano known as Arthur's Seat. A hearty Scottish breakfast is served on fine bone china at separate tables in the dining room; the marble fireplace with mirror above it is a lovely feature in this room.

RECOMMENDED IN THE AREA

Edinburgh Castle; Palace of Holyrood House; University of Edinburgh

Southside Guest House ♦♦♦♦

Map ref 10 - NT27
8 Newington Rd, EDINBURGH, EH9 1QS
E end of Princes St take North Bridge to the Royal Mile, continue S 0.5m, house on right

Ⓣ 0131 668 4422
Ⓕ 0131 667 7771
Ⓔ info@southsideguesthouse.co.uk
Ⓦ www.southsideguesthouse.co.uk

8 rooms, S £45-£70, D £70-£140,
No smoking

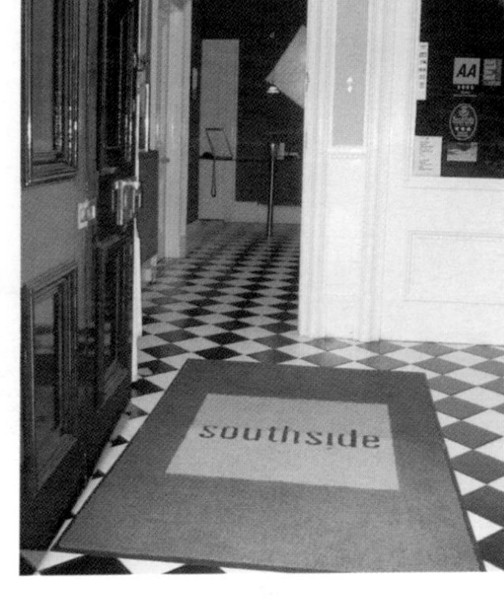

RECOMMENDED IN THE AREA

Edinburgh Castle; Edinburgh Festival Theatre; The Palace of Holyroodhouse

Southside is an elegant sandstone house in the centre of Edinburgh, only a few minutes from Holyrood Park. Owners Lynne and Franco have been involved in the hotel trade for many years and have happily made their home in the capital. Lynne is from the Highlands, and Franco hails from Florence. They offer individually designed, well-equipped bedrooms, with direct-dial telephones, DVD players, free wireless Internet access, and many other comforts. Two rooms have four-poster beds, and the remaining rooms come in a variety of colour schemes and bed sizes. Breakfast is guaranteed to satisfy with its great choice of traditional freshly cooked Scottish dishes, cheeses, oatcakes, fresh fruit and real coffee. Guests sit at separate tables in the attractive dining room. Look out for Tootsie the blind cat who prowls in the garden when she is not asleep.

Violet Bank House ♦♦♦♦♦

Map ref 10 - NT27
167 Lanark Rd West, Currie, EDINBURGH, EH14 5NZ
On A70 in village centre, corner Lanark Rd West & Kirkgate
T 0131 451 5103
E reta@violetbankhouse.co.uk
W www.violetbankhouse.co.uk
3 rooms, S £50-£100, D £70-£120, No smoking

Lying to the south of Edinburgh within easy reach of the airport and Herriot Watt University, Violet Bank is a lovely stone house with smart, very well-equipped bedrooms, stylish bathrooms and the very best in hospitality. Thoughtful little extras include fresh flowers, Crabtree and Evelyn toiletries, and tea and coffee facilities. The bathrooms are all en suite, a good size and beautifully kitted out. The inviting lounge overlooks the attractive rear garden, and delicious, perfectly presented breakfasts using excellent Scottish produce are served in the charming dining room. Afternoon tea in the lounge or garden is offered on arrival.

RECOMMENDED IN THE AREA
Edinburgh Castle; Rosslyn Chapel; Malleny Gardens (NTS)

The Walton Hotel ♦♦♦♦

Map ref 10 - NT27
79 Dundas St, EDINBURGH, EH3 6SD
T 0131 556 1137
F 0131 557 8367
E enquiries@waltonhotel.com
W www.waltonhotel.com
10 rooms, S £35-£75, D £79-£139, No smoking

Set in the central New Town district of Edinburgh, the Walton is ideally placed for shopping in Princes Street. A genuinely warm greeting awaits you at this charming Georgian terrace house. It offers well-equipped en suite bedrooms decorated in attractive styles. A host of extras includes toiletries, writing desks with telephone and Internet connections, and hospitality trays. Traditional Scottish breakfasts, a variety of continental choices or the vegetarian menu ensure that there is something for everyone. Rare among the city-centre hotels, the Walton has off-street parking.

RECOMMENDED IN THE AREA
Princes Street; Edinburgh Castle; Royal Botanic Garden

The Spindrift ♦♦♦♦

Map ref 10 - NO50
Pittenweem Rd, ANSTRUTHER,
Fife KY10 3DT
Entering town from W on A917, 1st building on left
T / F 01333 310573
E info@thespindrift.co.uk
W www.thespindrift.co.uk
8 rooms, S £32.50-£46, D £55-£72, No smoking, Closed 24-26 Dec

A unique feature of this house is the top- floor Captain's Room, made to resemble a shipmaster's cabin by the original owner. The east-facing window looks towards Anstruther harbour, which would once have been busy with tea clippers and the fishing fleet. All the individually furnished, spacious bedrooms are brightly decorated and have a wide range of extras; each has a private bathroom and, like the rest of the house, all are centrally heated. The attractive lounge has a well-stocked honesty bar for a pre-dinner drink, and enjoyable, home-cooked fare is served in an elegant dining room.

Recommended in the Area

Scottish Fisheries Museum; St Andrews; East Neuk coastal villages

The Roods ♦♦♦♦

Map ref 10 - NT18
16 Bannerman Av, INVERKEITHING,
Fife KY11 1NG
A90/M90 N onto B981, pass car park. Turn 1st right, then 1st left
T / F 01383 415049
E isobelmarley@hotmail.com
W www.theroods.com
2 rooms, S £25-£27, D £50-£60, No smoking

Despite its secluded setting in attractive gardens, this delightful house is within easy reach of both the railway station and the town centre. The two individually furnished bedrooms are both on the ground floor and have smart new bathrooms en suite. Thoughtful touches bring a personal feel to the rooms, which are equipped with direct-dial telephones, central heating and tea and coffee facilities. The lounge has an inviting open fire and breakfast is served at individual tables in the pretty conservatory. Evening meals are available by arrangement. Parking for four cars is provided. No dogs please.

Recommended in the Area

Culross Palace, Town House & The Study; Pittencrieff House Museum; Aberdour Castle

Dunclutha Guest House ♦♦♦♦

Map ref 10 - NO30
16 Victoria Rd, LEVEN, Fife KY8 4EX
A915, B933 Glenlyon Rd into Leven, rdbt left onto Commercial Rd & Victoria Rd, Dunclutha opp church on right

T 01333 425515
F 01333 422311
E pam.leven@blueyonder.co.uk
W www.dunclutha.myby.co.uk

4 rooms, S £28-£35, D £52-£60, No smoking

This former Victorian rectory has been upgraded to a good standard and is lovingly maintained. Its original splendour sits well with modern trappings, making this an impressive place to stay. Three spacious bedrooms and a cosy fourth room make up the en suite accommodation (one room has a private bathroom). All of the rooms are smartly decorated. The lounge is filled with interesting items as well as a piano, and is a sociable place in the evenings. The adjoining dining room is the setting for hearty breakfasts, which include delicious home-made preserves and bread.

RECOMMENDED IN THE AREA
St Andrews; Levens Links golf course; Fife Coastal Path

Mellondale ♦♦♦♦

Map ref 11 - NG88
47 Mellon Charles, AULTBEA, Highland IV22 2JL
A832 to Aultbea & Mellon Charles

T / F 01445 731326
E mellondale@lineone.net
W www.mellondale.co.uk

4 rooms, D £52-£56, No smoking in bedrooms or dining room, Closed Nov-Mar

A modern house set in landscaped grounds with panoramic views over Loch Ewe. You can relax in the attractive lounge throughout the day to watch television, play games, or just soak up the scenery. The pretty bedrooms, including two on the ground floor, are well equipped, with thoughtful touches like fruit and biscuits, complimentary toiletries and magazines. All of the rooms are en suite, with their own sitting areas, and those overlooking the loch enjoy stunning sunsets. The bright dining room is just the place to linger over delicious home-cooked breakfasts, and feast on the views.

RECOMMENDED IN THE AREA
Inverewe Gardens; Gairloch Heritage Museum; Beinn Eighe Nature Reserve

The Old Minister's House ♦♦♦♦♦

Map ref 12 - NH81
Rothiemurchus, AVIEMORE, Highland PH22 1QH
B970 from Aviemore signed Glenmore & Coylumbridge, establishment 0.75m at Inverdruie
T / F 01479 812181
E theoldministershouse@btinternet.com
W www.theoldministershouse.co.uk
4 rooms, S £35-£40, D £60-£80, No smoking

Built in 1906, The Old Minister's House stands in well-tended grounds close to Aviemore. Dylis Stretton, a runner-up for AA Landlady of the Year 2005, and her husband Paul, warmly welcome you into their home and are always on hand to offer advice and information. Being keen naturalists they are able to pass on first-hand knowledge of the local wildlife, including possible sightings of otters and ospreys. The house is beautifully furnished and immaculately maintained. The attractive, well-equipped bedrooms - with both bath and shower - are sizeable and come with tea and coffee facilities. Lavish Scottish breakfasts are served in the dining room and there is an inviting lounge too.

Recommended in the Area

Cairngorms National Park; Strathspey Steam Railway; RSPB Nature Reserve

---

Lyn-Leven Guest House ♦♦♦♦

Map ref 9 - NN05
West Laroch, BALLACHULISH, Highland PH49 4JP
Off A82 signed on left West Laroch
T 01855 811392
F 01855 811600
W www.lynleven.co.uk
12 rooms, S £24-£35, D £48-£60, Closed Xmas

Beautifully situated, this guesthouse maintains high standards in all areas. Highland hospitality puts guests at their ease, and the spectacular views of Loch Leven guarantee plenty to talk about. Bedrooms vary in size, are prettily decorated, and have showers en suite and some thoughtful extras. The spacious lounge and smart dining room make the most of the scenic outlook, and delicious home-cooked evening meals and breakfasts are served at separate tables. You can enjoy the lovely gardens that surround the property, and there is ample parking.

Recommended in the Area

Dragon's Tooth Golf Course, Ballachulish; Stalker Castle, Fort William National Trust for Scotland Centre, Glencoe

Craiglinnhe House ♦♦♦♦♦

Map ref 9 - NN05
Lettermore, BALLACHULISH, Highland
PH49 4JD
From village A82 onto A828, Craiglinnhe 1.5m on left
T 01855 811270
E info@craiglinnhe.co.uk
W www.craiglinnhe.co.uk
5 rooms, S £40-£65, D £56-£80, No smoking, Closed Jan

RECOMMENDED IN THE AREA
Glencoe; Fort William; Whisky distillery

Brian Hitchcock and Derrick Armitage offer a haven of relaxation and exemplary hospitality. The two are much travelled, and have filled their home with artworks, rugs and furnishings from all over the world. The stunning views across Loch Linnhe to the village of Onich epitomize the western Highlands, and you will never tire of gazing up to the Ballachulish Bridge and the Pap of Glencoe. The Victorian stone house has been modernised with comfort uppermost in mind, and the result is a choice of stylish en suite bedrooms with showers. A video and CD player are provided in each room (there is a library of videos and CDs to choose from), along with hairdryers and hospitality trays. While Derrick cooks tasty breakfasts and evening meals, Brian mans the front of house and serves drinks. There is an elegant sitting room, and you can expect to hear all sorts of glorious classical music being played at Craiglinnhe.

Shorefield House ♦♦♦♦

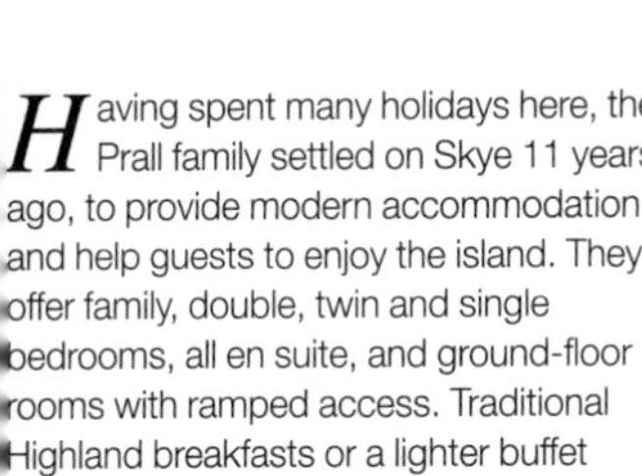

Map ref 11 - NG35
Edinbane, EDINBANE, Highland
IV51 9PW
12m from Portree & 8m from Dunvegan, off A850 into Edinbane, 1st on right

T 01470 582444
F 01470 582414
E shorefieldhouse@aol.com
W www.shorefield.com

5 rooms, S £32-£45, D £64-£90, No smoking, Closed Nov-mid Mar

Having spent many holidays here, the Prall family settled on Skye 11 years ago, to provide modern accommodation and help guests to enjoy the island. They offer family, double, twin and single bedrooms, all en suite, and ground-floor rooms with ramped access. Traditional Highland breakfasts or a lighter buffet alternative are served in the dining room (special diets catered for). The adjoining conservatory has books, games and a television, and there is a large garden with a children's play area. Packed lunches can be ordered, and there are excellent local restaurants for evening meals.

Recommended in the Area

Dunvegan Castle & seal colony; Skye Riding Centre; Talisker Whisky Distillery

---

Ashburn House ♦♦♦♦♦

Map ref 12 - NN17
8 Achintore Rd, FORT WILLIAM, Highland PH33 6RQ
500yds S of town centre on A82

T 01397 706000
F 01397 702024
E christine@no-1.fsworld.co.uk
W www.highland5star.co.uk

7 rooms, S £35-£50, D £70-£100, No smoking

Wonderful views of Loch Linnhe and the Ardgour Hills can be enjoyed from many of the bedrooms here, as well as the conservatory lounge. This imposing Victorian property is just a 5-minute walk from the centre of Fort William. A loving restoration has brought the house back to its former glory, including a magnificent barley twist pine staircase. Bedrooms are individually designed and spacious, with little luxuries and en suites, hairdryers and hospitality trays. Wake up to the aroma of Christine MacDonald's freshly baked scones and plan your day out with the knowledgeable Willie.

Recommended in the Area

Nevis Range Gondola; Ben Nevis; Jacobite Steam Train

Distillery House ♦♦♦♦♦

Map ref 12 - NN17
Nevis Bridge, North Rd,
FORT WILLIAM, Highland PH33 6LR
A82 from Fort William towards Inverness, on left after Glen Nevis rdbt

T 01397 700103
F 01397 702980
E disthouse@aol.com
W www.stayinfortwilliam.co.uk

10 rooms, S £25-£45, D £50-£96, No smoking

Distillery House is a conversion of three houses in the extensive grounds of the former Glenlochy Distillery, originally used to house distillery staff. It stands on the banks of the River Nevis at the end of the West Highland Way (a long distance walk from Glasgow), but just a 5-minute walk from the centre of Fort William. The well-equipped en suite bedrooms have tea and coffee trays and hairdryers. You are greeted with a complimentary whiskey and home-made shortbread, and there's a reading lounge furnished with chesterfield sofas. Breakfast, including kippers, haggis, home baking, seasonal fresh fruits, preserves and cereals, is served at individual tables in the airy dining room.

RECOMMENDED IN THE AREA

Ben Nevis & Distillery Visitor Centre; Skiing & walking in Nevis range; West Highland Way

---

The Grange ♦♦♦♦♦

Map ref 12 - NN17
Grange Rd, FORT WILLIAM,
Highland PH33 6JF
A82 S from Fort William, 300yds from rdbt left onto Ashburn Ln, at top on left

T 01397 705516
F 01397 701595
E info@thegrange-scotland.co.uk
W www.thegrange-scotland.co.uk

4 rooms, D £98-£110, No smoking, Closed Nov-Mar

Years of careful planning and hard work have gone into the restoration of this lovely property, to provide only the highest standards. Meticulous attention to detail is evident throughout the house, and warm Highland hospitality is assured. Attractive decor and pretty fabrics are used to stunning effect in the charming bedrooms, all of which have beautiful views over Loch Linnhe. All of the rooms have quality en suites. There is an abundance of books and fresh flowers in the comfortable lounge, and the dining room provides a lovely setting for the extensive breakfast, which is a really good start to the day.

RECOMMENDED IN THE AREA

Ben Nevis; Jacobite steam train; Loch Ness

Mansefield Guest House ♦♦♦♦

Map ref 12 - NN17
Corpach, FORT WILLIAM, Highland
PH33 7LT
2m N of Fort William A82 onto A830, house 2m on A830 in Corpach
Ⓣ 01397 772262
Ⓔ mansefield@btinternet.com
Ⓦ www.fortwilliamaccommodation.com
6 rooms, S £20-£30, D £40-£58, No smoking

Mansefield House is a former manse set in mature gardens overlooking .och Linnhe with great mountain views. 'he friendly, family-run guesthouse rovides en suite bedrooms with ountry-style decor and Laura Ashley urnishings, plus complimentary toiletries nd hospitality trays. You can even equest blankets if you prefer them to luvets. The cosy sitting room overlooks ne garden, and a roaring coal fire burns n cold evenings as you browse the many books, magazines and tourist information available. Delicious home-cooked breakfasts and pre-booked evening meals are served at individual tables in the attractive dining room. Packed lunches are also available.

RECOMMENDED IN THE AREA

Treasures of the Earth Exhibition, Corpach; Ben Nevis; Boat trips to Seal Island, Loch Linnhe

---

Foyers Bay House ♦♦♦♦

Map ref 12 - NH42
Lochness, FOYERS, Highland
IV2 6YB
Off B852 into village
Ⓣ 01456 486624
Ⓕ 01456 486337
Ⓔ carol@foyersbay.co.uk
Ⓦ www.foyersbay.co.uk
6 rooms, S £32-£48, D £54-£66, No smoking in bedrooms

Set on the quiet, undeveloped side of Loch Ness among hillside woodlands with a colourful bundance of rhododendrons, this delightful house has tunning views with forest walks and nature trails. The igh-ceilinged rooms have original wood panelling and ornices. There is a comfortable lounge adjacent to a lant-filled conservatory café-restaurant, where aditional breakfasts are served or you can enjoy a appuccino or a delicious evening meal. The attractive bedrooms, which vary in size, all have bath or shower rooms en suite, direct-dial telephones, tea and coffee facilities and fresh fruit. There are self-catering lodges also available.

RECOMMENDED IN THE AREA

Inverness; Loch Ness; Glen Affric

An Cala Guest House ♦♦♦♦♦

Map ref 12 - NJ02
Woodlands Ter,
GRANTOWN-ON-SPEY, Highland
PH26 3JU
From Aviemore on the A95 bear left on the B9102 at the rdbt outside Grantown. After 400yds, 1st left & An Cala opp
T / F 01479 873293
E ancala@globalnet.co.uk
W www.ancala.info
4 rooms, S £35-£45, D £52-£60, No smoking, Closed Xmas, New Year

The large Victorian house is set above the town and surrounded by well-tended gardens. Val and Keith Dickinson provide an attractive setting where you can relax. They offer four beautifully decorated bedrooms with king-size or four-poster beds and antique furniture, and smart bathrooms complete with good toiletries. A wood-burning stove makes the lounge extra cosy in winter, and the dining room is the setting for freshly cooked evening meals and tasty breakfasts. The house is in the Cairngorms National Park, and Grantown is an easy walk away. Ask Keith, a qualified outdoor activities instructor, for local information and advice.

RECOMMENDED IN THE AREA
The Malt Whisky Trail; Ballindalloch Castle; Osprey Centre, Boat of Garten

Rossmor Guest House ♦♦♦♦

Map ref 12 - NJ02
Woodlands Ter,
GRANTOWN-ON-SPEY, Highland
PH26 3JU
A95 from Aviemore to Grantown-on-Spey, left at rdbt entering town through pine woods, Rossmor on left opp park
T / F 01479 872201
E johnsteward.rossmor@lineone.net
W www.rossmor.co.uk
6 rooms, S £30-£35, D £54-£70, No smoking

An original staircase, stained-glass windows and brass fittings are impressive features of this beautiful Victorian villa with superb views over the Cromdale Hills. Each of the en suite bedrooms has a refreshment tray, and for special occasions there is a Tudor-style four-poster bed. Relax in the lounge and enjoy the views after a day in the country. A wide choice of breakfast dishes includes fish or a fruit and cheese platter. A drying room for wet days, a lock-up for skis and fishing rods, and a garage for motorbikes and bicycles are bonuses.

RECOMMENDED IN THE AREA
Cairngorm Mountain; Malt Whisky Trail; Osprey Centre

Acorn House ♦♦♦♦

Map ref 12 - NH64
2A Bruce Gardens, INVERNESS, Highland IV3 5EN
From town centre onto A82, on W side of river, right onto Bruce Gardens

T 01463 717021 &
F 01463 714236
E enquiries@acorn-house.freeserve.co.uk
W www.acorn-house.freeserve.co.uk

6 rooms, S £35-£50, D £58-£65, No smoking in bedrooms or dining room

A strong Scottish theme, with much memorabilia and bold use of tartan in the decoration and fabrics, distinguishes this Highland guesthouse. Acorn House is an attractive property set in a quiet residential area, just a 5-minute walk from the city centre. The well-equipped rooms are all en suite, some with the extra luxury of four-poster beds, and there is a sauna and a Jacuzzi, which are very popular after a busy day touring. Traditional Scottish food is served in the pretty dining room at breakfast and in the evening, and after-dinner coffee can be enjoyed in the comfortable lounge. Expect a warm, friendly welcome.

RECOMMENDED IN THE AREA

Eden Court Theatre; Fort George; Loch Ness

Ballifeary Guest House ♦♦♦♦♦

Map ref 12 - NH64
10 Ballifeary Rd, INVERNESS, Highland IV3 5PJ
Off A82, 0.5m from town centre, turn left onto Bishops Rd & sharp right onto Ballifeary Rd

T 01463 235572
F 01463 717583
E william.gilbert@btconnect.com
W www.ballifearyhousehotel.co.uk

6 rooms, S £35-£65, D £60-£70, No smoking, Closed 25-28 Dec

Guests return again and again to this peaceful detached house and garden. Bill and Morag Gilbert put their guests before anything else, and it is easy to feel pampered and spoiled in their stylish home. Bedrooms come in various sizes and are well equipped and furnished, while the lounge offers a chance to unwind in elegant surroundings. Delicious breakfasts, made from fresh local produce when possible, are served at separate tables in the dining room. This pleasant residential area is within walking distance of the town centre and Eden Court Theatre.

RECOMMENDED IN THE AREA

Loch Ness & Urquhart Castle; Numerous golf courses; Inverness Castle & Cathedral

The Lodge-Daviot Mains ♦♦♦♦♦

Map ref 12 - NH73

Daviot Mains, Daviot, INVERNESS, Highland IV2 5ER

Off A9 5m S of Inverness onto B851 signed Croy. B&B 1m on left

T 01463 772215
F 01463 772099
E info@thelodge-daviotmains.co.uk
W www.
thelodge-daviotmains.co.uk

7 rooms, S £35-£40, D £70-£90, No smoking, Closed 2 wks mid Oct

This lovely small country house offers luxury accommodation just south of Inverness amid 80 acres of pastureland. The wealth of local attractions include castles, distilleries, standing stones, mountains, beaches, golf courses and not least Loch Ness. The Hutcheson family have been welcoming guests for 20 years and won the AA Guest Accommodation of the Year for Scotland 2005. Named after local rivers, the attractive bedrooms have coordinated furnishings - the master bedroom has a four-poster bed and the Victorian bathroom was brought from the owners' former house. One room is on the ground floor for easy access. After a busy day you can relax in the elegant public rooms hung with original artworks. The cooking is excellent, with a wide choice at breakfast and an optional dinner - both offer the best of traditional Scottish dishes using local produce.

Recommended in the Area

Loch Ness; Culloden Battlefield (NTS); Cawdor Castle

*M*oyness House ♦♦♦♦♦

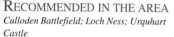

Map ref 12 - NH64

6 Bruce Gardens, INVERNESS, Highland IV3 5EN

Off A82 Fort William road, almost opp Highland Regional Council headquarters

T / F 01463 233836
E stay@moyness.co.uk
W www.moyness.co.uk

7 rooms, S £35-£38, D £70-£76, No smoking

RECOMMENDED IN THE AREA

Culloden Battlefield; Loch Ness; Urquhart Castle

*R*estoring this gracious Victorian villa to its former glory is a labour of love for Jenny and Richard Jones, who spent several years continuing the work begun by Richard's parents, the former owners. They still have plenty of time to care for their guests, who find this quiet residential area ideal for touring the beautiful Highlands. Inviting public rooms overlook the garden to the front, and the pretty walled garden to the rear is a favourite spot in warm weather. Bedrooms are attractively decorated and have bath or shower rooms en suite, and hospitality trays to make your stay comfortable.

Trafford Bank ♦♦♦♦♦

Map ref 12 - NH64
96 Fairfield Rd, INVERNESS, Highland
IV3 5LL

Off A82 at Kenneth St, Fairfield Rd 2nd left, 600yds on right

T 01463 241414
F 01463 241421
E enquiries@invernesshotelaccommodation.co.uk
W www.traffordbankhotel.co.uk

5 rooms, S £50-£60, D £75-£98,
No smoking

Recommended in the Area

Cawdor Castle; Culloden battlefield; Loch Ness

Luxurious accommodation and Highland hospitality go hand in hand at this guesthouse run by Lorraine Freel and Koshal Pun. This multilingual pair can welcome you in Italian, French, Hindi and Swahili. Located within walking distance of the city centre and the Caledonian Canal, Trafford Bank was built in 1873 and was once the local bishop's home. Lorraine's flair for interior design is combined with antiques and contemporary furniture, some of which she has designed herself; the dining-room chairs are a special feature, and there is unusual lighting and original art throughout the house. The bright bedrooms are individually themed; all are en suite and have enticing extras like Arran aromatic products and Skye soap. Breakfast is prepared using the best Highland produce and served on Anta pottery in the stunning conservatory. There are two spacious lounges and the house is surrounded by gardens that you can enjoy.

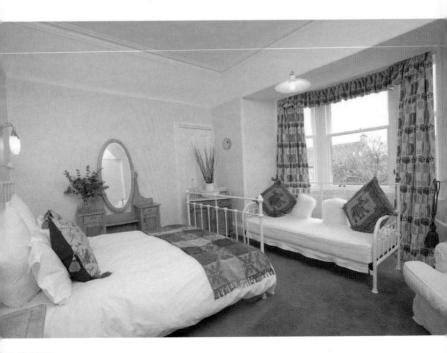

*W*estbourne Guest House ♦♦♦♦

Map ref 12 - NH64
50 Huntly St, INVERNESS, Highland
IV3 5HS
A9 onto A82 at football stadium, over 3 rdbts & Friars Bridge, 1st left onto Wells St & Huntly St
Ⓣ / Ⓕ 01463 220700
Ⓔ richard@westbourne.org.uk
Ⓦ www.westbourne.org.uk
10 rooms, S £35-£45, D £54-£70, No smoking, Closed Xmas, New Year

RECOMMENDED IN THE AREA

Loch Ness; Inverness Castle; Culloden Battlefield

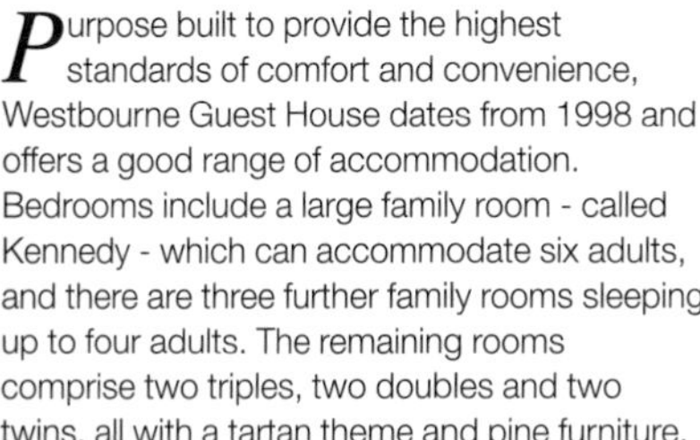

Purpose built to provide the highest standards of comfort and convenience, Westbourne Guest House dates from 1998 and offers a good range of accommodation. Bedrooms include a large family room - called Kennedy - which can accommodate six adults, and there are three further family rooms sleeping up to four adults. The remaining rooms comprise two triples, two doubles and two twins, all with a tartan theme and pine furniture. The Anderson room on the ground floor offers easy access to both the dining room and the car park. All the rooms are en suite and thoughtfully equipped with radio alarms, hairdryers, trouser presses and hospitality trays. Selected rooms are also fitted with a safe. A full Highlander's breakfast is served, with a vegetarian alternative, and other special diets can be catered for. No smoking throughout the house.

Osprey Hotel ♦♦♦♦♦

Map ref 12 - NH70
Ruthven Rd, KINGUSSIE, Highland PH21 1EN
A9 into Kingussie, hotel at S end of the main street
T / F 01540 661510
E aileen@ospreyhotel.co.uk
W www.ospreyhotel.co.uk
8 rooms, S £30-£45, D £60-£74, No smoking

Expect warm hospitality, comfortable accommodation and fine food at this informal guesthouse in the Spey valley. Surrounded by the mountains of the Grampians, it stands next to the memorial gardens in the peaceful centre of the village. Its reputation for good food is well deserved, with lavish dinners based on fresh local ingredients served in the dining room, and hearty breakfasts including home-made breads and preserves. Relax with a drink after dinner in one of two lounges, before retiring to the well-equipped en suite bedrooms. All rooms are fitted with refreshment trays, hairdryers and electric blankets.

RECOMMENDED IN THE AREA
Ruthven Barracks; Highland Wildlife Park; Cairngorm Mountain & Funicular

The Sheiling Guest House ♦♦♦♦♦

Map ref 12 - NC86
MELVICH, Highland KW14 7YJ
In village on A836
T / F 01641 531256
E thesheiling@btinternet.com
W www.thesheiling.co.uk
3 rooms, D £64, No smoking, Closed Oct-Apr

'Come and be spoiled' is the generous invitation from Joan and Hugh Campbell. They are superb hosts, and their charming home is extremely comfortable. With its glorious coastal views, the Sheiling offers attractive bedrooms with pretty soft furnishings, and smart en suites. Generous refreshment trays and toiletries add to the pleasure of being pampered. Breakfast is a sumptuous affair served at one large table, and afterwards you can walk in the 15 acres of grounds.

RECOMMENDED IN THE AREA
Castle of Mey; RSPB Forsinard; Strathnaver Museum

Corriechoille Lodge ♦♦♦♦

Map ref 12 - NN28
SPEAN BRIDGE, Highland PH34 4EY
Off A82 signed Corriechoille, continue 2.25m, left at road fork (10mph sign). At end of tarmac, turn right up hill & left

T 01397 712002
W www.corriechoille.com

4 rooms, S £36-£40, D £52-£60, No smoking, Closed Nov-Mar

Dating in parts from the 18th century, the constantly improving Corriechoille ('forest of the glen') has been in its time a farmhouse and fishing lodge for the Inverlochy Estate. Now it provides stylish accommodation and informal hospitality in a rural location with views towards the Nevis range and surrounding mountains. These views benefit the first-floor lounge and some of the bedrooms, including a choice of two doubles and two family suites twins. All rooms are spacious and have en suites, and are thoughtfully equipped with tea and coffee provisions. In addition to the hearty breakfast, home-cooked candlelit dinners are offered along with a varied wine list and a range of single malts.

Recommended in the Area

Ben Nevis; Loch Ness; Glencoe

Golf View House ♦♦♦♦

Map ref 12 - NH78
13 Knockbreck Rd, TAIN, Highland IV19 1BN
A9 onto B9174 at Tain, 0.5m house signed on right

T / F 01862 892856
E golfview@btinternet.com
W www.golf-view.co.uk

5 rooms, S £28-£45, D £52-£60, No smoking, Closed Dec-Jan

Originally a manse, this sandstone house has been converted into a top-notch guesthouse with amazing views across the golf course to the Dornoch Firth beyond. Bedrooms are a mixture of modern and traditional, and one room has a four-poster bed. The refined lounge has large picture windows, and the dining room, with individual beech tables, is the setting for traditional breakfasts featuring good local produce. There is a storage room for your golf clubs or bike, and a drying room to hang wet clothes should you get caught in a downpour.

Recommended in the Area

Glenmorangie Distillery and Visitors Centre; Tain Pottery; 10 golf courses

Dromnan Guest House ♦♦♦♦♦

Map ref 12 - NH19
Garve Rd, ULLAPOOL, Highland
IV26 2SX
A835 S into town, left at 30mph sign
Ⓣ 01854 612333
Ⓔ info@dromnan.com
Ⓦ www.dromnan.com
7 rooms, S £25-£38, D £50-£60,
No smoking

Recommended in the Area
Corrieshalloch Gorge; Knockan Crag; Ferry to Stornoway, Lewis

Immaculate throughout, this friendly, family-run modern house stands in well-tended gardens on the outskirts of Ullapool. The attractive bedrooms have bathrooms en suite and hairdryers and courtesy trays, and there is easier access ground-floor rooms. A feature of the house is the split-level lounge-breakfast room that overlooks the gardens and Loch Broom. Charlotte MacDonald's freshly cooked Highland breakfast or continental option can be enjoyed against the backdrop of the loch. Facilities at Ullapool Swimming and Leisure Centre free during your stay, and this is a handy base for touring the north-west Highlands or for catching the Stornaway ferry. No dogs except guide dogs.

The Haughs Farm ♦♦♦♦

Map ref 10 - NJ45
KEITH, Moray AB55 6QN
0.5m from Keith off A96, signed Inverness
Ⓣ / Ⓕ 01542 882238
Ⓔ jiwjackson@aol.com
Ⓦ www.
haughsfarmbedandbreakfast.net
3 rooms, S £28-£30, D £40-£44,
No smoking in bedrooms or dining room

You are assured of a warm welcome at this comfortable farmhouse on the outskirts of town. The friendly owners have been providing bed and breakfast for over 40 years in this lovely part of Scotland. The large bedrooms, mostly with bathrooms en suite, offer a comprehensive range of accessories including individual basins and tea facilities. The large lounge has scenic views of the surrounding countryside, and meals are served in the sunroom overlooking the garden. The land of this mixed farm is now rented to a neighbouring farmer, but you will always receive a traditional farmhouse stay here.

Recommended in the Area
Whisky Trail, Keith; Baxters Visitor Centre, Fochabers; Moray coast

Loch Leven near Kinross, Perth & Kinross

*T*igh Na Leigh Guesthouse ♦♦♦♦♦

Map ref 10 - NO24

22-24 Airlie St, ALYTH,
Perth & Kinross PH11 8AJ

A926 onto B952, 0.5m on left after St Ninian's Church

Ⓣ 01828 632372
Ⓕ 01828 632279
Ⓔ bandcblack@yahoo.co.uk
Ⓦ www.tighnaleigh.co.uk

5 rooms, S £35, D £80-£100, No smoking, Closed Nov-Feb

This guesthouse in the heart of Alyth is an absolute delight - it's big on food, hospitality and service. A bit daunting from the outside, inside the property is superb, lovingly modernised and furnished with an eclectic mix of contemporary and antique furniture. The large, individually decorated bedrooms comprise a four-poster, twin, double and single, equipped with all the necessary amenities. Every room is en suite and some have spa baths. Pre-dinner drinks are provided in one of two inviting lounges, followed by a delicious home-cooked meal in the huge conservatory (where breakfast is a treat too) overlooking the lovely garden.

Recommended in the Area

Scone Palace; Glamis Castle; Dunkeld Cathedral

Adam Guest House ♦♦♦♦

Map ref 10 - NO12

6 Pitcullen Crescent, PERTH,
Perth & Kinross PH2 7HT

From town centre over bridge onto A94 Coupar road, house on left

T / F 01738 627179
E enquiresadam@aol.com

4 rooms, S £25-£35, D £46-£55,
No smoking

RECOMMENDED IN THE AREA

Scone Palace; Cherrybank Gardens; Glamis Castle

The friendly Wilson family have run this stylish guesthouse for over 16 years, and Jane is ably assisted by daughter Josie her son Stewart. All three enjoy meeting the visitors who come to stay from all over the world. The attractive en suite bedrooms are well equipped and carefully maintained, and have smart bathrooms and plenty of home comforts. Downstairs, there is a pleasant lounge and a cosy dining room. Breakfast is served at individual tables in the dining room, a traditional Scottish choice guaranteed to set you up for the day. The Adam Guest House is handily located beside the Coupar Angus road and has a parking area.

Dalhenzean Lodge ♦♦♦♦

Map ref 10 - NO17
GLENSHEE (SPITTAL OF),
Perth & Kinross PH10 7QD
On A93 2m S of Spittal of Glenshee
T 01250 885217
F 0871 7335419
E mikepurdie@onetel.com
2 rooms, S £35, D £45-£50

A really warm welcome makes guests feel immediately at home at this well-equipped guesthouse. It was built as a lodge in 1715, but there's nothing old-fashioned about the accommodation: the bedrooms are beautifully decorated and filled with thoughtful extras and modern comforts. Rooms are either en suite or have private facilities. The scenery is hard to beat. With the imposing presence of Meall Uaine in one direction and Shee Water in another, it is well placed for fishing, hill-walking, climbing and skiing, and there are many places of historic and scenic interest nearby. Hearty breakfasts prepare you for these outdoor pursuits, while a conservatory makes the most of the view.

Recommended in the Area

Glamis Castle; Balmoral; Edradour Distillery

The Glenholm Centre ♦♦♦♦

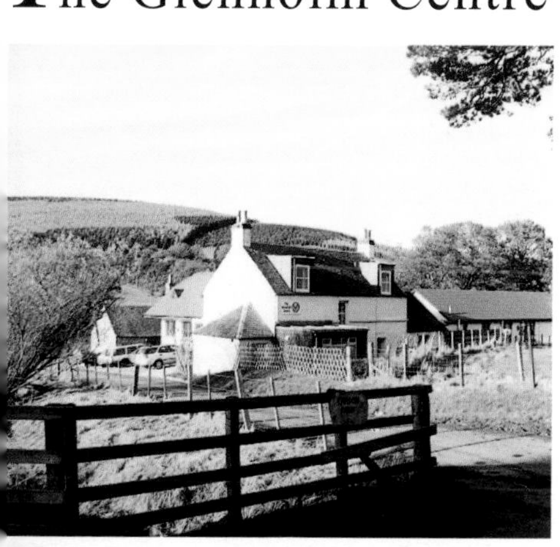

Map ref 10 - NT13
BROUGHTON, Scottish Borders
ML12 6JF
2m S of Broughton. Off A701 to Glenholm, on right before cattle grid
T / F 01899 830408
E info@glenholm.co.uk
W www.glenholm.dircon.co.uk
4 rooms, S £27-£29.50, D £48-£53, No smoking, Closed Jan

Over 1000 acres of farmland surround this converted school house set in a peaceful valley. Neil Robinson returned from Zambia where he met Fiona Burnett, and the pair now run this welcoming guesthouse on the family farm. Wholesome cooking is a special feature, and home-baked breakfasts are the highlight of any stay; all tastes can be catered for. The en suite bedrooms are bright and airy, and a family suite is available in an adjacent cottage, with room for up to four people. Fridges, direct-dial telephones and videos add to the comfort. The Centre is licensed.

Recommended in the Area

Dawyck Botanic Gardens, Broughton Gallery. John Buchan Museum

Ruthven House ♦♦♦♦♦

Map ref 10 - NT83
COLDSTREAM, Scottish Borders
TD12 4JU

From Coldstream turn at Mercedes Garage N onto Guards Rd, after 3m Ruthven signed on right

Ⓣ 01890 840771
Ⓕ 01890 840680
Ⓔ gradidge@worldonline.co.uk
Ⓦ www.bordersovernight.co.uk

4 rooms, S £35-£40, D £60-£70,
No smoking

Elizabeth Gradidge, AA Landlady of the Year 2005, gained her prestigious award for the high standards of hospitality and accommodation she has built up with her husband since 1999. Their impressive Victorian family home stands in 7 acres of well-tended grounds in beautiful Borders countryside, with stunning views of the Cheviot Hills. The spacious bedrooms are beautifully furnished and very well equipped, and the attractive bathrooms have extraordinary free-standing bathtubs. There is a comfy drawing room, and hearty breakfasts are served in the dining room with delicious evening meals by arrangement. The gardens are delightful, with a lawn gently sloping to paddocks. Ruthven is an ideal base for exploring the Borders, or for fishing - in the nearby River Tweed and Whiteadder Water - golf and walking. If you have an interest in Scottish history, there are several castles to visit in the area. Themed workshop weekends at the house, including cookery courses, are also available.

RECOMMENDED IN THE AREA

Floors Castle, Kelso; Lindisfarne, Holy Island; Alnwick Castle and Gardens

Crailing Old School B&B ♦♦♦♦

Map ref 10 - NT62
CRAILING, Scottish Borders
TD8 6TL
A698 onto B6400 signed Nisbet, Crailing Old School also signed
T / F 01835 850382
E jean.player@virgin.net
W www.crailingoldschool.co.uk
4 rooms, S £26.50-£28.50, D £53-£64, No smoking, Closed 24-27 Dec, 2 wks Feb & Nov

This delightful Victorian village school has been imaginatively renovated to combine original features with modern comforts. The sizeable bedrooms are beautifully maintained and decorated, and filled with homely extras. The lodge annexe suite lies just 10 yards from the house and has easy ground-floor access. The best of local ingredients go into the tasty breakfasts, served in the stylish lounge-dining room (evening meals by arrangement). Jean Leach-Player was a runner-up AA Landlady of the Year in 2002, 2003 and for 2005. This is a good area for outdoor pursuits including fishing, walking and, in particular, golf. Ray Leach is a golf professional and can advise on the 22 courses in the vicinity.

Recommended in the Area

St Cuthbert's Way; Teviot and Tweed rivers; Roxburghe Championship Golf Course

---

The Black Bull Hotel ♦♦♦♦

Map ref 10 - NT54
Market Place, LAUDER, Scottish Borders TD2 6SR
On A68 in village centre
T 01578 722208
F 01578 722419
E enquiries@blackbull-lauder.com
W www.blackbull-lauder.com
8 rooms, S £50, D £75-£90, No smoking, Closed 1st 2 wks Feb

The family-run Black Bull lies in the heart of the Borders, with some of the best forest, coastal and hill walking in Scotland, and great fishing too. This 18th-century coaching inn has been ftransformed into a perfect country retreat only 30 minutes from Edinburgh. The lovely en suite bedrooms are furnished in period character, and have fresh flowers, luxury toiletries and tea and coffee facilities. The cosy bar and four dining areas, all with old wooden floors, are charming, the main dining room being a former chapel. The tremendous range and quality of the food makes this a pub worth travelling to. AA Scottish Pub of the Year 2005-2006.

Recommended in the Area

Edinburgh Castle; Thirlestane Castle; Rosslyn Chapel, Roslin

Fauhope House ♦♦♦♦♦

Map ref 10 - NT53
Gattonside, MELROSE,
Scottish Borders TD6 9LU
0.7m N of Melrose over River Tweed. N off B6360 at Gattonside 30mph sign (E) up long driveway
T 01896 823184
F 01896 822245
E fauhope@bordernet.co.uk
3 rooms, S £40-£45, D £70-£80, No smoking

Fauhope House is a fine example of the arts and crafts style of architecture of the 1890s. Inside, stunning floral displays enhance the designs, and lavish drapes and fine furniture grace the drawing room and the magnificent dining room where full Scottish or a continental breakfast is served. The en suite bedrooms are luxurious with generous sizes, individual furnishings and thoughtful extras. Sheila Robson is an experienced host who continually pleases her discerning guests. Melrose has a good choice of restaurants and pubs, accessed via a Georgian suspension bridge spanning the Tweed.

Recommended in the Area

Abbotsford House; Melrose Abbey; Roxburgh Golf Course

Glen Orchy House ♦♦♦♦

Map ref 13 - HU44
20 Knab Rd, LERWICK, Shetland
ZE1 0AX
Next to coastguard station
T / F 01595 692031
E glenorchy.house@virgin.net
W www.guesthouselerwick.com
24 rooms, S £42.50, D £69

Once an Episcopalian convent, this smart hotel has swapped an austere past for the modern comforts expected by discerning guests. It offers several new bedrooms in a non-smoking wing, which come equipped with satellite television and air conditioning, as well as some older but equally appealing rooms. One of the lounges has an honesty bar, and there are plenty of books and games for wet days. Delicious three-course dinners and substantial breakfasts are served in the dining room. Fax and VCR facilities are available on request.

Recommended in the Area

Shetland scenery; Pictish broch on the Island of Mousa; St Ninian's Isle

Daviot House ♦♦♦♦

Map ref 9 - NS32
12 Queens Ter, AYR, South Ayrshire
KA7 1DU
Off A719 onto Wellington Sq & Bath Place, turn right
Ⓣ 01292 269678
Ⓕ 01292 880567
Ⓔ annthedaviot@aol.com
Ⓦ www.daviothouse.com
5 rooms, S £28-£35, D £50-£60, No smoking

Ann Vance always provides a warm welcome to her Victorian terrace home, set in a quiet residential area just a stroll from the beach and town centre. The house retains much original character, and the attractive en suite bedrooms include three suitable for families. Each room has a radio alarm, hairdryer and a hospitality tray. There is a comfortable lounge and dining room, where a full home-cooked Scottish breakfast is served. Ann is a member of Golf South Ayrshire and can provide a booking service for the local municipal courses.

RECOMMENDED IN THE AREA

Burns Cottage; Royal Troon & Turnberry golf courses; Culzean Castle

---

Balkissock Lodge ♦♦♦♦ 

Map ref 5 - NX08
Balkissock, BALLANTRAE,
South Ayrshire KA26 0LP
Off A77 1st left S of river, 3m to T-junct. Turn right, Lodge signed 1m ahead
Ⓣ 01465 831537
Ⓔ info@balkissocklodge.co.uk
Ⓦ www.balkissocklodge.co.uk
4 rooms, D £58-£75 No smoking

RECOMMENDED IN THE AREA

Galloway Forest Park; Culzean Castle; Logan Botanical Garden

Built as a shooting lodge for the Laggan Estate, this charming Georgian house has a peaceful setting in 1 acre of garden and woodland. Fran and Denis Sweeney offer high standards of hospitality and housekeeping. The bedrooms are stylish and thoughtfully equipped with extras such as electric blankets. Retire to the lounge with its log fire after a day walking, cycling, fishing or playing golf. The couple take great pride in their evening meals, which include fish and game dishes using home-grown and local produce. The extensive breakfast menu is imaginative with alternative fish and cheese options together with home-made breads and preserves.

Cosses Country House ♦♦♦♦♦

Map ref 5 - NX08
Cosses, BALLANTRAE, South Ayrshire KA26 0LR
A77 S of Ballantrae onto inland road at caravan sign, house 2m on right
T 01465 831363
F 01465 831598
E info@cossescountryhouse.com
W www.cossescountryhouse.com
2 rooms, S £62.50, D £95, No smoking in bedrooms or dining room, Closed Nov-Feb

A charming country house set in a secluded valley with 12 acres of beautiful gardens and woodland. The house is filled with elegant furniture and treasures, and you are guaranteed a very special welcome. Two of the three suites have their own sitting rooms, and all are equipped with bathrooms en suite. Home-made biscuits, fruit, toiletries and writing materials are just some of the many extras. A pre-dinner drink is taken with the owners in front of a blazing fire in the lounge, and an excellent meal is served at the communal table. Home-grown and local produce also appears at the breakfast table.

Recommended in the Area

Culzean Castle & Country Park (NTS); Logan Botanic Garden; Turnberry Golf Course

---

Dunduff Farm ♦♦♦♦♦

Map ref 9 - NS21
Dunure, DUNURE, South Ayrshire KA7 4LH
On A719 400yds past village school
T 01292 500225
F 01292 500222
E gemmelldunduff@aol.com
W www.gemmelldunduff.co.uk
3 rooms, No smoking, Closed Nov-Feb

There are panoramic sea views from all the rooms at this working farm, parts of which date back to the 15th and 17th centuries. From its position above the Firth of Clyde, the sheep and beef farm looks out towards Arran and the Mull of Kintyre, and over to Ailsa Craig. Thoughtful touches are evident throughout the house, and the modern en suite bedrooms are well equipped. The genuine Scottish hospitality makes you feel at home, and there is a welcoming lounge. Specialities such as locally smoked kippers are served at breakfast, and there is a choice of places to eat in nearby Ayr.

Recommended in the Area

Dunure Castle; Burns Cottage; Culzean Castle & Country Park (NTS)

Ballochneck Country House ♦♦♦♦♦ 

Map ref 9 - NS59
Ballochneck Estate, BUCHLYVIE, Stirling FK8 3PA
A811 onto B835, left 300yds after speed-limit sign, 1m up driveway
T 01360 850216
F 01360 850376
E info@ballochneck.com
W www.ballochneck.com
2 rooms, D £145-£165, No smoking in bedrooms or dining room

This is a super house with lovely proprietors. Built in 1863 on the route from Stirling to Loch Lomond, Ballochneck is an impressive country house just 30 minutes from Glasgow and 1 hour from Edinburgh. The secluded house stands amid manicured lawns, rhododendrons, mature trees, ponds and stunning countryside. Bedrooms are spacious and the top floor has a games room with a full-size billiard table and a card room. There is a comfortable drawing room, and an elegant candle-lit dining room for the home-cooked fare. The conservatory has been planted up round the edges with a lovely selection of aromatic and structural plants.

Recommended in the Area
Menteith Hills; Loch Lomond & The Trossachs National Park; Bannockburn (NTS)

Arden House ♦♦♦♦

Map ref 9 - NN60
Bracklinn Rd, CALLANDER, Stirling FK17 8EQ
Off A84 Main St onto Bracklinn Rd, house 200yds on left
T / F 01877 330235
E ardenhouse@onetel.com
W www.ardenhouse.org.uk
6 rooms, S £32.50-£35, D £60-£70, No smoking, Closed Nov-Mar

Visitors to Arden House need not be alarmed if they are offered Janet for the night - the rooms are named after characters from the television series Doctor Finlay's Casebook. The fictional home of Doctors Finlay and Cameron is now owned by Ian and William, who offer a genuine welcome with tea and home-made cake on arrival. The en suite bedrooms have been refurbished and provided with thoughtful extras. A stylish lounge and bright dining room are inviting, and traditional Scottish breakfasts are a definite high spot of a visit.

Recommended in the Area
Loch Lomond & Trossachs National Park; Stirling Castle; Loch Katrine

Lubnaig House ♦♦♦♦

Map ref 9 - NN60
Leny Feus, CALLANDER,
Stirling FK17 8AS
From centre A84 W, right onto Leny Feus
T 01877 330376
E info@lubnaighouse.co.uk
W www.lubnaighouse.co.uk
8 rooms, S £40-£49, D £60-£68, No smoking in bedrooms or dining room, Closed Nov-Apr

Lubnaig House, built in 1864 on the edge of the Trossachs and just a short walk from the town centre, has been home to kilt-wearing Crawford Low and his wife Sue since the early 1990s. The key to their success is warm Scottish hospitality and a restful country house atmosphere. The bedrooms, with some on the ground floor, have shower rooms en suite and tea and coffee facilities. There are two cosy lounges, and an impressive dining room where hearty traditional breakfasts are served at individual tables. The gardens are a delight with a huge range of trees and shrubs, and seats to relax on.

RECOMMENDED IN THE AREA
Loch Lomond & The Trossachs National Park; Steampship Sir Walter Scott on Loch Katrine; Stirling Castle

---

Ashcroft Farmhouse ♦♦♦♦♦

Map ref 10 - NT06
EAST CALDER, West Lothian
EH53 0ET
On B7015, off A71, 0.5m E of East Calder, near to Almondell Country Park
T 01506 881810
F 01506 884327
E scottashcroft7@aol.com
W www.ashcroftfarmhouse.com
6 rooms, S £45-£60, D £64-£70, No smoking

Surrounded by open countryside yet only 10 miles from the centre of Edinburgh, this sprawling modern bungalow is set in a beautifully landscaped garden. Elizabeth and Derek Scott have been welcoming guests to their immaculate home for 43 years and their well-proportioned bedrooms are comfortably furnished. Each en suite room is named after a Scottish championship golf course, and has fluffy towels and good toiletries, and a hospitality tray with shortbread biscuits. The golf memorabilia is a talking point in the dining room, where delicious breakfasts made from fresh Scottish produce are served at individual tables. Home-made sausages and whisky marmalade are part of the morning treat. There is a video library in the lounge. Elizabeth was runner up AA Landlady of the Year 2005.

RECOMMENDED IN THE AREA
Edinburgh Castle; Royal Yacht Britannia; McArthurglen Designer Outlet

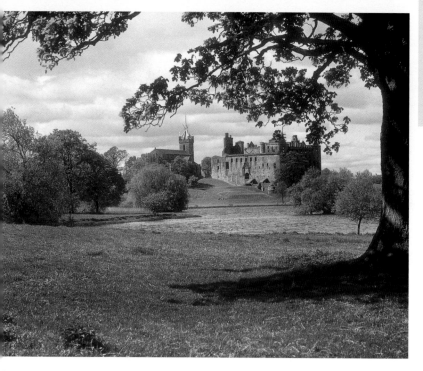

.inlithgow Palace, West Lothian

Bomains Farm Guest House ♦♦♦♦

Map ref 10 - NS97

Bo'Ness, LINLITHGOW, West Lothian EH49 7RQ

A706 1.5m N towards Bo'Ness, left at golf course x-rds, 1st farm on right

T / F 01506 822188
E buntykirk@tiscali.co.uk
W www.bomains.co.uk

3 rooms, S £35-£40, D £50-£60, No smoking

From its elevated location, this friendly farmhouse has stunning views of the Firth of Forth, Linlithgow nd the hills beyond. The warmth of the Kirk's welcome s apparent from the moment you step into the hallway vith its impressive galleried staircase. The bedrooms, amed after the Kirk's grown-up children, are beautifully lecorated, well equipped and enhanced by quality abrics and modern hand-painted furniture. All are en uite and come with hospitality trays. The traditional Scottish breakfast, served at a polished mahogany table with views towards the Ochil Hills, is prepared using local ingredients. The working farm is next to a golf course with fishing nearby, yet is convenient for visiting Edinburgh.

Recommended in the Area

Falkirk Wheel; Zebrugge-Rosyth Ferry; Edinburgh Airport

Wales

A selection of places to eat from the AA Restaurant & AA Pub guides

Restaurants

da Venditto (Italian)
7-8 Park Place, Cardiff CF10 3DP
Tel 029 2023 0781

The Cors Restaurant (Welsh)
Newbridge Road, Laugharne,
Carmarthenshire SA33 4SH
Tel 01994 427219

Ynyshir Hall (British)
Eglwysfach, Ceredigion SY20 8TA
Tel 01654 781209

Tan-y-Foel Country House (British)
Capel Garmon, Conwy LL26 0RE
Tel 01690 710507

The Old Rectory (British, French)
Llanrwst Road, Llansanffraid Glan Conwy,
Conwy LL28 5LF Tel 01492 580611

Penhelig Arms Hotel & Restaurant (British)
Terrace Road, Aberdyel, Gwynedd
LL35 0LT Tel 01654 767215

Ye Olde Bulls Head Inn (British)
Castle Street, Beaumaris,
Isle of Anglesey LL58 8AP
Tel 01248 810329

Walnut Tree Inn (Italian)
Llandewi Skirrid, Abergavenny,
Monmouthshire NP7 8AW
Tel 01873 852797

The Bell at Skenfrith (British)
Skenfrith, Monmouthshire NP7 8UH
Tel 01600 750235

The Chandlery (European)
77-78 Lower Dock Street, Newport
NP20 1EH Tel 01633 256622

The Welcome to Town (Welsh)
Llanrhidian, Swansea SA3 1EH
Tel 01792 390015

Fairyhill (Welsh)
Reynoldston, Swansea SA3 1BS
Tel 01792 390139

Pubs

Caesars Arms
Cardiff Road, Creigiau, Cardiff CF15 9NN
Tel 029 2089 0486

The Plough Inn
The Roe, St Asaph Denbighshire LL17 0LU
Tel 01745 585080

The Boat Inn
The Back, Chepstow,
Monmouthshire NP16 5HH
Tel 01291 628192

The Newbridge Inn
Tredunnock, Monmouthshire NP15 1LY
Tel 01633 451000

Pendre Inn
Pendre, Cilgerran, Pembrokeshire SA43 2SL
Tel 01239 614223

The George's Restaurant/Café Bar
24 Market Street, Haverfordwest,
Pembrokeshire SA61 1NH
Tel 01437 766683

White Swan Inn
Llanfrynach, Brecon, Powys LD3 7BZ
Tel 01874 665276

The Usk Inn
Talybont-on-Usk, Brecon, Powys LD3 7JE
Tel 01874 676251

The Talkhouse
Pontdolgoch, Caersws, Powys SY17 5JE
Tel 01686 688919

The Bear
Brecon Road, Crickhowell, Powys NP8 1BW
Tel 01873 810408

The Old Black Lion
Hay-on-Wye, Powys HR3 5AD
Tel 01497 820841

Dragon Hotel
Montgomery, Powys SY15 6PA
Tel 01686 668359

Blue Anchor Inn
East Aberthaw, Vale of Glamorgan CF62 3DD
Tel 01446 750329

The West Arms Hotel
Llanarmon Dyffryn Ceiriog,
Wrexham LL20 7LD
Tel 01691 600665

Dan y Coed ♦♦♦♦

Map ref 2 - SN53
Nant y Ffin, BRECHFA,
Carmarthenshire SA32 7RE
2m NE of Brechfa on B4310 on left
T 01267 253986
F 01267 253985
E stella@danycoed.co.uk
W www.danycoed.co.uk
2 rooms, S £30, D £60, No smoking

Forget about the car when you visit this modern bungalow, as there are great opportunities to explore the beautiful Cothi valley on foot, mountain bike or horseback. Two cosy bedrooms, one double with shower room en suite and a twin with a private luxury bathroom, are furnished with coordinated soft furnishings and stocked with fleecy dressing gowns and toiletries. Unforgettable Welsh breakfasts are served in the dining room, or on fine days on the veranda with a panoramic view across the valley to the towering Brechfa forest - with luck you may glimpse a red kite or buzzard soaring overhead.

Recommended in the Area

National Botanic Garden of Wales; Aberglasney; Dolaucothi Goldmines (NT)

Glasfryn Guest House & Restaurant ♦♦♦♦

Map ref 2 - SN53
BRECHFA, Carmarthenshire
SA32 7QY
M4 junct 49, A48 to Cross Hands, towards Carmarthen for 1m, 2nd left onto B4310, past gardens over A40, continue 6m into Brechfa
T 01267 202306
F 0870 1341770
E joyce.glasfryn@clara.co.uk
W www.glasfrynbrechfa.co.uk
3 rooms, S £37.50, D £55,
No smoking in bedrooms or dining room

Set in a picturesque valley ideal for touring south Wales, this large stone house exudes traditional Welsh hospitality. The late Victorian property has been refurbished to retain stone walls and stripped pine, and the accommodation has been extended into a large, bright conservatory. The pretty en suite bedrooms have power showers in the bathrooms. In the evening an imaginative à la carte is available, served in the smart dining room overlooking a pretty patio. This homely guesthouse is only 15 minutes from the National Botanic Garden of Wales.

Recommended in the Area

Aberglasney; Forest walks; Mountain biking in the forest

Laugharne Castle, Carmarthenshire

Capel Dewi Uchaf Country House ♦♦♦♦

Map ref 1 - SN42

Capel Dewi, CARMARTHEN,
Carmarthenshire SA32 8AY

On B4300 between Capel Dewi & junct B4310

T 01267 290799
F 01267 290003
E uchaffarm@aol.com
W www.walescottageholidays.uk.com

3 rooms, S £45, D £66, No smoking, Closed Xmas

Dating from the 18th century, this Grade II listed farmhouse stands in 30 acres by the River Towy with stunning country views. Private fishing and stabling for horses are available. The lovely garden includes a terrace, and inside a welcoming fire and period decor enhance the property's original features. Bedrooms are en suite or have private facilities, and come with hairdryers and hospitality trays. Fresh local produce is a feature of the memorable dinners and generous Welsh breakfasts, including home-grown vegetables. There's a lounge, with a piano, guitar and wind-up gramophone as well as the television, and the house has a residential licence.

Recommended in the area

National Botanic Garden of Wales; Aberglasney; Carreg Cennen Castle

Brynteilo Guest House ♦♦♦♦

Map ref 2 - SN62
Manordeilo, LLANDEILO,
Carmarthenshire SA19 7BG
On A40, 4m NE of Llandeilo & 8m SW of Llandovery
T 01550 777040
F 01550 777884
E enquiries@brynteilo.com
W www.brynteilo.com
11 rooms, S £45, D £60,
No smoking

Lovely countryside surrounds this friendly guesthouse in the heart of the Towy valley. The modern accommodation comes with a host of practical and homely extras. Each en suite room is equipped with a desk, teletext television, telephone with modem connection, and a hospitality tray. Several rooms are on the ground floor, and there is also a family room. A self-catering flat with a good range of equipment offers total privacy. Local produce is used wherever possible in the traditional breakfasts.

RECOMMENDED IN THE AREA
National Botanic Garden of Wales; Dinefwr (NT); Dolaucothi Gold Mines (NT)

Dolau Guest House ♦♦♦♦

Map ref 2 - SN42
Felingwm Isaf, NANTGAREDIG,
Carmarthenshire SA32 7PB
A40 onto B4310, 1.5m to Felingwm Isaf, right in village, over bridge on left
T 01267 290464
E brightdolau@aol.com
W www.dolau.com
3 rooms, S £28-£35, D £48-£56,
No smoking

Expect a warm Welsh welcome and plenty of individual attention at this lovely riverside house. The modernised property and 5-acre gardens run alongside the Cloidach Brook, where once there was a woollen mill. Carol and Bill Bright are happy to share their many interests - including cycling, painting, walking, needlework and gardening - and they still have time to spend with their three young grandchildren. Bedrooms are well equipped and cosy, with tea and coffee facilities, and are en suite or have private bathrooms. There conservatory breakfast room has separate tables.

RECOMMENDED IN THE AREA
National Botanic Garden of Wales; Aberglasney Gardens; Brechfa Forest

Coedllys Country House ♦♦♦♦♦

Map ref 1 - SN21
Llangynin, ST CLEARS, Carmarthenshire
SA33 4JY

T 01994 231455
F 01994 231441
E keith@harber.fsworld.co.uk
W www.coedllyscountryhouse.co.uk

3 rooms, S £42.50, D £70, No smoking, Closed Xmas

Recommended in the Area

Dylan Thomas Boathouse, Laugharne; Millennium Coastal Path; National Botanic Garden of Wales

Coedllys is the ultimate country hideaway. It is surrounded by its own farmland with a pretty woodland dell and lovely open views, known locally as Paradise Valley. Valerie and Keith Harber are mad about nature and conservation, and their sanctuary has provided a refuge for countless animals over the years. The large country house has been beautifully restored to provide elegant cottage-style rooms with antique furniture, luxurious fabrics and lavish thoughtful extras. Chocolates, fresh fruit, flowers and magazines join soft bathrobes and slippers, and comfy sofas to make a stay here truly special. Those spectacular views across the valley can be soaked up from the charming lounge, where a large wood-burning stove keeps the chill away. Breakfasts spoil you for choice, and delicious evening meals three nights a week are served around one large table.

Arosfa Harbourside Guesthouse ♦♦♦♦

Map ref 1 - SN46
Cardigan Bay, ABERAERON, Ceredigion SA46 0BU
A487 in town centre onto Market St towards sea, 150yds to Arosfa car park
T 01545 570120
E arosfabandb@aol.com
W www.arosfaguesthouse.co.uk
4 rooms, S £35-£45, D £56-£70, No smoking

Once the library of this historic town, the Georgian house is surrounded by similar fine properties overlooking the inner harbour. Most of the bedrooms have views over the water and are comfortably furnished with a sofa or fireside chair, complemented by modern bathrooms. Quality art and memorabilia enhance the stairways. The attractive dining room is the setting for memorable Welsh breakfasts, which include traditional farmhouse-cured bacon, laver bread, Aberaeron mackerel, fresh mushrooms, local cheeses, fresh fruit salad and home-made bread.

Recommended in the Area

Llanerchaeron (NT) ; Cors Caron National Nature Reserve; Devil's Bridge

---

Bodalwyn Guest House ♦♦♦♦

Map ref 2 - SN58
Queen's Av, ABERYSTWYTH, Ceredigion SY23 2EG
N along promenade towards Cliff railway. 1st right after Marine Hotel & over x-rds, guesthouse opp North Rd Clinic
T 01970 612578
F 01970 639261
E hilary.d@lineone.net
W www.bodalwyn.co.uk
8 rooms, S £35-£40, D £55-£65, No smoking, Closed 24 Dec-1 Jan

Bodalwyn is a restored Edwardian house, ideal for a relaxing break by Cardigan Bay or as a base for exploring the countryside. It is just a few minutes from the promenade, and close to Constitution Hill where you can ride on Britain's longest electric cliff railway. The accommodation includes spacious bedrooms and stylish modern bathrooms, with plenty of homely features such as bottled water and a hospitality tray. An elegant dining room with a conservatory extension offers individual tables at breakfast time, when a hearty Welsh spread is always on the menu. The house is completely non-smoking.

Recommended in the Area

National Library of Wales; Llanerchaeron (NT); Vale of Rheidol Railway

Afon View Non Smokers Guest House ♦♦♦♦

Map ref 5 - SH75
Holyhead Rd, BETWS-Y-COED,
Conwy LL24 0AN
On A5 150yds E of HSBC bank
T / F 01690 710726
E welcome@afon-view.co.uk
W www.afon-view.co.uk
7 rooms, S £27.50-£31, D £55-£70,
No smoking, Closed 24-26 Dec

Expect a warm Welsh welcome at this impressive stone house dating from the 1880s. Teresa and Keith Roobottom are a homely couple who enjoy looking after their guests. Their comfortable home has spacious, attractive bedrooms with dramatic views of the surrounding wooded hills. Some rooms have original slate and marble-effect fireplaces, and there is a four poster among the practical bed options. A pretty dining room is the setting for wholesome Welsh breakfasts, and there's a relaxing lounge where you can enjoy a hot drink or borrow a book.

RECOMMENDED IN THE AREA
Snowdon Mountain Railway; Bodnant Garden (NT); Conwy

Bryn Bella Guest House ♦♦♦♦

Map ref 5 - SH75
Lon Muriau, Llanrwst Rd, BETWS-Y-COED,
Conwy LL24 0HD
A5 onto A470, 0.5m right onto driveway signed Bryn Bella
T 01690 710627
E welcome@bryn-bella.co.uk
W www.bryn-bella.co.uk
5 rooms, D £52-£65, No smoking

There are stunning views of Betws-y-Coed and Snowdonia National Park from this elegant Victorian house. Joan and Mark Edwards thoughtfully provide a telescope to make the most of the scenery, and work hard to make a stay here homely and special. Bedrooms have been renovated to a good standard since they took over recently, and are equipped with fridges, electronic safes and microwave ovens, as well as tea and coffee facilities and hairdryers. An Internet connection is also available. Comprehensive breakfasts are served in the attractive dining room with wonderful views, and there's a comfortable lounge.

RECOMMENDED IN THE AREA
Mount Snowdon; Caernarfon Castle; Bodnant Garden (NT)

Penmachno Hall ♦♦♦♦

Map ref 5 - SH75
BETWS-Y-COED, Conwy LL24 0PU
A5 onto B4406 to Penmachno, over bridge, right at Eagles pub signed Ty Mawr
T / F 01690 760410
E stay@penmachnohall.co.uk
W www.penmachnohall.co.uk
3 rooms, D £70-£85, No smoking, Closed Xmas, New Year

Set in over 2 acres of mature grounds with mountain stream and woodland in Snowdonia National Park, this impressive Victorian rectory has been lovingly restored to provide high standards of comfort. It offers country-house style and quality furnishings while retaining original features. The en suite bedrooms come with a range of enticing extras. Commodious reception rooms, with fires in winter, welcome the weary on their return from an energetic day out in the surrounding countryside. The meals at Penmachno - dinner-party style around a central dining table - are a highlight and prepared using first-class local produce and there is an excellent wine list.

Recommended in the Area

Snowdon; Bodnant Garden (NT); Portmeirion

Whitehall Hotel ♦♦♦♦

Map ref 5 - SH87
51 Cayley Promenade,
Rhos-on-Sea, COLWYN BAY,
Conwy LL28 4EP
From A55 E or W Old Colwyn exit. At T-junct turn down to Promenade. Left at Promenade and travel W for 1.9m to Rhos on Sea. Left at Puppet Theatre. Hotel 5th on right
T 01492 547296
E mossd.cymru@virgin.net
W www.whitehall-hotel.co.uk
12 rooms, S £28.50, D £57-£63, No smoking

This comfortable family-run hotel overlooks the promenade of Rhos-on-Sea, between Llandudno and Colwyn Bay, and is an excellent base for exploring north Wales. The well-appointed en suite bedrooms include several family rooms and each room has a video and a CD player, and all have air conditioning. The extensive breakfast menu has over 30 choices, using local produce where possible. Tony and Maria are friendly hosts who have lived in Canada, the USA, and the Middle and Far East, so while the daily changing four-course dinners stress Welsh cuisine they also offer surprises from around the world. There is a cosy bar next to the dining room.

Recommended in the Area

Rhos-on-Sea beach; Snowdonia National Park; Bodnant Garden (NT)

Sychnant Pass House ♦♦♦♦♦

Map ref 5 - SH77

Sychnant Pass Rd, CONWY, Conwy
LL32 8BJ

1.75m W of Conwy. Off A547 Bangor Rd in town onto Mount Pleasant & Sychnant Pass Rd, 1.75m on right near top of hill

T 01492 596868
F 01492 585486
E bresykes@sychnant-pass-house.co.uk
W www.sychnant-pass-house.co.uk

10 rooms, S £70-£140, D £90-£170, No smoking in bedrooms or dining room, Closed 24-26 Dec

Recommended in the Area

Conwy Castle; Bodnant Garden (NT); Penryhn Castle (NT)

Set in the foothills of the Snowdonia National Park, Bre and Graham Carrington-Sykes's large Edwardian house stands in 3 acres of landscaped grounds with lovely views. Bedrooms, including suites and four-poster rooms, are individually furnished with great attention to detail. Named after TS Elliot's Practical Cats, McCavity's vies for the best room with a view, looking out to the mountains. Sitting rooms with deep sofas and attractive pictures are warmed by open fires in the chillier months. Chef Graham has a training background gained at Gleneagles, Turnberry and in Switzerland. He prepares imaginative dinners and suppers, served in the attractive candlelit dining room. New in 2005, the leisure suite and swimming pool is proving a highlight. Well-behaved children and pets are welcome and are given much attention by Conor, the son of the owners.

Llandudno, Conwy

Abbey Lodge ♦♦♦♦♦

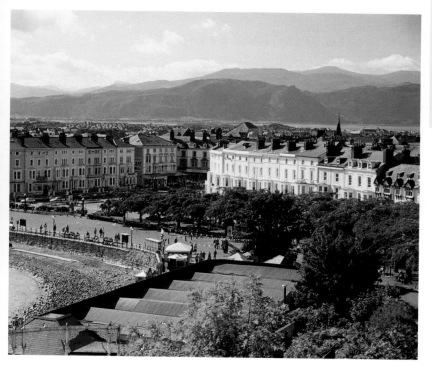

Map ref 5 - SH78
14 Abbey Rd, LLANDUDNO,
Conwy LL30 2EA
A546 to N end of town, onto Clement Av, right onto Abbey Rd
T / F 01492 878042
E enquiries@abbeylodgeuk.com
W www.abbeylodgeuk.com
4 rooms, S £50, D £75, No smoking, Closed 21 Dec-9 Jan

Abbey Lodge is an impressive white-painted property just a short walk along a leafy avenue from the promenade. The house was built in 1870 and has been restored to provide a country-house ambience with modern comforts. There is a sumptuous sitting room and a smart dining room where enjoyable breakfasts are served at one splendid table. Bedrooms are thoughtfully equipped with radios, and tea trays with mineral water and biscuits, and all rooms have luxurious bathrooms en suite. The gardens are a delight, particularly in summer.

Recommended in the Area

Conwy Castle; Bodnant Garden (NT); RSPB Reserve, Llandudno Junction

Brigstock House ♦♦♦♦

Map ref 5 - SH78
1 St David's Place, LLANDUDNO, Conwy LL30 2UG

A470 into Llandudno, left onto The Parade promenade, left onto Lloyd St, left onto St David's Rd & left onto St David's Place

Ⓣ 01492 876416
Ⓔ mtajmemory@brigstock58.fsnet.co.uk
Ⓦ www.brigstockhotel.co.uk

9 rooms, S £27, D £54-£62, No smoking, Closed Nov-Feb

Recommended in the Area

Snowdonia National Park; Welsh Mountain Zoo; Great Orme Dry Ski Slope

The lovely Edwardian property stands in a peaceful area of Llandudno only a short walk from the shops and the sea. The house is an ideal base for touring Snowdonia and Anglesey. Owners Martin and Alison Memory have completely updated Brigstock House over the past five years to provide rooms of a very high standard with new text televisions with either DVD or video, and hospitality trays with biscuits. Two superb suites are available for special occasions, each with a well-furnished lounge area, extra television, fridge and DVD, CD-radio-cassette player and other thoughtful extras. The candlelit restaurant has an extensive, freshly prepared menu and you can relax in the beautifully furnished lounge or garden with patio. A computer with broadband Internet access is available in the reception. Children over 12 years welcome.

Plas Rhos ♦♦♦♦♦

Map ref 5 - SH88
Cayley Promenade,
RHOS-ON-SEA, Conwy
LL28 4EP

A55 junct 20 for Rhos-on-Sea, follow Promenade signs, at seafront fourth building on left

T 01492 543698
F 01492 540088
E info@plasrhos.co.uk
W www.plasrhos.co.uk

8 rooms, S £40-£55, D £60-£90, No smoking, Closed 21 Dec-Jan

A yearning to live by the sea and indulge their passion for sailing brought Susan and Colin Hazelden to the north Wales coast. Running a hotel in Derbyshire for many years was the ideal preparation for looking after guests at their renovated Victorian home. Breakfast is a particularly memorable feature, taken overlooking the pretty patio garden. The two sumptuous lounges have spectacular sea views, comfy chairs and sofas, and interesting memorabilia, while the modest-size bedrooms have plenty of extras. One period room is furnished with a romantic half tester and antiques, and those same stunning views – ideal for honeymooners.

Recommended in the Area

Conwy Castle; Bodnant Garden (NT); Snowdonia National Park

Bron-y-Graig ♦♦♦♦♦

Map ref 5 - SJ04
CORWEN, Denbighshire LL21 0DR
On A5 on E edge of Corwen
T / F 01490 413007
E business@north-wales-hotel.co.uk
W www.north-wales-hotel.co.uk
10 rooms, S £39-£49, D £59, No smoking in bedrooms or dining room

It took Judith Sansom, Lorna Roberts and David Cowan 10 years to restore Bron-y-Graig, which now provides stylish accommodation with period character and excellent service. Now in their sixth successful year, Lorna, the chef, is convinced that guests keep returning for her food, served in the small restaurant and drawing room. Judith, a classics scholar, thinks it's for the extensive library of books and videos for adults and children, while David knows that it's the decor, the 4x4 minibus, the gardens and the woods. The bedrooms are all en suite, and the house is situated on the wooded slopes of the Berwyn Mountains in the beautiful Vale of Llangollen.

Recommended in the Area

Snowdonia National Park; National Whitewater Rafting Centre: Llangollen Steam Railway

---

Bach y Graig ♦♦♦♦

Map ref 5 - SJ07
Tremeirchion, DENBIGH, Denbighshire LL17 0UH
A55 onto A525 to Trefnant, left at lights onto A541 to x-rds with white railings, left down hill, over river bridge, right
T 01745 730627
F 01745 730971
E anwen@bachygraig.co.uk
W www.bachygraig.co.uk
3 rooms, S £38-£48, D £60-£68, No smoking, Closed Xmas, New Year

Edward the Black Prince once hunted in the area, Samuel Johnson visited here, and the wealth of oak beams and panelling, inglenook fireplace and Grade II listing testify to the farmhouse's historic character. Built in 1567, and reputed to be the first brick building in Wales, Bach y Graig is set in 200 acres with private fishing rights on the River Clwyd. The en suite bedrooms are furnished with fine period pieces and quality soft fabrics, and have tea and coffee trays - some rooms have antique brass beds. The ground floor has a quiet lounge and a sitting-dining room, featuring a superb Jacobean oak table where a scrumptuous Welsh breakfast is served.

Recommended in the Area

Bodnant Garden (NT); The Old Gaol, Ruthin; Tweedmill Factory Outlets, St Asaph

*B*arratt's at Ty'N Rhyl ♦♦♦♦

Map ref 5 - SJ08

Ty'N Rhyl, 167 Vale Rd, RHYL, Denbighshire LL18 2PH

A55 onto A525 to Rhyl, pass Sainsburys & B&Q, garden centre on left, Barratts 400yds on right

T / F 01745 344138
E EBarratt5@aol.com

3 rooms, S £45, D £70, No smoking in bedrooms or dining room

RECOMMENDED IN THE AREA

Bodrythan Hall; Bodnant Garden (NT); Local golf courses

David and Elvira Barratt have been at Ty'n Rhyl for over 13 years, a fabulous house set in 1 acre of walled gardens. David is a creative chef, inspired by his grandmother and an extended family who share a love of music, food and wine. The spacious en suite rooms are furnished with French beds and Louis XV-style pieces, and thoughtfully equipped with clock radios, hospitality trays, sweets, toiletries and clothes wash. Plump sofas make for a comfortable bar, while the lounge is an elegant retreat with wood panelling and a fireplace made from Catherine of Aragon's bedstead. Mealtimes are flexible and special diets are catered for.

*F*irgrove Country House B & B ♦♦♦♦

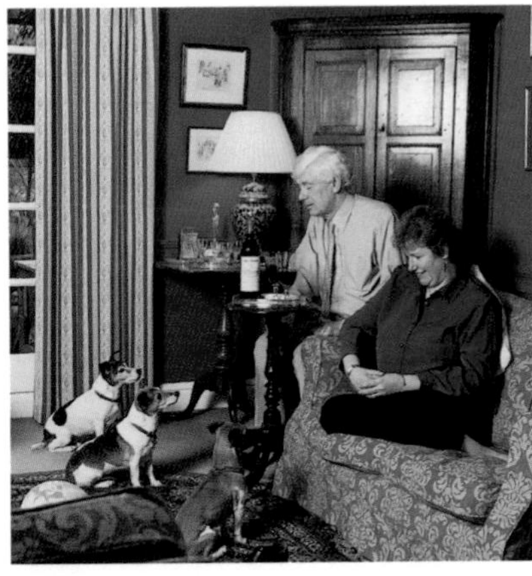

Map ref 5 - SJ15

Firgrove, Llanfwrog, RUTHIN, Denbighshire LL15 2LL

Exit Ruthin on A494 to Bala, at minirdbt take B5105 to Cerrig-y-Drudion. Pass church on right & Cross Key Inn on left. Firgrove is 0.25m on right

T / F 01824 702677
E meadway@firgrovecountryhouse.co.uk
W www.firgrovecountryhouse.co.uk

3 rooms, D £56-£70, No smoking, Closed Dec-Jan

RECOMMENDED IN THE AREA

Offa's Dyke Path; Bodnant Garden (NT); Historic Chester

Firgrove was once an old stone house on Lord Bagot's estate. In 1800 it was dramatically altered by the addition of a Georgian brick façade, and Lord Bagot used it as a guesthouse separate from his stately pile. Anna and Philip Meadway proudly continue the tradition. The Grade II listed building has been brought up to date with well-equipped bedrooms and modern comforts. The well-proportioned rooms exhibit many original period features, plus smart bathrooms designed for pure pampering. One room has an attractive four-poster bed, while another is a suite with an open fire, small kitchen and a sitting room. Home-made or local produce features in the memorable breakfasts served in the elegant dining room. The immaculate garden is an ongoing labour of love, planted with beautiful trees and shrubs, and there are inspiring views of the Vale of Clwyd.

Snowdon Mountain Railway

Erw Feurig Guest House ♦♦♦♦

Map ref 5 - SH93
Cefnddwysarn, BALA, Gwynedd
LL23 7LL

3m NE of Bala off A494. 2nd left after telephone box, B&B signed

T / F 01678 530262
E erwfeurig@yahoo.com
W www.erwfeurig.com

4 rooms, S £30-£40, D £42-£45, No smoking, Closed 24-26 Dec

A warm welcome awaits you at this extended farmhouse, which is set in 200 acres of sheep and cattle grazing land. Gareth and Glenys Jones are the third generation of the family to live at Erw Feurig, where homely accommodation is offered in family, double and twin rooms, each having a hospitality tray and toiletries. Two rooms are en suite and the ground-floor twin has private facilities. A cosy lounge is provided and breakfast is served in the pleasant dining room, at separate tables if preferred. Fishing is available on the farm. Sorry no dogs or smoking indoors.

Recommended in the Area

Ewe-phoria – Agri Theatre and Sheepdog Centre; National White Water Centre; Llyn Tegid Narrow Gauge Steam Railway

Llwyndu Farmhouse ♦♦♦♦

Map ref 5 - SH61

Llanaber, BARMOUTH, Gwynedd
LL42 1RR

A496 towards Harlech. Where street lights end, on outskirts of Barmouth, take next right

T 01341 280144
F 01341 281236
E Intouch@llwyndu-farmhouse.co.uk
W www.llwyndu-farmhouse.co.uk

7 rooms, D £74-£80, No smoking, Closed 25-26 Dec

RECOMMENDED IN THE AREA

Cader Idris; Portmeirion; Centre for Alternative Technology

The converted farmhouse has been known for its 'hospitality, song and good ale' since the 16th century. Among the original features are a circular stone staircase, inglenook fireplaces, exposed beams and mullioned windows. The bedrooms are modern and well equipped, and some have four-poster beds. There are more rooms in the converted granary next to the house, but all rooms are en suite and have hospitality trays. There is a cosy lounge to relax in or to chat to fellow travellers. Breakfast specialities are kippers or naturally smoked haddock, Glamorgan vegetarian cutlets or local herb sausages, and smoked bacon and laver bread. Candlelit dinners in the licensed period-furnished dining are a treat of imaginative food, local produce, fine wines, and a little music thrown in for a great experience. This is a wonderful area for walking, either in the Rhinog Mountains or the nearby Panorama Walk with stunning views across Cardigan Bay to the Llyn Peninsula.

Pengwern Farm ♦♦♦♦

Map ref 5 - SH46
Saron, CAERNARFON, Gwyned
LL54 5UH
From Caernarfon take A487 S, pass supermarket on right, take 1st right turn after bridge 2m to Saron, through x-rds, farm is 1st drive on right

T 01286 831500
F 01286 830741
E janepengwern@aol.com
W www.pengwern.net

3 rooms, S £45, D £60-£70,
No smoking, Closed Nov-Mar

Pengwern is a delightful farmhouse surrounded by 130 acres of beef and sheep farmland running down to Foryd Bay, noted for its bird life. There are fine views from many bedrooms over to Anglesey, and the top of Snowdon can be seen on clear days. Bedrooms are generally spacious, and all are well equipped with modern facilities, including bath and shower rooms en suite, and tea and coffee facilities. A comfortable lounge is provided and good home cooking is served. The farmhouse is a good base from which to explore Snowdonia National Park and the historic town of Caernarfon.

RECOMMENDED IN THE AREA
Plas Newydd, Anglesey (NT); Caernarfon Castle; Electric Mountain

---

Bron Rhiw Hotel ♦♦♦♦ 

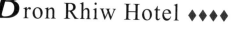

Map ref 5 - SH43
Caernarfon Rd, CRICCIETH,
Gwynedd LL52 0AP
Off High St onto B4411

T 01766 522257
E bronrhiwhotel@amserve.com
W www.bronrhiwhotel.co.uk

9 rooms, S £35-£37.50, D £56-£64,
No smoking, Closed Nov-Feb

Siân and Claire extend a warm welcome to Bron Rhiw, built in 1857 as a hotel just a short walk from the seafront. The bedrooms provide high standards of comfort and modern facilities and are thoughtfully furnished. All have bathrooms en suite and beverage trays. The ground-floor areas include a sumptuous lounge with wonderful sunset views, a cosy bar, and an elegant dining room for imaginative dinners and outstanding breakfasts. Cooked to order, using local produce including Welsh sausages, local bacon and free-range eggs, breakfast sets you up for a busy day playing golf, walking, sailing, birdwatching, cycling, sightseeing or even relaxing.

RECOMMENDED IN THE AREA
Criccieth Castle & beaches;
Llyn Peninsula; Snowdonia National Park

Cefn Uchaf Farm Guest House ♦♦♦♦

Map ref 5 - SH43
Garndolbenmaen, CRICCIETH,
Gwynedd LL51 9PJ
3m N of Criccieth. Off A487 between Dolbenmaen & Bryncir signed Cefn Uchaf
T 01766 530239
E cefnuchaf@tiscali.co.uk
W www.criccieth.co.uk/cefnuchaf
8 rooms, S £40-£50, D £50-£60, No smoking

RECOMMENDED IN THE AREA
Snowdonia National Park; Criccieth Castle; Ffestiniog Railway

Set at the gateway to the Llyn Peninsula overlooking Cwm Pennant valley, Cefn Uchant, meaning the highest ridge, is a great base for exploring or walking the mountains of Snowdonia and the coast. The large modernised farmhouse offers comfortable accommodation and a relaxed friendly atmosphere. The en suite bedrooms all have tea and coffee trays. Start the day with a wholesome, traditional breakfast and spend the evening exploring the farm, walking by the river, or relaxing in the lounge with a drink. There is plenty of room for children to play and friendly animals including sheep, ducks, rabbits, peacocks and chickens. Fishing available in season.

Tyddynmawr Farmhouse ♦♦♦♦♦

Map ref 2 - SH71
Cader Rd, Islawrdref, DOLGELLAU,
Gwynedd LL40 1TL
From town centre left at top of square, left at garage onto Cader Rd for 3m, 1st farm on left after Gwernan Lake
T 01341 422331
3 rooms, S £45, D £60, No smoking, Closed Jan

Birdwatchers, ramblers, photographers and artists see these spectacular surroundings as a paradise, and the farmhouse accommodation appeals equally to those just happy to sit and look. Olwen Evans prides herself on her home cooking and warm hospitality. Oak beams and log fires lend character to the stone house, and bedrooms are spacious and furnished with Welsh oak furniture; one room has a balcony, and a ground floor room benefits from a patio. The en suites are large and luxurious. This breathtaking mountain setting is about 3 miles from the historic market town of Dolgellau.

RECOMMENDED IN THE AREA
Walking - Cader Idris, Precipice Walk, Torrent Walk, Maddach Estuary Walk; Steam railways; Centre for Alternative Technology

Tyddyn Du Farm Holidays ♦♦♦♦♦

Map ref 5 - SH53
Gellilydan, Ffestiniog, PORTHMADOG,
Gwynedd LL41 4RB
1st farmhouse on left on A470 after junct A487 & A470, near Gellilydan
T 01766 590281
E theaa@snowdoniafarm.com
W www.snowdoniafarm.co.uk
4 rooms, S from £40, D from £65,
No smoking

Warm hospitality is extended at this working farm where stables and barns have been converted to luxury accommodation. The four suites are all on the ground floor and come with beverage trays with biscuits and welcome cake on arrival. Some have Jacuzzi baths and large separate showers - one bathroom even has a therapeutic air bath. Each suite has a microwave and toaster and a full-size fridge. Breakfast ingredients can be left for you but if you decide not to self-cater a superb breakfast is served in the 400-year-old farmhouse. Candlelit dinners, featuring traditional farmhouse cooking, are served four nights a week during the summer. The farm is family orientated and children are encouraged to meet the animals, collect eggs, and feed the chickens, ducks, lambs and ponies. (But this is also an excellent place for couples celebrating special occasions.) The immediate area has an abundance of wonderful mountain, forest and lakeside walks. Well-behaved pets welcome.

Recommended in the Area

Portmeirion Italianate Village; Ffestiniog Railway; Llechwedd slate mines

Tre-Wyn ♦♦♦♦

Map ref 5 - SH48
Maenaddwyn, LLANERCHYMEDD, Isle of Anglesey LL71 8AE
A5025 to Benllech Bay, B5108 to Brynteg x-rds, take Llannerchymedd road 3m to Maenaddwyn. Right after 6 houses, 0.5m to farm

T 01248 470875
E nia@trewyn.fsnet.co.uk
W www.trewynfarm.co.uk

3 rooms, No smoking

RECOMMENDED IN THE AREA

Beaumaris Castle; Oriel Mon Heritage Centre, Llangefni; Anglesey Sea Zoo

Nia Brown gives an extremely friendly welcome to her spacious farmhouse, while husband Brian looks after the 240-acre mixed farm. The attractive bedrooms are well equipped and furnished, and the dining room and the lounge with its log fire look out across the gardens to the countryside. A variety of breakfasts are created from local produce, including free-range eggs from the farm. You are welcome to explore the farmland and from the front of the house there is a great view towards Bodafon Mountain - from mountain itself you can see over Anglesey. Apart from lovely local walks, there is a cycle route nearby and many coastal paths for birdwatchers.

Penylan Farm ♦♦♦♦

Map ref 2 - SO51
The Hendre, MONMOUTH, Monmouthshire NP25 5NL
B4233, B4347 NW to Newcastle, 1st left for 1.5m, next left, farm 0.5m on right

T 01600 716435
F 01600 719391
E penylan@fsmail.net
W www.penylanfarm.co.uk

3 rooms, S £28-£32, D £50-£55, No smoking

RECOMMENDED IN THE AREA

Offa's Dyke Path; Wye Valley; Brecon Beacons National Park

Penylan is a working farm and Dave and Cathy Bowen welcome you to share their idyllic country retreat, once part of the Hendre Estate owned by the famous Rolls family. The converted granary, set in a courtyard, houses bedrooms furnished to a very high standard, and features tea and coffee facilities and a private lounge with a television. Breakfasts specialities include local meat from an award-winning butcher in Monmouth and home-made preserves. There are plenty of opportunities to explore the farm and watch the calves being fed. An ideal place for walking nearby and in the Wye Valley, and convenient for the Brecon Beacons too.

Cwmbach Cottages Guest House ♦♦♦♦

Map ref 2 - SS79
Cwmbach Rd, Cadoxton, NEATH,
Neath Port Talbot SA10 8AH
1.5m NE of Neath. A465 onto A474 & A4230 towards Aberdulais, left opp Cadoxton church, guesthouse signed
T 01639 639825
E l.morgan5@btinternet.com
W www.cwmbachcottages.co.uk
5 rooms, S £34-£38, D £52-£58, No smoking

Three former miners' cottages have been converted into a guesthouse that happily caters for all comers. A drying room for wet gear acknowledges the needs of walkers and bikers, while a bike shed and car park are useful. Inside there are thoughtfully furnished bedrooms, including one on the ground floor. Lynda and Lawrence Morgan also offer self-catering lodges. A smart lounge and cosy breakfast room with separate tables are provided, and in the garden a decking area overlooks the water garden and wooded hills beyond.

Recommended in the Area

Aberdulais Falls (NT); Neath Abbey; Gnoll Estate

Dulais Rock ♦♦♦♦

Map ref 2 - SS79
Main Rd, Aberdulais, NEATH,
Neath Port Talbot SA10 8EY
M4 junct 43, follow signs for Aberdulais Falls for 3m
T 01639 644611
F 01639 646611
E stay@dulaisrock.co.uk
W www.dulaisrock.co.uk
3 rooms, S £55-£62.50, D £55-£62.50, No smoking in bedrooms or dining room

The innovative refurbishment of the 350-year-old Dulais Rock has harmoniously blended the old with new styles. Hospitality is paramount at this historic inn, and fine cuisine is a passion of the hosts who continue to raise standards. The en suite bedrooms occupy the roof space of the original mill above the Mediterranean-style restaurant. Dinner is a highlight using carefully chosen ingredients with a varied selection of wines. Each of the bars has a distinct atmosphere, with antique wood, leather furniture and real open fires, offering an Italian style café menu.

Recommended in the Area

Neath Abbey; Aberdulais Falls (NT); Afan Forest Park and Countryside Centre

The Inn at the Elm Tree ♦♦♦♦♦

Map ref 2 - ST38
ST BRIDES WENTLOOGE,
NEWPORT NP10 8SQ
4m SW of Newport. On B4239 in St Brides village
T 01633 680225
F 01633 681035
E inn@the-elm-tree.co.uk
W www.the-elm-tree.co.uk
10 rooms, S £80-£90, D £80-£130

This stylish barn conversion on the tranquil Wentlooge Levels has produced an inn that oozes with hospitality. Individually decorated bedrooms combine the traditional and the contemporary - hand-made brass beds, beamed ceilings, hand-made pine furniture and sumptuous fabrics, together with minimalist bathrooms (some with a spa bath), ISDN lines and business services. Meticulous attention to detail, lots of personal touches and little added luxuries make for a perfect stay. The restaurant rests on its long-standing reputation as one of the most distinguished in the area, and you can dine by logs fires in winter or in the pretty courtyard in summer. An extensive choice of mouth-watering dishes includes Welsh Black beef, local seafood and game in season, with the emphasis on quality organic ingredients.

Recommended in the Area

Tredegar House, Newport; Cardiff Millennium Centre & Stadium; Roman Legionary Museum, Caerleon

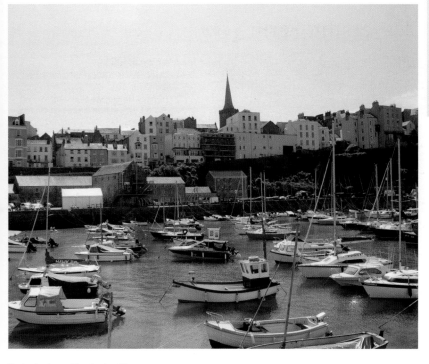

Tenby harbour, Pembrokeshire

*E*rw-Lon Farm ♦♦♦♦

Map ref 1 - SM93
Pontfaen, FISHGUARD,
Pembrokeshire SA65 9TS
5.5m SE of Fishguard on B4313
Ⓣ 01348 881297
3 rooms, S £35, D £52-£56,
No smoking, Closed Dec-Feb

RECOMMENDED IN THE AREA

Castell Henllys; Strumble Head; St David's Cathedral

Traditional Welsh hospitality is offered by the friendly McAllister family at their comfortable farmhouse. It is a beef and sheep farm looking over the lovely wooded Gwaun Valley at the foot of the Preseli Hills. The thoughtfully furnished and well-equipped bedrooms - two doubles and one twin - are all en suite and have clock radios, hairdryers, shaving points and tea and coffee facilities. A relaxing lounge is also provided. Standards are high throughout and a homely atmosphere prevails. Mrs McAllister serves up fine examples of traditional farmhouse cooking, where the size of the portions matches the warmth of the welcome.

Poyerston Farm ♦♦♦♦

Map ref 1 - SM90

Cosheston, PEMBROKE, Pembrokeshire SA72 4SJ

A477 towards Pembroke Dock, through Milton village, Poyerston 0.75m on left opp Vauxhall garage

T / F 01646 651347
E poyerstonfarm@btinternet.com
W www.poyerston-farm.co.uk

6 rooms, S £35-£40, D £56-£70, No smoking, Closed Xmas

RECOMMENDED IN THE AREA

Pembroke Castle; Oakwood Theme Park; Pembrokeshire Coast Path

Poyerston stands on a family-run, 400-acre dairy and beef farm. The impeccably maintained Victorian farmhouse is well placed for the Pembrokeshire coast and countryside, and for Tenby with its historic harbour and beautiful beaches. Bedrooms are all en suite and furnished to a high standard and are well equipped - some are in the adjacent former dairy. Ground-floor bedrooms and family rooms are available. There is a cosy lounge and an elegant dining room where delicious Aga-cooked breakfasts set you up for the day. This room extends into a conservatory with access to the well-maintained gardens. The guesthouse is a convenient stopover for the Pembroke Dock ferry to Ireland. Children are very welcome.

The Waterings ♦♦♦♦

Map ref 1 - SM72
Anchor Rd, High St, ST DAVID'S, Pembrokeshire SA62 6QH
On A487 on E edge of St David's
T / F 01437 720876
E waterings@supanet.com
W www.waterings.co.uk
5 rooms, S £40-£80, D £70-£85, No smoking in bedrooms or dining room

RECOMMENDED IN THE AREA
Ramsey Island boat trips; Pembrokeshire Coast National Park; Whitesands Beach

The Waterings is set in 2 acres of landscaped grounds only a short walk from the 800-year-old cathedral, which hosts an annual music festival. The magnificent coastline with its abundance of birdlife is also within easy reach. The en suite bedrooms in this spacious accommodation are all on the ground floor and come with tea and coffee facilities. Breakfast, prepared from a good selection of local produce, is served in a smart dining room in the main house. Outside amenities include a picnic area and barbecue, a croquet lawn and a nine-hole putting green.

Giltar Grove Country House ♦♦♦♦

Map ref 1 - SN10
Penally, TENBY, Pembrokeshire SA70 7RY
2m SW of Tenby. Off A4139, 2nd right after railway bridge
T 01834 871568
E giltarbnb@aol.com
W www.giltargrovecountryhouse.co.uk
6 rooms, S £35, D £60-£70, No smoking, Closed Dec-Feb

Owner Sarah Diment describes her lovely late Victorian country house as 'a warm, comfortable and friendly home run by warm, comfortable and friendly people' - a really welcoming atmosphere is assured. Giltar Grove has a beautiful, tranquil setting just a stroll from the spectacular coastal path and close to several lovely beaches. Originally a working farm, the house has been beatuifully restored and retains many original features. The charming bedrooms are all en suite, and two have four-poster beds. Tea and coffee facilities are provided, and a full traditional or vegetarian breakfast is served in the magnificent conservatory.

RECOMMENDED IN THE AREA
Pembrokeshire Coast National Park; Magnificent beaches; Historic castles

Rosendale ♦♦♦♦

Map ref 1 - SN10
Rosendale, Lydstep, TENBY,
Pembrokeshire SA70 7SQ
From Tenby A4139 3m W towards Pembroke, through Lydstep, Rosendale on right after village

Ⓣ 01834 870040
Ⓔ rosendalewales@yahoo.com
Ⓦ www.rosendalepembrokeshire.co.uk

7 rooms, S £25-£30, D £50-£60, No smoking, Closed Dec-Jan

Set in the pretty village of Lydstep, just a 10-minute drive from Tenby, Rosendale is ideally situated for exploring the beautiful coast and countryside of Pembrokeshire. There's plenty to do, from golf, birdwatching and surfing, to visiting the many castles, gardens and beaches in the area. Walkers are welcome, and the Pembrokeshire Coast Path is just a 15-minute walk away. Some bedrooms are on the ground floor but all are en suite, while useful extras include clock radios, hairdryers and beverage trays. A hearty full English breakfast is served in the attractive dining room, and after a day's exploring you can relax in the large cosy lounge. Off-road parking is available.

Recommended in the Area

Local gardens; Pembroke Castle; Manorbier Bay

Llanddetty Hall Farm ♦♦♦♦

Map ref 2 - SO02
Talybont-on-Usk, BRECON,
Powys LD3 7YR
7m SE off B4558

Ⓣ / Ⓕ 01874 676415

4 rooms, S £32, D £48-£54, No smoking, Closed 16 Dec-14 Jan

Recommended in the Area

Brecon Beacons National Park; Hay-on-Wye; Aberglasney

This listed farmhouse is part of a sheep farm in the Brecon Beacons National Park. The Brecon and Monmouth Canal flows through the farm at the rear, while the front of the house overlooks the River Usk. Bedrooms, including one on the ground floor, feature exposed beams and polished floorboards. Three rooms are en suite and one has a private bathroom - all have radio alarms and tea and coffee facilities. There is a lounge with a television, and a dining room where breakfast is served at an oak refectory table, and evening meals by arrangement. This is a no smoking house and dogs are not permitted.

The Usk Inn ♦♦♦♦

Map ref 2 - SO02
Station Rd, Talybont-on-Usk,
BRECON, Powys LD3 7JE
Off A40 6m E of Brecon

T 01874 676251
F 01874 676392
E stay@uskinn.co.uk
W www.uskinn.co.uk

11 rooms, S £60-£85, D £90-£125, No smoking in bedrooms or dining room, Closed 25-27 Dec

RECOMMENDED IN THE AREA

Brecon Beacons National Park; Blaenavon World Heritage Site; Hay-on-Wye

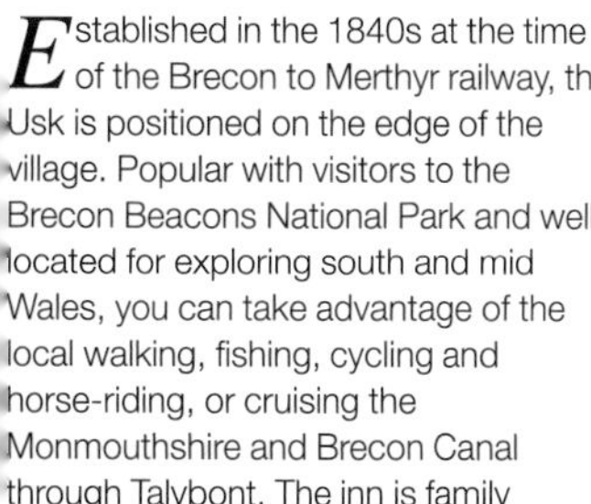

Established in the 1840s at the time of the Brecon to Merthyr railway, the Usk is positioned on the edge of the village. Popular with visitors to the Brecon Beacons National Park and well located for exploring south and mid Wales, you can take advantage of the local walking, fishing, cycling and horse-riding, or cruising the Monmouthshire and Brecon Canal through Talybont. The inn is family owned and personally run in a friendly manner by Michael and Barbara Taylor, who have many years of experience in the hospitality industry. It has been renovated to a high standard: public areas have a wealth of charm, while the thoughtfully equipped en suite bedrooms, each individually decorated and furnished with locally made pine furniture, include some rooms with four-poster beds. The inn's deserved reputation for good food is recognised by the AA Rosette, complimented by excellent beers and an interesting wine list.

Glangrwyney Court ♦♦♦♦♦

Map ref 2 - SO21

CRICKHOWELL, Powys NP8 1ES

2m SE of Crickhowell on A40 near county boundary

T 01873 811288
F 01873 810317
E info@glancourt.co.uk
W www.glancourt.co.uk

5 rooms, S £50-£70, D £55-£75, No smoking in bedrooms or dining room

Recommended in the Area

Brecon Beacons National Park; Danyrogof Caves; Big Pit

A Grade II listed country house, Glangrwyney Court is set in the national park midway between Abergavenny and Crickhowell. The interior is furnished with antiques, porcelain and paintings, and log fires welcome guests in winter weather. Breakfast is served in the elegant dining room and you can relax in the sumptuous lounge. There is a good choice of bedrooms, including single, twin, double and family rooms. All rooms are en suite or have private facilities, and come with tea and coffee equipment, and wonderful views over the garden and surrounding countryside. The Master Suite has the additional luxury of an extra deep bath, while the twin room has its own Jacuzzi. Croquet, boules and tennis are available in the grounds and activities such as pony trekking, golf, fishing and shooting can be arranged. There are many lovely walks in the area, with the Brecon Beacons and Black Mountains within easy reach. Children and pets welcome.